MANAGING YOUR MIND

THE MACMILLAN COMPANY
NEW YORK · BOSTON · CHICAGO · DALLAS
ATLANTA · SAN FRANCISCO

MACMILLAN AND CO., LIMITED
LONDON · BOMBAY · CALCUTTA · MADRAS
MELBOURNE

THE MACMILLAN COMPANY
OF CANADA, LIMITED
TORONTO

MANAGING YOUR MIND

You *Can* Change Human Nature

BY

S. H. KRAINES, M.D.

Assistant Professor of Psychiatry, University of
Illinois Medical School; Diplomate of the
American Board of Neurology and Psychiatry

AND

E. S. THETFORD

THE MACMILLAN COMPANY, NEW YORK

1947

TABLE OF CONTENTS

MANAGING YOUR MIND

CHAPTER I

INTRODUCTION

The concept of happiness has undergone radical modifications and there have always been widely varying definitions of the term, but however different the phraseology or even the basic ideal, the human goal has always been the same. Sometimes the present world has offered so many difficulties, so many obstacles to the securing of satisfactions here and now, that persons, or even whole peoples, have developed elaborate philosophical or theological superstructures of belief to guarantee an other-worldly happiness. Between the hedonist, who feels that he has fulfilled his highest moral obligation when to the fullest capacity he has gratified his pleasure-seeking impulses, and the stoic, who, by cultivating an attitude of indifference to pleasure and pain alike, would thus render himself immune to the ravages of all emotions, there are countless variations and interpretations of what constitutes happiness.

A *sine qua non* of happiness is health. Happiness and health, as we conceive them, are positive and not negative states. Freedom from physical aches and pains and release from mental distress and turmoil are tremendously important, but they are only steps toward a more positive state—one in which there is vigor and vitality, strength and force. The very etymology of the word health (A. S. *"hāl,"* meaning whole or sound) indicates one thesis of this book; namely, that man is a total organism, his physical and his psychological conditions being not separate entities but different aspects of the one totality. You have had innumerable experiences of having your body affect your disposition; you have had headaches that "ruined your day"; you have been irritable and "crabby" because of a nagging, persistent pain; you have been "blue" and depressed in spirit after a long illness which has left you physically "below par." It perhaps has not been so apparent to you that the principle also works in reverse. *Our emotional states as definitely determine the well-being of our bodies as they reflect it.* This entire book is given over to the demonstration of the validity of this statement, and what is vastly more important, to a detailed explanation of the technique whereby you can control the situation. If you would have that "wholeness" and that "soundness" which the word health connotes, then you must learn so to organize and control your body, mind, and emotions that instead of operating at cross-purposes they will work together, as a totality, to help you in your pursuit of happiness. It is a strange and difficult situation which we have to manage. The essence of the difficulty lies in the fact that our bodies have, through a long, long evolutionary process, become so organized that they function automatically in response to the demands of our emotions; but—and this is the "joker"—the type of response which our bodies are prepared to make is wholly inadequate for meeting the multitudinous and highly complex claims of our "civilized" life. Not only is it inadequate; it is itself the source of one of our major difficulties. With our desires and our fears, that is, with our emotions, we constantly call on our bodies for help. Our bodies respond automatically with the only kind of help that they "know" to furnish; and we almost as automatically inhibit or prevent these physical preparations from being released in action. The result [1] is the creation of countless physical and psychologic symptoms, ranging all the way from high blood pressure to hysterical paralysis, from peptic ulcers to insomnia, from aphonia to impotence.

We have said that the task is a difficult one, and it is. However, it is possible of achievement, and the more nearly you approximate this "management" of your emotions, the richer will be your rewards in health and happiness. Two things are essential: (1) insight into the mechanism whereby emotions are translated into

[1] *Vide* Chap. VI.

symptoms and (2) the desire and the determination to make whatever changes are necessary. We shall have much to say about both of these requirements; but that you may have a general idea of what this book offers and of what demands it will make upon you, let us say a few words here about insight and determination.

Insight into the mechanism by which emotions are translated into symptoms.—No one wishes to be ill or unhappy. No, that statement is not quite true. Some persons are so ill, so poorly integrated, so maladjusted and inadequate for the demands of life that they seem to glory in their misery and to enjoy their suffering. The vast majority of persons, however, wish to be well. They go to doctors; they swallow literally tons of medicine; they take up all sorts of food fads; and they join strange cults. The self-prescribed medicines, the fads, and the cults may be innocuous, they may be temporarily alleviating, or they may be definitely harmful. One thing is certain: they are not curative; for only when the causes are adequately dealt with can you hope for permanent cure. Go to your physician and avail yourself of all that medical science and knowledge can give you, but don't expect your physician to be a magician. Your intellectual understanding of the relationship between emotionalism and physical symptoms will no more cure a headache which has its origin in infected sinuses than it will set a broken bone. On the other hand, if you are retarding your recovery or if your physician assures you that your symptoms have no organic basis, then insight into the cause of your difficulties can be of incalcuable value. The fact that there is no organic basis for your symptoms does not make them less real or less disturbing, but it does mean that you cannot expect your physician to cure you unless you assume your share of the responsibility and do what only you can do: change from within. The more intelligence you bring to bear on the solution of any problem the better chance you have of solving it. Therefore you need to understand just as clearly as possible the whys, the hows, and the wherefores of your situation. You need to understand yourself in terms of your age-old inheritance; you need to understand your own primary needs and the social demands in terms of which you seek your happiness; you need to understand why your body acts as it does and how to make it your ally instead of your enemy; you need to understand that human nature is capable of modification and redirection; and you need to know how to go about changing it. Such understanding is vitally important; but it is only a preliminary step and it becomes truly significant only when it is taken so seriously that its implications are followed out, when it is implemented with action—*your* action.

The desire and the determination to change.—You can pay or persuade someone else to clean your house, keep your books, cook your meals, drive your car, manage your business, do your work; but only you can live your own life; only you can change the pattern of your actions, your thoughts, and your feelings; only you can reshape your life so that it more nearly conforms to what you wish. All your intellectual awareness of why you are as you are and all your theoretical acceptance of both the possibility and desirability of managing your life differently will profit you nothing unless you have both the will and the determination to make the changes which you know can and should be made. Your doctor tells you that your heart is "sound"; but it goes right on beating too fast and "pounding in your ears." He will explain to you, as does this book, *why* you have the disturbing symptom: because you are in the habit of over-reacting to too many stimuli, because you take things too hard and are always worried, fearful, and apprehensive. Such an explanation should reassure you that you are not going to die of heart trouble; but the reassurance will be superficial and that symptom, or some other one, will continue unless you set about changing yourself, removing the cause.

Such change is not easy. The more deeply ingrained are your habits of emotional thinking and instability, the more chronic are your over-reactions and your tendency to "feel" about life and all its exigencies instead of reasoning and acting on the basis of your logical conclusions—the more difficult will your task be. It will take time and persistent effort; you will be discouraged and tempted to give up your efforts; you will need encouragement, and you should get it from your physician or from someone else who knows enough and is objective enough to help you. Reading this, or any other, book will not cure you of anything; it will, however, point the way which will enable you to facilitate your physician's efforts in your behalf, to rid yourself of many disturbing or distressing symptoms, and to prevent the creation of new or additional troubles. Granting all the fortuitous circumstances and all the external and uncontrollable factors which may affect your life, we still maintain that in large degree your health and your happiness are in your own hands. If you are willing to take over the management of your own life, this book is for you.

CHAPTER II

MAN VERSUS ANIMAL

The purpose of this chapter is threefold: (1) to emphasize the fact that the mind neither exists nor functions as an entity separate from the body; (2) to point out the basic fundamental drives which are the common denominators in all "thinking," whether it be that of amœba or man; and (3) to indicate that the "superiority" of man's thinking ability lies in the complexity of his brain which enables him to "choose" responses rather than respond in reflex fashion to environmental stimulus. Each of these discussions will have to be given in abbreviated form; adequately dealt with each would demand a separate volume.

Just why does Man have such an exalted opinion of himself? It is a both exhilarating and humbling experience to examine the invisible world under a microscope or to search the starry heavens with a telescope. Perhaps if we did enough of both and let our imaginations play with the ideas and fancies thus aroused, we might gain some true perspective on the importance of our own great-little lives. We are so used to thinking of ourselves as a "special creation" of transcendent importance or as "the highest form of animal life" that we rarely stop to ask what superiority is represented by the word "highest." (Did you ever wonder whether Brother Dinosaur as he went swashbuckling through the world also dreamed himself the "highest form of animal life," because at the moment he happened to represent the crescendo of the evolutionary wave?) Called upon to substantiate this claim of superiority, most of us would reply in some such terms as "Well, man *thinks*," "Man has a better *mind*." Indeed, the technical designation of man is "homo sapiens," man wise or discerning. When we consider the

6

artful ingenuity displayed in inventing death-dealing weapons with which to kill each other, or remember that countless thousands go hungry in a world of plenty, we could think that "homo sap" would be a more accurate designation. If the ability to think is indeed our mark of distinction, then we need to know all we can about the mind—what it is, how it functions, how we can best use it.

There is no such thing as the mind.—"But," you say, "I make decisions; I solve problems; I use my judgment." True. You do. Look a little closer. Is some separate entity, some distinct and exclusive part of your organism performing these acts, or are you rather responding to a situation in terms of myriads of previous experiences which your total organism has undergone? Just as the rhythmic, smooth, and unbroken movement of the trained dancer seems to be a graceful undulating movement, but is in reality composed of innumerable small contractions of individual muscle fibers moving in such rapid succession as to "appear" smooth, so the mind, seeming to make decisions and to solve problems with relative simplicity, is in reality merely reacting to stimuli in terms of patterns established by countless hitherto experienced pains, frustrations, and successes. Man's body, including his brain, is composed of billions of cells which can be seen and studied under the microscope. These cells, useless by themselves, but capable of acting as an effective organism when in total harmony, differ from each other in form and function but not in basic nature. *Nor does the total body,* composed as it is of all these cells, *act in a manner different in principle from that which is characteristic of the simplest form of animal life,* for example, that of our microscopic progenitor, the amoeba.

We will leave to the philosopher the fascinating and as yet unanswered question, "What is Life?" and turn to those facts which we do know. All animals, single or multicellular, are capable of ingesting and excreting food; of moving toward pleasure and away from pain or danger; of being stimulated or depressed; and of reproduction. As you read this discussion of the private life of the amœba, two major points will become increasingly apparent to you: (1) that the motivating, actuating drives are for amœba and man essentially identical, and (2) that man has an infinitely greater technique of control over his environment than does the unicellular form of life; a much more complex mechanism with which to satisfy his needs; and, as a consequence, potentially much more freedom. In actuality, "civilization" has so elaborated and complicated his fundamental desires that his problems are much more multiform and acute and his chances of frustration much more numerous. You said that one evidence of your "mind" is that with it you make decisions. The amœba also "decides." Swimming about in stagnant water, the amœba, if he is to continue his "pursuit of happiness," must find food and escape danger. If his proud race is not to be obliterated, he must reproduce. And you?

The amœba is wholly dependent on the environment. The amœba grows colder when the surrounding temperature grows colder; his movements are determined almost entirely by the movements of the surrounding waters; his food must be brought within relatively easy grasp before it can be seized; and danger is not perceived until it is close enough to be felt. Placed in fresh water he dies; if the water becomes too hot or too cold he dies; but granted a livable environment, he will make all the "decisions" necessary to satisfy his basic drives for self-preservation and for propagation. Elementary biology books speak of chemotropism, heliotropism, and thermotropism, terms indicating that the primitive organism is drawn toward certain substances or foods, is drawn toward certain intensities of light, moves toward certain conditions of warmth. Because these elements benefit the organism we speak of these attractions or "tropisms" as inherent drives; yet one might just as well speak of the animal's "deciding" to go in this direction or that.

In other words, *the faculty of deciding, in its primitive state, is in reality merely doing that which is conducive to the best de-*

velopment of the organism. Those objects or stimuli which attract the organism are said to be pleasurable; and "deciding" to do something means, in primitive animals, doing that which is most pleasurable, escaping that which is painful.

The positive pole of attraction which draws the animal and the negative from which the animal runs rarely exist in pure form; here as elsewhere it is a matter of degree, of relativity. Usually some elements in the situation are mildly pleasurable or are strongly pleasurable; whereas others are either mildly annoying, painful, and irritating or else definitely and strongly dangerous and therefore to be feared. Contrast the words "like" and "love," dislike" and "hate" and you will be aware not only of the diametric opposition between pleasure and pain but also—and this fact is important—that pleasure and pain are *relative* and not absolute states.

What then will determine the amœba's (or man's) "decisions," his course of action? Two things: the *strength of the stimulus* and the *condition of the organism*. Properly, they should not be spoken of as though they were separate and distinct; for, in reality, the latter to a large extent determines the former. Stimuli are attractive to the organism when they can satisfy some organismal need, but not otherwise. Thus, if the animal is hungry, the sight or smell of food will draw him rapidly toward the stimulus; but if the animal is not hungry then the same stimulus may have no effect. One must always consider the condition of the animal, the "state of mind" of the organism, before avowing that a certain stimulus will or will not attract. The same is true with minor dangers or irritations; if the organism is "below par," or is already disturbed by some other source, a mildly irritating stimulus may be reacted to violently. You can readily think of dozens of your own experiences which substantiate this theory that the strength of the stimulus is determined by the condition of the organism. Is taking a bath merely part of the day's routine, or after a hot, dusty trip does "the benison of hot water" make you feel like writing "An Ode to the Bathtub?" Have you ever had to eat two Thanksgiving Day dinners on the same day? Does your neighbor's radio, which ordinarily you literally do not hear, "drive you wild" when you have a splitting headache? Have you ever "lost your temper" over some trivial, inconsequential incident and admitted later that it so affected you not because of its own intrinsic nature but as a "last straw." The hungry amœba will scuttle just as fast as the surrounding water will permit in an effort to overtake and enfold a passing bit of food; the well-fed amœba will let the same bit of food drift unmolested past his metaphorical nose. Likewise, man will expend his energy in direct proportion to the urgency of his desire either to obtain or avoid; and that urgency, in turn, will be determined by the condition of his organism.

What will the amœba do if confronted simultaneously by a pleasurable and by a dangerous stimulus? Just what you or anyone else would do. To be more explicit, one might answer in terms of physics: the direction which the organism will take will be the resultant of the two forces. Imagine a canoe being pulled by two ropes and in opposite directions. The canoe will travel in the direction of the stronger pull. If the two ropes are not pulling in opposite directions but at an angle to each other, the boat will move in a "resultant" direction between these two pulls. In the same way the organism responds to the forces of danger (pain) and of pleasure; the organism will travel in a direction which is a resultant of these forces; and the stronger the force, i.e., the greater the danger or the pleasure, the more influence will that force have on the organism. When the amœba is drawn toward some stimulus, for any of the above reasons, we may say that he has an emotion of pleasurableness. The "emotion" is merely the state of the organism as it is going through the motions towards pleasure or away from danger. Running away from danger and pain, the animal has the emotion of fear. Emotion is, therefore, a *state of the organism while it is responding to a stimulus*.

Apply to yourself all that has been written in the foregoing pages and you will realize that you, no less than your far away progenitors, respond to pleasure and to pain and that your "decisions," in the last analysis, are dependent upon the forces in the environment, the direction of their pull, and the condition of the organism. Recall some of the "decisions" you have made today. You ordered steak rather than fish because you *like* steak better; you shopped because you *needed* something for your comfort or pleasure or because you *enjoy* "just looking"; you went to work by bus rather than the street car, because you *wished* to ride through the park, etc. Likewise in more complex situations, the same pleasure-pain principle, though less obvious, still operates. Why do you decide to vote for a certain congressman, or why, when you are already overworked, do you decide to take an extension course in accounting? In the one instance, the congressman has promised to reduce taxes, a promise which if redeemed will in the future increase your pleasure; in the other, the knowledge gained will, you hope, increase your earning ability and hence your happiness.

The purpose of this discussion has not been to reduce you to the status of the amoeba but merely to establish kinship and to give you a key to unlock the door of understanding. Turn now to the other side of the picture and see the vast differences which exist—differences in equipment and therefore in potentiality, differences in opportunity and therefore in responsibility.

In a blithe manner calculated to horrify our scientific brethren and even our own inclinations, we summarize the long, long, evolutionary process and tell you that by the time Man comes upon the stage, two tremendously important things have happened: (1) relative independence of the environment has been achieved, and (2) the brain has been acquired. Development of the ability to breathe the oxygen directly from the air instead of from the water gave the animal more freedom to move and direct his activities. Land animals still needed water for their chemical processes to work and to carry on life; so they developed tissues which carried water within them, thereby giving them greater independence of the chemical activity of the surrounding waters. Our bodies are two-thirds water. Finally, since chemical activity of the body is more or less dependent upon a certain minimum of temperature, and since physical activity practically ceases when the body becomes the same temperature as the freezing external temperature, the next level of animals developed their own temperature-regulating mechanism which maintained a constant internal temperature so that the physiologic-chemical process could go on relatively independent of the environment. Further independence was achieved by the development of the senses of smell, hearing, and vision which enabled the animal to perceive at ever greater distances the pleasures and dangers of the environment, an awareness which would have been valueless had he not also been acquiring the kind of brain which enabled him to: (1) delay his responses, (2) profit by his past experiences, and (3) select the most effective response.

Thomas Hardy once said that human consciousness is a bad accident. Whether you agree or disagree probably depends upon the "state of your organism"; but one thing is certain: it is an accident which would not have occurred had it not been for the development of the brain and the central nervous system. The lowest amphibians have brains, the frog, for example, having a rather nice brain. All fish with spinal columns have brains; all animals that run on four legs or walk on two have brains. What good are they; and how do they differ?

Brains function, among other ways, as *stations of delay*. Animals without brains respond immediately and reflexly when stimulated. The reason for this immediate reflex response, which is unvarying in character, is that the stimulus on touching the surface of the organism creates an impulse which travels inward and stimulates the whole cell, which then reacts immediately and reflexly. In animals with a central nervous system, the stimulus produces an impulse which travels to the central nervous system, and in the central nervous system the impulse is delayed by traveling to several different centers. When the animal finally responds, he does so by using several specialized parts which have been stimulated by the impulse, and thus his reaction is more efficient. In other words, the brain acts as a station of delay in which the impulse can be examined, and the most efficient of the various mechanisms to deal with the situation can be brought into coördinated activity. In actual practice the delay lasts only a fraction of a second, but that is time enough. Thus, if the amœba is touched by an irritating stimulus it immediately withdraws with its entire body. If the frog is touched on its hind leg with such a stimulus the impulse travels to the spinal cord and causes the leg to contract, removing the leg alone from the irritation, or, a moment later, the animal may contract both legs into a jumping response, so that he can most effectively escape from the danger threatened if the irritation is strong enough to arouse the entire animal. When man is driving an automobile and suddenly perceives a pedestrian before him, the impulse goes from his eyes to his brain, where the impulse is then relayed to the centers controlling the right foot which is raised from the gas pedal and placed on the brake. In both the frog and man, the impulse has been delayed in the central nervous system for the ultimate purpose of permitting the organism to select the best possible type of response to meet the situation, instead of producing a general and reflex response which is ineffective and actually dangerous to the organism. In man responses may be so trained as to be automatic, yet should a stimulus arise with which he has had no experience, then between the time that the impulse reaches the brain, and the time that he reacts, man is testing the possibilities of the best type of response. This *testing of the possibilities is called thinking.* In its oversimplified sense, that's all that thinking is—testing the possibilities for the best response. And thinking is possible simply because the brain is a station of delay where such testing is possible. Only to the extent that animals can delay their responses, are they capable of thinking.

It becomes evident that man is not the only animal capable of delay, capable of selecting his responses, capable, that is, of thinking; he is merely that animal capable of the greatest delay, the widest range of selection, of being, therefore, the greatest thinker. You will notice the deliberate repetition of the word "capable"; for tragically few persons take advantage of their superior brain. We have been marvelously clever and sometimes it would seem devilishly ingenious in our manipulation of the physical universe, in extending our technique of control over the physical environment. We have used our brains to conquer the land, the sea, and the air; but we have not used our brains to learn to live happily within ourselves or with each other. Bombers in the air, mines in the sea, armies marching across the land—terrifying moments of wondering whether Man's cleverness, Man's ingenuity may not end in self-defeat, self-destruction. They need not. We respond reflexly, as the lower animals do, to situations which call rather for delayed responses with wise selection. We are pursued by unreasoning fears, dominated by unreasonable hatreds. We need not be. This book is written out of the conviction that it is possible to do something; that man can change the environmental pressure to a "normal" force and direction; and, most important of all, that he can alter his attitudes and reaction patterns in such a way as to make them his servants, not his master, his friendly ally and not his enemy. Neither task is easy, but both are possible; and both are necessary if we are in any adequate sense to achieve pleasure and avoid pain. The fact that we are subject to the same fundamental drives as are the lower forms of life does not mean that we are also limited as are they in our technique of achievement. Indeed, we have so enlarged and elaborated our conception of the meaning of "security," the significance of perpetuating the species, that we can no longer secure our values by the old, primitive methods. In addition to wanting food to satisfy the hunger of the moment and to escape an animal larger or stronger than we, and in addition to feeling the biological urge to reproduce, we want food for tomorrow, security for our old age and for our children; we want status, recognition, response, love, affection, a sense of our own

importance, variety, amusement, etc. All these multifarious wants
and wishes stem from the two fundamental needs; but the fact
that they are offshoots does not mean that they are less real or less
insistent. Paradoxically enough as we reduce the number of actual
dangers in our environment, as we perfect our food-getting techniques, we multiply our needs and desires in other directions, so
that Man is forever seeking, forever striving.

Not only are our desires complex, but the environment in which
they must be achieved has its own peculiar complexity which must
be recognized and dealt with. Man-made civilization has done
queer things to man. Not only is it possible, thanks to the superiority of our brains, for man to delay his responses and thereby
choose the most effective one to meet a particular situation; but
the very nature of our civilization makes it necessary for us to
learn to postpone present desires for future satisfactions. Even
our primary desire for food is satisfied in an indirect, circuitous
fashion. A well-fed beetle basks in the sunshine; along comes a
hungry robin, devours the beetle at one gulp, flies to a near-by tree
and while he is singing the song of the well-filled stomach, a hungry cat crawls stealthily up the tree, catches and eats the robin, and
goes on his way purring with contentment until he meets a hungry
and sharp-toothed weasel that sucks the cat's blood and no doubt
prays devoutly that he will not encounter another hungry animal
that is stronger than he.

Even our not so remote primitive ancestors employed much the
same *directness* in the satisfaction of their hunger. Armed with
clubs and later with traps they went forth from their caves, caught
and killed their prey, and devoured it.

There are no such direct satisfactions for us. In our moments
of greatest inertia we dream of South Sea islands with a tempting
variety of food (and other delights) forever within hand's reach;
but most of the time most of us are too engrossed with the complicated business of "making a living" even to have time for such
dreams. For long years we go to school to learn enough to secure

a job which will pay enough so that we can buy food. Civilized man not only feels the hunger of the moment but his mind is so constituted that remembering the past, he can look forward to the future and so is often willing to forego an immediate satisfaction for what he considers will be a greater although a postponed pleasure. One example will suffice.

A boy just out of high school is offered a job paying what appears to an eighteen-year-old a magnificent salary. What "future" is there in the job? He refuses the offer and instead works his way through college, and then through four more years of professional training. Then, if he is fortunate, after a few more years spent in establishing himself in his chosen field, he has some modicum of financial security. For ten or twelve years he has lived in comparative privation for the sake of a future greater security, plus, of course, recognition, status, and the pleasure of doing the work he most wishes to do.

Recapitulating this chapter we may say: (1) Man, like all other animals, is motivated in his actions by two basic drives—self-preservation and race perpetuation. (2) His patterns of reaction are established on the pleasure-pain principle. (3) Pleasure and pain are relative, not absolute, values: their intensity being in large measure determined by the condition of the organism and, in the case of man, by internal attitudes. (4) The function of the mind, which has no reality apart from the total organism, is an integrating and a directing one, its purpose being to enable the organism to achieve satisfaction and to avoid danger. (5) Man differs from other animals in at least three important respects: (a) his relative independence of the physical environment; (b) the greater complexity of his desires and his dangers which include the future as well as the present; and (c) his vastly superior brain which enables him to delay his responses, select the most effective one, respond to and control his environment far more adequately than can any other form of animal and far more "intelligently" than he is in the habit of doing.

CHAPTER III

AUTOMATIC BODIES IN A CHANGING WORLD

A curious situation has arisen because man's organism—with the best intentions in the world—has made many of our responses automatic (via the autonomic nervous system). This automaticity is designed for a totally different stage from the one on which we must play out the "Human Comedy"; and the result is that, far from making our orientation to the environment more efficient, it has created a whole new set of problems. If we are to solve the problems, and we must if we are to be healthy and happy, we need to understand the "workings" of our nervous systems, especially as they are affected by our emotions.

Do you realize that when you "get mad," your whole body gets mad at the same time, and that when you are happy, your whole body reflects the state of your emotion? Do you know that when you hate someone or feel angry or frightened, your blood pressure goes up, and your stomach is less capable of digesting food? Are you aware that any illness is intensified and prolonged, if the patient is worried or distressed? In our effort to understand and classify the complex activities and abilities of man we have fallen into the habit of speaking of "body" and "mind" as though they were two separate entities, distinct in origin and in function. (The confusion becomes worse-confounded when speculations extend to include a third part, "the soul".) Increasingly, doctors, psychologists, and philosophers are coming to realize both that man is a total organism, and must be so understood and treated, and that there is no such thing as emotion divorced from the body that reflects and expresses it.

To appreciate the complexity of man's ever present and engrossing problem of how living in the environment in which he does he can achieve pleasure and avoid pain you must understand three concepts or principles: (1) It is not the specialization (marvelous and intricate though that specialization be) of the various organs which constitute man's total organism, his "mind-body," but the *organization* of these parts into a smoothly working system which makes it possible for man to be efficient and successful in avoiding pain and achieving pleasure. (2) This coördination is accomplished on an automatic and involuntary level by the operation of the *autonomic nervous system*. (3) A higher degree of integration is made possible through the functioning of the voluntary nervous system and particularly of the *cortex*. (4) Since for civilized man the environment means not only the physical universe but the social, economic, and cultural milieu as well, and since man's basic needs to get food and to escape physical danger have been so enlarged and expanded, we shall try to show two things: (*a*) why the autonomic system faced with a new type of problem for which it was not primarily designed sometimes interferes rather than helps; and (*b*) how, by greater utilization of the latent powers of the cortex, we can control the autonomic nervous system, thereby bringing about a smoother and more efficient functioning of our total organism in the pursuance of our goals.

First, consider the question of *organization*. The ultimate purpose of specialization, whether it be in an automobile factory, a professional field, or the human organism, is increased efficiency. The animal organism is not a collection, but a highly integrated set of organs, each performing its own special work, but each dependent on the coöperation of the other organs. For example, the stomach and gastrointestinal tract will take care of the ingestion and digestion of food, *provided* the muscles seek out and seize the food; and the muscles, in turn, do their work only *provided* the brain orients the organism toward food and consequent pleasure. This coöperation calls for a highly complex but efficient organization. See how interdependent these organs are. When digestion is going on, the blood must be drawn from the muscles to the stomach; and vice versa, when the muscles are in action, the blood must be shifted to them from the stomach. To accomplish this blood transportation and to provide a fluid mechanism for carrying to all other organs the food which has been digested by the intestinal system, the *heart* and circulating system are called into play. The heart not only adjusts but is itself very adjustable, being able to change its tempo according to whether we are resting or exercising. To aid in the controlling and regulating of the utilization of food, special *glands* supply internal secretions, called hormones (as insulin from the pancreas). The *liver* helps process the food. The *lungs* furnish oxygen from the air; and the *spleen* and *bone marrow* are special organs to supply the blood cells which carry oxygen. In other words, the entire organism has gone in for specialization, a specialization designed so to increase the efficiency of the automatic processes that the entire animal can more easily obtain sustenance and more surely ward off danger.

Just as a government needs not only an executive but a legislative body or just as a play needs not only trained actors, skillful designers, and efficient property men but also a stage director; so all these specialized organs, efficient as they are within themselves, and working as they do in automatic fashion, need to be integrated so that there is harmony in their activity. Some of this integration is carried on by means of hormones in the blood stream, hormones which come from such glands of internal secretion as the pituitary, the thyroid, and the adrenals. Even more of the work of integration comes about through the operation of the involuntary nervous system.

The *autonomic* or *involuntary* nervous system, as its name implies, is not under voluntary control but acts automatically. Having its center at the base of the brain, in a structure called the hypothalamus, it is connected with practically every portion of the body. It is amazing that an organ no bigger than is the hypothalamus— it is about the size of an ordinary postage stamp—can and does control so much of our lives. There are two divisions of this system: the sympathetic and the parasympathetic, the former serving to stimulate and increase activity; the latter, to quiet and to conserve and build up energy. They are alike in that they work automatically, but diametrically opposed in purpose and function. A branch from each part goes to every organ in the body; and, as a rule, when one system is active, the other is not in operation. This division of labor means that the body tends to respond as a unit to either the one system or the other. Remembering this fact will help when we come to discuss the variety and widespread nature of symptoms.

The purpose of the autonomic nervous system is so to integrate all the organs that the animal or man can succeed in his effort either to get food or to escape danger; or, in the case of the parasympathetic division, to permit the total organism to rest and build up new energy. Look at what happens when the sympathetic portion is stimulated. The blood pressure is increased, the heart beats faster, the blood vessels contract, the stomach dilates, the gastric secretion tends to diminish, the intestines relax, the heat regulation is changed so that more heat is lost, the adrenal glands are stimulated, the liver secretes more glycogen which changes to blood sugar, the blood clots more easily: in other words, the sympathetic nervous system automatically increases the activity of every organ, prepares the total organism to meet the immediate situation. The reverse situation obtains when the organism is resting: the parasympathetic system automatically slows down the activity of each organ.

In association with the hypothalamus, which controls the involuntary nervous system, there are at the base of the brain several masses of nerve cells termed the basal ganglia, which automatically coördinate the sensations from the skin, muscles, and those portions of the organism which are under conscious control.

See how beautifully this whole system works. You are walking in a forest and suddenly step on a snake. The snake coils ready to strike. What do you do? Your brain, having received the danger signal by way of the optic nerves, makes you "decide" to run. In the split fraction of a second during which you are "deciding," your body has begun to operate automatically in such a way as to implement your decision. The hypothalamus becomes active and stimulates the glands which supply sugar to your running muscles, raises the blood pressure, and increases the heart rate so as to supply more blood to your muscles and brain; your stomach and intestines stop their work of digesting food so that no energy will be deflected from the running muscles; your basal ganglia permit the muscles to work in smooth harmony—in fact, once you've "decided" to run, it is as if a multitude of orders had been given to the various organs of your body, orders which are automatically executed.

(Dare we dream that in some happy future, Society will have so perfected its organization that whatever part needs care will automatically receive care, that there will be a "parasympathetic system" to work constructively in times of peace and quiet, a "sympathetic system" to be called into automatic and efficient play in times of distress and danger?)

Perhaps you are saying, "What does all this elementary physiology have to do with my headache?" or "I'm not interested in all this stuff about basal ganglia and parasympathetic systems. What I wish to know is, 'Why do I get up dead tired every morning, no matter how many hours I have slept?'" One need not be a master mechanic in order to drive an automobile; but one does need to know a little of the principles involved and observe at least a few of the rules of the road, if he wishes to avoid difficulty. If you are innocent of all mechanical information, don't "tinker" with your car; you'll do more harm than good. And don't try to be your own physician. We can neither "turn in" the old body for a new one, nor even buy new parts. On the other hand, we can use our intelligence to keep our cars and our bodies in good running condition and to get from them their best possible performance. It is important that you understand how your body "behaves" if you are to keep it from "misbehaving"; so look for a moment at the working of the *voluntary nervous system*.

As the hypothalamus is the most important part of the involuntary or autonomic nervous system, so the *cortex* is in the *voluntary*. The cortex which makes *conscious* control possible is a thin layer composed of myriads of cells and sheathing the entire brain in much the same manner as the skin covers the body. Though the constituent cells have many different and specialized functions, the various parts work harmoniously; and the cortex, accordingly, operates as a unit. In lower forms of animal life, the basal ganglia are the terminus for sensory fibers and for those involved in the involuntary nervous system and so function as the "brain." In higher forms and in man in particular, the structure is much more complex; and, consequently, a far more efficient functioning of the entire organism is made possible. The operation of the cortex is made possible by a great mass of nerve fibers connecting it with the basal ganglia and the spinal cord. These fibers are "conductors," relaying messages to and from the cortex. The picture is that of countless sensory fibers; e.g., visual, auditory, olfactory, gustatory fibers, and fibers which bear the messages of pain, heat, touch, and position carrying their messages to the cortex which in this instance acts as a receiving station. The involuntary nervous system also sends messages via the secondary fibers *to* and receives "replies" *from* the cortex.

The cortex, then, plays a double rôle: the passive one of receiving impulses and the active one (and it is in this ability that man's "superiority" lies) of *correlating* these impulses, *choosing* the responses, and, by sending out nerve fibers to various muscle groups, *controlling* activity. It is the inherent ability of the cortex to delay responses which makes awareness, consciousness, and control possible. The amazement which you may have felt as you watched a giant switchboard in operation would be slight in comparison with that you would feel were it possible graphically to describe the complexity, the intricacy, the precision, and the efficiency with which these two systems—the voluntary and the involuntary—do their separate and coöperative work.

If we look at the long, long procession of Life, it would seem that countless changes and developments have taken place in an effort to make animals more and more "master" of themselves and of their environment. The goals have not changed; they have been modified, enlarged, and enhanced; but their basic nature has remained essentially the same: all life seeks to obtain satisfactions and to avoid danger or pain. The amazing change lies in the ever-improving mechanism wherewith to realize these goals. Whether there is a "purpose" directing these changes is a question for intellectual gymnasts and one not likely soon to be definitely answered; but one fact seems patent: the newer parts which came into being, survived, and were integrated in each succeeding evolutionary phase actually did serve the condition better.

The paradox for man lies in the fact that though it is essential that many functions operate automatically so as to give greater freedom for the orientation of the organism in meeting the problems which are constantly confronting him, yet, the nature of our civilized life being what it is, this very automaticity is often self-defeating. Let us be more specific. What happens when primitive man unexpectedly meets a lion? The man jumps and runs as fast as he can. The jumping and running represent a highly complicated series of activities. Through his sensory fibers he sees, hears, or smells something which he *recognizes* as being dangerous. It is because the nerve fibers send messages to the highly sensitized cortex that such awareness, such recognition is made possible through the process of remembering and discriminating. Such perception having taken place, both the involuntary (automatic) and the voluntary (cortical-spinal) systems go into action to meet the situation. Impulses travel rapidly to the hypothalamus which, when so stimulated, immediately discharges its sympathetic or stimulating apparatus which is always utilized when action is desired. Thus while the function of consciousness is primarily that of selecting and adopting the "best" procedure to follow in any given situation, the actual operation of the organism tends to be largely on an automatic level.

Two points thus become clear: First, the mere seeing of objects does not arouse the cortex sufficiently to stimulate the hypothalamus; the *stimulus must be interpreted as dangerous before* the organism orients itself toward danger. Second, once an idea has been "perceived" as dangerous, forces of the body are *set into motion automatically* so that even if the body does nothing in the face of danger it is left with raised blood pressure, rapid heart, increased blood sugar, etc.

What happens to "civilized" man? He has reduced the actual physical dangers of his environment, but he has in their place a whole host of ideational dangers (worries and fears) which are none the less insistent because they are intangible. You are afraid of losing your job; you dread the prospect of penniless old age; you earn enough to feed and clothe your family, but not enough to educate them properly; other men are more successful, win more recognition, etc. What are the doubts, fears, worries that "dog" you by day and haunt you by night? The man who "has everything," who "does not have a care in the world" exists nowhere except in the imagination of someone else. Every man confirms the truth of the old proverb, "Man is born to trouble as the sparks fly upward." Our reach forever exceeds our grasp, and achieved satisfactions are always followed by new desires. Many of our satisfactions must be delayed, postponed. When primitive man felt anger (a kind of fear), he released his emotion with his fists, his teeth, or a convenient stone. How many times in your adult life when you have been "fighting mad" have you actually fought? We are neither making an apologia for, nor condemning civilization; we are merely stating a fact. Here we are equipped with an organism geared for automatic response to stimuli, but placed in a situation which a large part of the time makes such immediacy of response either impossible or undesirable. The autonomic nervous system does not know that you must sit quietly when you are in a "boiling rage"; instead it gets you ready to do something; it does not distinguish between fear of a lion and fear of an employer's wrath, and in both instances mobilizes the organism's resources for flight or for fight. Far from being conversant with Emily Post, the involuntary nervous system has not even heard of the Ten Commandments. It has been engrossed through countless ages with perfecting a series of systems to enable the organism effectually to cope with the environment; and the drastic changes in environmental demands have been comparatively so sudden that the established automaticity often works as a hindrance rather than as a help.

It is of the utmost importance that we all realize the full import of the preceding paragraphs. When man perceives dangers, his physical organism prepares for a physical struggle, and if there is no release of the extra energy thus mobilized, disturbances of physical function will result. Thus, often the blood pressure remains elevated and persons "develop" high blood pressure; or the blood sugar becomes elevated and the persons "develop" diabetes; or the digestive ability of the stomach remains permanently impaired and facilitates the production of peptic ulcer. Our everyday or slang expressions for describing states of fear or anger—"worried sick," "so mad I could pop," "blind with rage," "trembling like a leaf," "shaking in my shoes," "burned up," "letting off steam," etc., are not found in medical textbooks; and yet they accurately describe just what does happen when external circumstances or our own attitudes constantly stimulate the physical organism to prepare for a type of activity which it rarely is permitted to perform. It is a good deal like lashing a tethered horse, or constantly building up the fire under a boiler that does not have adequate safety valves.

This situation of living one kind of life and being "geared" to live a totally different kind is one which calls for neither regret, which is futile, nor censure, which is equally profitless, but for clear understanding. In moments when "the world is too much with us" we dream vaguely of the joys of primitive life; but in actuality we prefer to have our cabin in the woods supplied with running water (preferably hot) and our porches screened. We poetize and sentimentalize about sleeping on pine boughs and drinking "Adam's ale" as it gushes from the spring; but we see to it that our mattresses have inner springs and that we are inoculated against typhoid. Granting that primitive man did not have to worry about how he was to pay next month's rent and that he probably did not have spastic colitis, high blood pressure, or any of the other ills which are concomitants of our high tension way of life, most of us most of the time would not willingly forego the conveniences and advantages of our civilization, with all its inhibitions, limitations, and frustrations. Even if we would, we can't. Nor do we need to abandon ourselves to an attitude of hopeless resignation, of saying, "Well, the Big Experiment slipped up somewhere and gave us the wrong kind of bodies with which to meet our kind of world."

Have you noticed that two or three times already this book has spoken of "attitudes" as if they were of equal importance with the external environment? They are, and for civilized man perhaps even more important. Something *can* be done about changing attitudes; and thanks to the cortex, we can do less automatic responding and more by way of real thinking.

CHAPTER IV

EMOTIONAL THINKING

This paradoxical chapter heading might as well have been "Illogical Thinking" or "Primitive Thinking," for all three phrases indicate the point we wish to demonstrate; namely, that most of what we loosely term "thinking" is not thinking at all. *Thinking* is a cortical process—delayed, unhurried, logical—based on facts, not wishes or fears, a selected response which implies discrimination. Dozens of times each day we begin a statement, "I think . . ." but rarely does what follows represent any such dispassionate and objective activity as that indicated by the foregoing definition of thinking.

Before proceeding to the discussion of emotional thinking, we need to clarify two preliminary points: (1) the close relation between thinking and feeling, and (2) the difference between emotion and emotional thinking.

List all the emotions which you experience: love, liking, fear, anger, dismay, confusion, bewilderment, homesickness, loyalty, patriotism, disgust, resentment, antagonism, joy, despair, aspiration; make your list as inclusive as possible and then scrutinize it carefully and see whether every item does not represent some variation or modification of the two basic emotions of pleasure and pain. Perhaps you will be interested to note that many more synonyms for pain than for pleasure come readily to your mind. The reason may be that joy is its own sanction; and we seek explanation, and hence words, only for pain and suffering. Do you talk as much about your undeserved good fortune as you do your "bad breaks"? Are you as voluble about your good health as about your aches and pains? Are you as articulate in praise of your children's accomplishments as you are eloquent about their failures and short-comings? Clarence Darrow used often to say that there was no such thing as pleasure—only pain and the absence of pain, the latter being a negative and not a positive state. Those of us who knew the positive joy he took in his family and his friends, in his books, and in confounding his opponents realize that he was merely stating dramatically the fact that the gaining of satisfaction brings at least temporary cessation from effort; whereas frustration, pain, and their host of brothers leave the organism in unrest and demand that something more be done. The physical, mental, and emotional aspects are simply *aspects,* not separate entities, of the functioning of the total organism. It cannot too often or too strongly be stressed that we are total organisms with all parts mutually interrelated and interdependent. There would be no problem were it not for the peculiar circumstances under which we live. The well-fed cat purrs "happily," his *emotion* apparently reflecting the fact that his *mind* has directed his *body* to a bowl of milk or an unwary mouse, with satisfying results—so far as the cat is concerned. He does not worry about where tomorrow's salmon is coming from nor the superior beauty of the next door Persian. The simpler the needs of the organism, the less "dangerous" the environment, the closer will be the harmony of feeling, thinking, and bodily activity. But life is not simple for any child of man; his basic wants have been augmented by countless wishes and desires; his environment has become complicated and demanding; and his organism is not so constituted as to make achievement easy. He must develop a new technique—one which makes increasing use of his cortical ability, one which substitutes logical, objective control for instinctive, emotional responses. We must postpone the satisfaction of many desires and circumvent rather than attack most dangers. Civilization has "thrown a monkey wrench" into the smooth working together of body, mind, and emotion, of activity, thinking, and feeling. We are so constituted that the three *should* operate as a unit; civilization is so organized that they do not. The pleasure-pain principle still operates; but to "feel" better physically and to be "happier" emotionally, we must delegate more and more responsibility, more and more control to our "cortical" minds.

Though the phrase "emotional thinking" is used more or less invidiously, do not be misled into believing that there is an implicit belittling of the value of emotion. Brain and heart, mind and emotion must work together, if we are to achieve happiness. Mind without emotion is sterile; emotion without mind is devastating. Cold, objective, dispassionate reason, unanimated by emotion, is like an architecturally perfect house, unlighted, unwarmed, uninhabitable; uncontrolled, undirected emotion is like a forest fire which consumes, destroys, blots out the beauty of the earth. The whole plea of this book is that we let our minds so control, so direct that there be less devastation—personal and social—and more light and warmth.

Even for primitive man, "a stranger and afraid, in a world he never made," the plot had begun to thicken, the dangers to multiply and be less subject to direct assault, the satisfactions to be more complex and less directly obtainable. Even he could not rely solely on his autonomic nervous system, his physiologically automatic responses. *Because he had to, he started to think.* Since so much of our own so-called thinking follows the same pattern as that formulated by our primitive progenitor, it behooves us not to smile too superciliously at the more obvious illogicality of his thought processes, and also to check rather carefully our own performances. If we scrutinize the customs, ceremonials, and rituals—the way of life—of primitive man, we see that most of his activities expressed belief in the *law of contagion* and in the *law of similarity.* According to the law of contagion, the part partakes of the nature of the whole, and association is misconstrued as identity. The law of similarity assumes that things which appear alike *are* the same. Thus primitive man was very careful to keep his nail parings, hair combings, clothes, or any other of his possessions from falling into the hands of his enemy. If they were lost, he was lost. If primitive man wished to destroy his enemy and could not secure some part of his victim's person or belongings, he could make an image representing his enemy, and, by destroying it, bring destruction to his foe. Even so intangible a possession as a name came to be identified as being an actual part of its owner, and was carefully concealed from one's enemy.

Do you ever use this primitive thinking? Why does a hideously ugly and uncomfortable chair in which Napoleon is reputed to have sat command a price to stagger the imagination, let alone the purse? What gives "relics" their value? Have you ever in a burst of anger torn up a photograph or a letter? Why do we lay wreathes of flowers at the feet of a marble statue? How many "keepsakes" of no intrinsic value do you cherish as invaluable? Why do we resent the familiar use of our first names by disliked persons or casual acquaintances? Why do we invoke the names of patron saints or national heroes? Why do we not name our children Xantippe or Judas, Machiaevelli or Ananias?

Or take the matter of superstitions. You don't have them; we don't have them; they are the silly beliefs of *other* persons. Perhaps a battalion of black cats crossing your path gives you no qualms; it makes no difference to you over which shoulder you see the moon; you live in a city apartment and are not disturbed about whether things should be planted in "the light of the moon" or the "dark of the moon"; with impunity you open umbrellas in the house and have no forebodings when mirrors crash to the floor; you are punctilious about returning borrowed salt and are not afraid to wear opals. But do you have "lucky numbers" or do you carry a "good-luck" piece? You don't "really believe" in it; but you would be very uncomfortable if you lost it. One brilliant physicist always draws from his pocket his rabbit's foot and lays it beside him on the table when he is playing bridge. (Incidentally, he is an excellent bridge player.) Relatively few office buildings or hotels have a thirteenth floor. It is easy to laugh derisively at the superstitions of others, for they are so patently absurd; our own we do not recognize. "But," you say, "what difference does it make if I keep a cracked teacup because it has certain associations for me?" "Why shouldn't I carry a protective medal with me when I go on journeys, if it makes me feel safer?" No reason at all, *provided* you realize just what you are doing, provided you do not confuse your "primitive thinking" with logical reasoning, provided you know that you are feeling and not thinking.

There is a point, however, beyond which this substitution of feeling for thinking, this reacting to situations in terms of their emotional connotations and associations can be detrimental; and particularly is this statement true if the associations are unconscious. Before discussing the significance of this statement, we should like to draw your attention to the question of *symbolization*.

Webster defines the word symbol as "That which stands for or suggests something else by reason of relationship, association, convention, or accidental but not intentional resemblance." One of the simplest uses of symbols is shown in such everyday expressions as: "Brave as a lion," "crafty as a fox," "happy as a lark," "hard as a stone," "capricious as an April day," "meek as a lamb," etc. Or we shorten the simile into a more emphatic form and speak of a man as being a "snake," a "rat," a "tower of strength," a "dynamo." Not only individual persons but groups also we thus "symbolize": the Republican elephant, the Democratic donkey, the American eagle, the Chinese dragon, the Russian bear, the British lion, the Irish shamrock, etc. Every decorator of a display window knows the value of symbols. Hearts and cupids; cherries and hatchets; clay pipes, shamrocks, and donkeys; rabbits and chickens; pumpkins and turkeys; Santa Claus and reindeer *mean* respectively Valentine's Day, Washington's Birthday, St. Patrick's Day, Easter, Thanksgiving, Christmas. The flag of every nation is a symbol of what that country stands for; a coat of arms is "the outward and visible sign" for a host of ideas, traditions, ideals. The meanings represented by symbols grow, deepen, intensify, and sometimes disappear according to the experiences associated with them. Do you respond emotionally to a cross, a crescent, a six-pointed star, or a lotus blossom? It depends on whether you are Christian, Mohammedan, Jew, or Buddhist. Moreover, the quality of your response will be proportionate to the intensity of your sense of identification with the group so represented, so symbolized. In connection with the statement that symbols may change in meaning, did you read of the store owner who at great expense had removed from the decoration of his building the Indian swastika, symbol of good luck, because of the sinister associations which that sign now carries?

Likewise, by facial expression and by gesture we represent or symbolize our feelings, our attitudes. The clenched fist, the lifted eyebrow, the bowed head, the open arms, the extended hand, the drooping mouth, the compressed lips, the "set" jaw, the shrugged shoulder; all these symbols and countless others tell in brief and condensed form what we are thinking, what we are feeling.

Symbols, then, are short-cut methods by which we interpret our relationship to the environment, a kind of shorthand which we both read and write. Things are symbols; gestures are symbols; words are symbols. The process of symbolization is a circular one; first, through *experience* we learn the *meaning* (its use, its potentiality for giving pleasure or pain) of an object; through repeated experience associations come to be identified with the meaning so that in time not only the object but the very word which represents or symbolizes it is capable of simultaneously conveying the denotative meaning and evoking the connotative associations. It is important to remember that symbols do not have preëxistent meanings, that the meanings grow out of experience; and it is equally important to remember that experience is always, to some extent, an emotional process.

If we are to understand our own tendency to "emotional thinking" we must remember that the vast majority of our meanings, symbols, ideas—call them what you will—are indirect acquisitions; we adopt them, for the most part unconsciously, from the milieu in which we live. Persons who have never handled or in any way been endangered by a gun shudder at the sight or even mention of a death-dealing weapon. Children fear or trust the corner policemen not in terms of direct dealings with him but according to whether they have heard "he will help you get across the street," or "he will take you away and lock you up if you are bad." One need not be bitten by a black widow spider or have his hand burned off in order to develop a hearty respect for the pain which both spider and fire are capable of giving. "All to the good," you object, "this passing on, this absorbing of meanings is valuable and timesaving; otherwise, each generation would have to start 'from scratch'; there could be no progress." And you are right. The trouble, however, is that we inherit not only the wisdom of the ages but misconceptions and distorted meanings along with their feeling tones which may be so pervasive as to continue operation long after the person so "infected" has intellectually emancipated himself from the misconception. A university professor (in the department of Social Science, incidentally) was heard to say, "I never quite get over my feeling of surprise when someone I really like and respect turns out to be a Republican." He had grown up in a "solid party state" where "nobody" was a Republican. One of his earliest memories was of his distress when he heard that Mr. M. was a Republican. Not having even the vaguest notion of what horrible reality the word represented, he nevertheless besought his father "to make Mr. M. stop being a Republican."

Do you, too, still have "inherited" feelings despite your intellectual awareness of their lack of factual basis?

Since we are primarily acting and feeling, rather than thinking, beings and since our acceptance of symbols or meanings is an emotional rather than a logical one, we are inclined on the one hand to let them operate without subjecting them to the cold light of reason or our own experience, and on the other hand to become resentful and defensive when these "taken for granted" ideas or beliefs are challenged. In other words, we accept the full emotional tone with which symbols, whether they be words or visible signs, are charged, and act in accordance with the emotions thus stimulated. All the rabble-rousers, the evangelists, the dictators recognize full well the value of catch words, of emotionally toned symbols, and use them often to achieve ends which are a distortion of the original meaning. It is, for example, a rather grim travesty that the cross, symbol of a religion the founder of which obviously cared enough about justice, brotherhood, and the worth of the individual man to be willing to die for His belief, has so often been used to arouse hatred, persecution, and injustice.

Another characteristic of emotional thinking is revealed in our tendency to generalize; we carry the emotional tone from one experience to another situation which may appear to be, but is not, identical (law of similarity). If you "know" that all Englishmen are humorless and reserved, that all Chinese are sinister, that all Russians are morbid, that all Negroes are shiftless, that all Yankees are shrewd and all Southern women are charming, that all church members are hypocrites, that all judges can be "bought," that all artists are temperamental, that no woman can drive a car decently, that all politicians are "crooks," that all men are conceited and all women gossips, and so on *ad infinitum,* then check your "knowledge" against the number of confirmatory instances which you actually know.

We generalize about individual persons as well as about groups. How reluctant we are to change our first impressions; we love and hate at first sight, and interpret succeeding actions as proof for or evidence against. It is amazing how good a case can be made for or against anyone, provided the judge knows ahead of time what the verdict is to be! "Only 'sissies' wear spats"—C. B. wears spats: one count against him; how rapidly the others pile up! He "flops" his hands. His voice is too high-pitched. He wears overshoes and carries an umbrella. His is the neatest desk in the office; it's disgusting for a *man* to be so tidy. You hear that he was seen at a concert, and it is rumored that he has a secret vice—reading poetry. Then one black day he seals his doom forever—he gives you his favorite recipe for salad. He is not a man at all; just a "born old-maid, wearing pants." You "knew it the first time you saw him wearing his sissy spats." On the most absurd, trivial, inconsequential bases we make "snap judgments," and then take great pride in proving that we were right. Mr. W. is a reserved and rather silent man: "thinks he's too good for other persons; he certainly is a snob." Mr. H. greets casual acquaintance and friend effusively: "just a politician with his hand-shaking and boot-licking." Miss L. carries a heavy burden of mascara on her lashes and applies rouge and lip stick with more generosity than artistry: "You can't tell me; any girl who gets herself up like that is bound to be a cheap, common piece." Mr. F. is not the barber's best customer, nor does he think that patriotism necessarily excludes objective criticism or a sense of humor: "Look at that wild-eyed, long-haired Russian. Did you hear him say, 'Only an adolescent with a changing voice could hope to sing *The Star Spangled Banner?*' I'll bet he's a Communist. If he doesn't like it here, why doesn't he go back to Russia?" Not these identical speeches but dozens of similar ones we make and hear every day; and all of them are the reflection of emotional thinking, a pseudothinking which does not arrive at conclusions after the examination of facts but one based on wishes or fears or on preconceived notions about our fellow men. The more intense the emotion that accompanies our prejudices the more difficult is it for us to isolate and evaluate facts.

For your own amusement and edification make a list of objects or situations which arouse an emotional response in you, an emotion which is not an inherent part of the stimulus but which exists because of some association which you have made. How do you "feel" about oatmeal, white flowers, onionskin paper, train whistles at night, the fragrance of new cut grass, petunias, Brahms' Waltz in A Major, candlelight, even numbers, the letter F, the figure 3, leather buttons? Perhaps you do not feel anything at all about any one; but it is certain that every human heart is haunted by fragrances, sounds, sights, memories. Since emotion or feeling is integral with experience—pleasurable emotions being the concomitant of the achievement of desired satisfactions or the escape from danger, and painful emotions being the accompaniment of the contrary type of experience—there is no possibility or even desirability of eliminating emotion from human life. Two things, however, are both possible and desirable.

In the first place, being aware of the emotional nature of many of our responses we can learn to be objective by analyzing specific situations, facing facts as they actually exist, "cortically" determining our course of action instead of "reflexly" responding in terms of our wishes or our fears. Wishes and fears may act as a goad toward effort; but the one is impotent, the other paralyzing unless they serve to stimulate the kind of logical, evaluating, rejecting, choosing, planning which will enable one to achieve his wishes and to escape his fears. One may lie in bed and dream endlessly of being a great lawyer, of winning fame and fortune, of halting forever the miscarriage of Justice; but the successful practice of law calls for a great deal more than wishing. Or one may worry, stew and fret about the prospect of losing one's job to the extent not only of losing it but one's health and happiness as well.

In the second place, we can stop the irradiation of harmful emotions and keep them from becoming chronic. How many times have you "taken out" on your wife or children your irritation with your employer or your concern about your financial condition? How many possible but highly improbable dangers have you worried about until your body is in a constant state of tension and your temper explosive? Do you know persons who say almost with pride, "I've always been a great worrier," or "I never have been able to control my temper"? What does your worry profit you? Where does your uncontrolled anger lead? Headaches, insomnia, digestive upsets, palpitating hearts, decreased efficiency, lessened happiness. Logical thinking is not easy. Of course it is "natural" to wish to kick the chair over which one has stumbled. Be "natural" and what do you have? A bruised toe to keep your aching shin company. Logical thinking is urged, not because it is easy or particularly pleasant but because it is essential if we are to live with maximum pleasure and minimum pain in this "civilized" environment, for the control of which our total organism is not any too well adapted. Just as lower forms of life developed special sense organs wherewith to master their environment so man, to meet his special situation, must utilize the latent powers of his cortex.

CHAPTER V

MAKING ALLIES OF OUR ATTITUDES

Even more than we ordinarily realize are we creatures of habit: our bodily functions, the minutiae of our daily lives, and our very attitudes are so "grooved" that they operate automatically without our conscious volition or awareness. These general attitudes play a tremendously important rôle so far as our health and happiness are concerned; so it behooves us not only to discriminate between beneficial and detrimental attitudes but also, having seen the harm "bad" habits can do, to change them. Habits are formed, not given; and as surely as they can be established in the first place, they can be broken and replaced. *We can change human nature;* and we'd better!

We have pointed out the automatic nature of many of our physiological functions, the purpose of the automaticity being the more efficient functioning of the total organism. In much the same way a large proportion of our daily activities are automatic. We establish a routine for ourselves, and for the most part quite unconsciously follow it. Without reflection or deliberate deciding we automatically get up when the alarm clock shatters our peace; automatically wash and dress (putting on the same shoe first every morning); automatically eat breakfast and glance through the paper; and automatically leave the house at the same time we left yesterday and will tomorrow.

There are countless different routines, but the point is that you have *yours* and follow it automatically. The world's work and your own would never be accomplished were it not possible for us thus automatically to attend to the minutiae of living. Whether this tendency to routinism is an ally or a hindrance depends on two things: the nature of the habit itself and our attitude toward the value of the habit. Obviously, habits of slovenliness, laziness, and procrastination interfere with rather than further efficiency and so are self-defeating. Even our good habits can become a hindrance if we regard them as fetishes and are unduly concerned or upset when, as is inevitable, they must at times be modified or abandoned.

Just as many of our physiologic functions are automatic and just as many of our daily activities are habitual in nature so also many of our general attitudes, the reaction patterns with which we meet life, are unconsciously acquired, automatic in nature and self-perpetuating.

Are you aggressive or submissive? Hypersensitive or callous? Sympathetic or indifferent? Even-tempered or volatile? Stormy or placid? Self-accusatory or self-indulgent? Inclined to brood over or to forget your mistakes? Understanding or condemnatory? Self-reliant or dependent? Impulsive or deliberate? Overwhelmed by a sense of your general worthlessness or exalted by a conviction of your superiority? How do you meet new or difficult situations—with self-confidence or with dread? Can you laugh at your own mistakes and stupidities, or do you take yourself seriously? Do you think the best of others or do you hope for the worst? Do you "fly off the handle" and do you "boil inside"? Whatever may be your answer to any or all of these questions, there are two which are even more important. *How did you get that way? Should you like to be different?*

The answer to the first question, "how did you get that way?" calls for discussion. A categorical answer would be: "Most of our general attitudes are those which are inculcated in us by and unconsciously adopted by us from our early environment."

We affectionately call children "little monkeys," and they are just that. They imitate the speech, the mannerisms, the actions, the attitudes of those who make up their little world. Mr. B. had his hand badly injured in an accident. His two-and-a-half-year-old son insisted on having *his* hand swathed in bandages and a pillow placed in his crib on which to rest *his* hand. Mr. T., a gentle-voiced and gentle-mannered man swears consistently, automatically, and apparently in an utterly dispassionate fashion. His three-year-old son in a soft and entirely unexcited voice accompanies his play with a running commentary which is the horror of his neighborhood and would be the envy of a sailor.

Children imitate not only the external manners of others but their attitudes as well. Children come into the world neither trailing Wordsworthian "clouds of glory" nor as "limbs of Satan," but rather as putty or clay, capable of being shaped along lines of loveliness or distorted into grotesques. You cannot unlive your own childhood; but you can better understand your present personality in terms of it; and the understanding of why you are as you are is the first step in the technique of changing yourself.

Between the extremes of the nearly ideal home wherein parents genuinely care for and respect the personalities of each other and their children and where there is both community and diversity of interests and the other extreme of bitter antagonism and brutal domination there are a thousand and one variations. It stands to reason and to universal experience that if two persons live under the same roof—no matter how large a house it may cover—there are inevitable differences of opinion, divergent interests and inclinations. What happened in your home? Were there frank and objective discussions leading to compromise solutions; or was every minor incident made the excuse for a major assault, with your father announcing, "So long as I pay the bills around here, you'll do what I say," or with your mother resurrecting every past real or imagined grievance, nagging persistently until she eventually had her way? Did you learn that you too could have *your* way, if you were disagreeable enough for a long enough period of time? Did you secretly hate one of your parents for his or her treatment of the other, and then did you feel guilty for not loving them equally as children are supposed to do? Bad as is the atmosphere of constant quarreling and contention, even worse is one of grim silence in which neither physical nor verbal blows are exchanged but there is a sense of constant tension, of bottled-up emotions which may at any moment explode. Did you feel helpless, not knowing what was expected of you, not knowing what it was all about? Did your parents share the responsibility of your guidance, or were you told, "Wait until your father hears about this," with the result that you came to regard him as little more than a punitive agency? Did one shove all the responsibility on the other with a, "Ask your mother" or a, "You'll have to do whatever your father says"? Worse yet, did you learn that there was so much friction between them that if one said "No," you could almost certainly wangle a "Yes" from the other? It is a tragic thing that the child is so often made the battleground on which parents fight their unending struggle to establish their "rights." Many a mother, unsatisfied in her own emotional life, attempts in her devotion to her children to find self-release. Though she would gladly die for her children, she refuses them the right to live their own lives; binds them tight with the "silver cord"; and in her effort to protect them from suffering makes them dependent, incapable of coping with the problems which inevitably they must meet.

Were you disciplined or directed? Were you allowed to make decisions for yourself and abide by the results of your own wisdom or foolishness? Were your childish mistakes treated as such, or were they magnified out of all proportion? Were you bewildered because one day you were laughed at and another frowned upon for the same action? Were you encouraged to be honest? It is doubtful that many parents give verbal instruction to their children on the advantages of being dishonest; but if a child's telling the truth brings about dire consequences, he soon learns to be evasive. It is an interesting fact that in practically every case of a problem child it is the parents rather than the child that need treatment. Lessening the tension of the home atmosphere often entirely dissipates the child's troubles.

Many factors in the early environment, other than the parents' relation to each other and to the child, enter into the formation of general attitudes. The following list of questions is by no means exhaustive, but it may indicate how numerous are the molding influences.

Were you an only child? Were you spoiled and pampered? Do you still wish to be the center of attention and feel that your wishes have priority claims? Were you one of several children and were invidious comparisons constantly made? Do you today, no matter how well you accomplish a task, feel that others could have done it better? Did you fight your own battles, or did you have an older brother to fight them for you? Now when confronted with a difficult situation, do you automatically tackle it yourself or do you expect someone else to help you out? Do you meet persons easily and feel comfortable in their presence, irrespective of whether their financial and social status is identical with or different from your own? Did you "belong" in your neigborhood; that is, was the financial and cultural status of your family about on a par with that of others whom you knew? Were you "too good to associate" with other children, or were they "not allowed to play with" you? Did you have little or much company? Were you told to speak when you were spoken to, or accepted as a part of the family, not necessarily the most important part, but important in your own right? Did you feel free and proud to bring your school companions home with you? How did your family get along with the neighbors? Did you learn early to play with groups of children? Were you a leader, a hanger-on, an outsider, or a coöperating participant? Which are you today?

This list of questions could be multiplied indefinitely and then could not possibly hope to cover all the multifarious factors which have gone into making you or us as we are today. If you have any characteristics about which you are inclined to say, "I've always been that way," try to push your memory back as far as you can and see whether you can trace the origin of your attitude. The point of such a procedure is not *to give you an alibi* for your present failures or inadequacies—there is nothing more tiresome than a person who is forever excusing his own shortcomings by placing the responsibility on someone else—but if you understand *why* you feel and respond to life as you do, then you lose your sense of guilt or self-intolerance and realize that *if you could learn one habit of reaction, it is possible to learn another,* that you can change, that you do not have to be "that way." Unlearning a habit and substituting another is a difficult task. If, from the time of your earliest memories, you have felt shy, insecure, seclusive you cannot one night decide that you would prefer being self-confident and assured and hope that the next day you can go forth wearing your new attitude as you would a new suit of clothes. If you have always been hypersensitive to criticism, "sensing" derogatory implications in whatever another says or fails to say, it will take *time and persistent effort* to get to the place where you see yourself in some true proportion and cease being troubled over every casual comment. Being intellectually convinced that your intolerance of the foibles or differences of others is a reflection of ingrained prejudices and emotional thinking is only the first step toward arriving at the mature stage of judging in terms of facts and realities; but it is an essential step.

Appreciation of the rôle played by early environment in the determination of future reaction patterns and attitudes focuses our attention on the necessity of providing children with as nearly ideal growing situations as possible. In the last few years we have learned much about the care and feeding of babies, with a consequent dramatic lowering of the rate of infant mortality. If we are to have children grow straight and tall in spirit and personality as well as in body then we must give as much care and attention to teaching *by example* healthful habits of thinking and feeling as we now do to diet and exercise. Modern surgery can perform miracles in straightening crooked bones, and modern psychiatry has achieved wonders in straightening out crooked and distorted personalities; but in both instances the procedure is time-consuming, painful, and certainly not so satisfactory as correctly developed limbs or personalities would be.

In addition to the personal relationships within the family, there are other environmental influences which, while equally potent, are less obvious. Do you have prejudices against any race, religion, or institution? Did you early learn to take it for granted that your own particular group was superior, and all others were to be scorned or at best pitied? Was the reverse true—were you "fed" with stories of injustice and mistreatment suffered by your group, so that you started life with a crippling sense that all the odds were against you? There is no gainsaying that our society is so organized that minority groups do find life more difficult, are discriminated against, are treated in a manner which belies our political mouthings about "democracy" or our religious protestations of belief in the "brotherhood of man"; but it is equally incontrovertible that there is more than one attitude with which the deplorable situation can be met. The following incidents are illustrative. In a midwestern university Miss F. was failed in a course because of flagrant dishonesty on her examination. In conference with the instructor she admitted that she had cheated but kept reiterating, "Others cheat. It's just because you are a Southern man and have a prejudice against our race that you fail me." So habituated was she to thinking of herself as a martyr to race prejudice that no amount of talk or even her own admission could change her attitude. In the same university, Mr. M., a member of the same race was ready to take the examination for his Ph.D. degree. Despite the fact that his scholastic record was superior, he postponed for one quarter the taking of his examination saying, "I'm sure that I could pass the examination now; but I wish to do more than just pass. I wish to have my record stand on its own merit and not have anyone say, 'He did well for one of his race.'" He took his degree with the highest honors that the university gives.

Was your family interested in community and national affairs.

and if so were their attitudes partisan or broadly tolerant? Were they self-seeking, or did they identify their interests with those of a larger group? Was your father fortunate enough to be doing work he liked, or was he just making a living? Did you get the idea that work and drudgery are synonymous? Was your mother's life circumscribed by circumstance or inclination to the routine of tending to the house and the children?

What are your own present social attitudes? Do you feel that life owes you a living, do you have a philosophy of "everybody for himself and the devil take the hindmost," or do you genuinely feel that you are your brother's keeper and that your responsibility to society is in direct proportion to your abilities and your advantages? Which philosophy did you daily see lived and exemplified by your family? Are you preoccupied with the minutiae of other persons' lives, or are you more concerned about situations of wider significance? How do you feel when one of your opinions is challenged? Are you annoyed and defensive, or do you listen with your mind as well as your ears?

We have talked almost exclusively about those factors in the environment which exert an almost unconscious influence, those attitudes which we appropriate through imitation. There may also be definite, traumatic or injuring experiences which will form the basis of a "general attitude" which becomes extensive in its manifestation. *Physical illness or handicaps* fall in this category.

J. P., a young man of quite ordinary achievements and abilities, has an overweening sense of his own importance. He is thoroughly insulated in a sense of self-esteem and toward his every utterance assumes the attitude—"Sir Oracle speaks. Let no dog ope his mouth." Any opposition or even the expression of a divergent point of view meets with a violent temper outburst to be followed by brooding sulkiness. As a child he was desperately ill with rheumatic fever followed by a long convalescence which necessitated his being confined to bed for a period of three years. The family was warned to avoid all excitement, to keep the patient calm, to let him have his own way. The result was that he developed into a full-fledged tyrant. Fear that John might have a heart attack made the family accede to his slightest whim and made of his every caprice a binding obligation. Confined as he was for the years between twelve and fifteen, he missed the harsh but effective discipline that comes from association with other boys. Even when he was well enough to return to school, he did not have enough physical strength for participation in active sports and so devoted himself to reading. He would make such unpleasant scenes at home whenever his will was crossed that his family followed the way of least resistance and gave in on every issue. Now, fifteen years later, he continues the same bullying technique of control. His will is law; his desires sacred; his opinion incontrovertible; his statements final. Needless to say he has few friends and makes life miserable for those who cannot escape coming into contact with him.

It is, of course, easy to understand how parents wish to coddle and pamper a sick child; but it is fortunate for the child that the majority of illnesses are of short enough duration so that the patient is soon back in a normal environment and able to pursue a normal life.

Physical handicaps are often the basis of inferiority feelings. We prate a good deal about our desire to be individualists; but in reality most persons are at heart conformists and feel happier if they are not too startlingly different in any direction. Cross-eyes, a harelip, deformed limbs—even being too short, too tall, too fat or too thin—can make life miserable. We carry our desire to be "one of the gang" even further: if all the other girls in the seventh grade have "permanents" and wear sweaters, there is no peace in Susan's heart or for her family until she too has her hair kinked and is supplied with sweaters, however unbecoming they may be; if "all the other kids" wear their hair "slicked back," Tom will go about with a perpetually wet head and spend hours brushing his unruly mop of hair in an effort to make it look like every one else's.

Mr. K. B., a person of fine physique and excellent mental ability, is painfully shy and seclusive. He magnifies the achievements of everyone else and minimizes his own. He suffers tortures over every real or imagined inadequacy. He was born with only one ear. At home, he constantly heard variations of, "The poor child; we never mention it. He is so dreadfully sensitive"; at school he was promptly christened, "One Lug." His father's business necessitated frequent moves; so Kenneth was subjected to many new adjustments with the inevitable curiosity and pity. He became hypersensitive; was sure that whenever he heard unexplained laughter it was from persons making fun of him; and finally came to feel that he was a freak, an object of revulsion to every one who saw him. Little was known about plastic surgery in his youth. Later he had a series of operations performed, and now only careful scrutiny would reveal the difference between his two ears. However, the attitude of sensitivity, of inferiority, is so deeply ingrained that he is sure that everyone notices the difference and either pities him or is revolted.

There may also be specific experiences which are so emotionally disturbing as to color the entire after-life of a person, to make it easy for him to develop a distorted attitude toward himself and toward others. One example will suffice.

H. F. is untiring in his efforts to make life better and easier for others. A brilliantly successful lawyer, he could win both personal fame and great fortune for himself; but he devotes nine tenths of his time and ability to "no-fee" cases. Though he spends his life trying to secure justice and mercy for others, he has no faith in life so far as his own life is concerned. He takes it for granted that his acquaintances will prove faithless, that his wife will desert him, that his children are sorry to be his, that he can count on no one or nothing. He gives devotion, loyalty, and effort; he expects indifference, distrust, betrayal. He is miserably unhappy and makes others feel likewise.

His father was a harsh and tyrannical man who worked hard to provide his family not only with necessities but with luxuries as well but who ruled with an iron hand. At the age of seven H. was called home from school to find his mother a suicide, her body still hanging. On a sadistic impulse of cruelty the father said, "Now you will be sorry that you were not kinder to your mother." Not only was H. bewildered by the loss of his one haven of refuge, but he felt vaguely that he was somehow responsible. His loss of security plus a sense of guilty responsibility became the groundwork against which he judged all future relations and activities. Since that one devastating experience he has always felt that he had no right to happiness, that his own nature is such as to make any kind of permanently meaningful relationship impossible.

Fortunately the reverse side of the picture is equally true. A chance experience can be sufficiently affecting to bring about a desired change of attitude.

P. R. was one of many children in a home where there was never quite enough money, where the father was constantly harassed by his inability to provide more adequately, and the overworked mother was irritable and short-tempered. Polly was full of life and apparently had a special talent for getting into mischief. Her older brothers and sisters were models of good deportment in school and learned their lessons easily and well. Polly was as slow about learning her "three R's" as she was quick to get into trouble. As a child she was always spoken of as "a little devil," a "hellion," or a "dumbbell." She accepted the terms and all their implications and lived by the theory that since she had the name, she might as well have the game. One day when she was in the sixth grade Polly was amazed when her teacher, having to leave the room, asked her to take charge during her absence. Years later speaking of the incident she said in effect, "No one could know what that request meant to me. I kept thinking, 'I can't be so dumb or so bad as every one says or she would never have asked me.' I learned more in the remainder of that year than I had in the preceding five and a half years put together."

Whether our general attitudes are imitative in origin or whether they are rooted in some particular experience, they are for the most part taken for granted, accepted almost fatalistically as though they were an inescapable part of our personalities. It cannot too strongly be emphasized that these attitudes are *learned* responses and they are capable of modification or elimination, provided the person is both intellectually convinced that some other attitude would be more productive of happiness and efficiency and is willing to expend the requisite energy and effort to bring about the change.

Check over the following list of attitudes; see which ones are predominately characteristic of your personality; decide which ones are assets and which are hindrances. The list is only partial and there are countless variations and degrees of each attitude listed.

IMMATURE, HARMFUL ATTITUDES	MATURE, CONSTRUCTIVE ATTITUDES
Intolerance	Tolerance
Hypercriticism	Understanding
Hypersensitivity	Objectivity
Dependence	Self-reliance
Defensiveness	Open-mindedness
Irritability	Calmness
Resentment	Forgiveness
Suspiciousness	Fair-mindedness
Inferiority	Self-respect
Inadequacy	Self-confidence
Self-pity	Facing facts
Egocentricity	Concern for others
Self-importance	Respect for others
Self-indulgence	Self-discipline
Selfishness	Generosity
Laziness (mental as well as physical)	Industry
Excessive pride	A sense of proportion
Excessive humility	Poise

A word of warning should be inserted here: *any virtue carried to excess becomes a vice.* We would all agree that *self-tolerance* is a desirable attitude. To demand the impossible of one's self, to reproach and condemn one's self for failures or mistakes, to expect a machine-like perfection and a complete realization of one's goals and ideals result in nothing but chronic dissatisfaction and a paralyzing sense of frustration. Understanding one's limitations and taking them into account in the evaluation of any success or failure does not, however, mean going to the opposite extreme of expecting nothing of one's self and constantly indulging in self-exculpation. Self-tolerance must not be confused with self-indulgence. *Pride,* likewise, is an admirable characteristic. Pride of one's abili-

ties, one's achievements, one's family, one's country, etc., to be constructive and valuable must be based on a true sense of values. The
man who is "too proud" to take a job which he considers beneath
his station and ability, and as a consequence permits his family to
suffer deprivations, is not truly proud; he merely has an inflated
idea of his own importance. There are many situations in life
which we are powerless to change or escape; they must be accepted
with some decent *humility,* some awareness of our relative impotence and unimportance. At the other extreme is the cringing,
fawning, worm of the dust, self-depreciation immortalized in the
character of Uriah Heep. Avoidance of extremes, the cultivation
of the "golden mean" is essential for the development of a well-
balanced, well-integrated personality. Don't let your self-confidence
become belligerent aggressiveness; your self-respect, self-adulation;
your tolerance, indifference; your generosity, prodigality.

SPECIFIC ATTITUDES

Most of our specific attitudes reflect our basic underlying general
patterns of reaction; i.e., if we are overcritical, we constantly find
new stimuli to evoke the critical attitude, or if we are inclined to
be hypersensitive, then we seize upon a thousand and one occasions
to be hurt. If, on the other hand, we are for the most part understanding and tolerant, then in the majority of situations our habitual or general attitude will be called into play. The cure or cultivation of such specific attitudes obviously must be directed not toward
a particular situation, but toward basic causes.

There are, however, countless specific attitudes which need direct
attention. You, for example, tend to be an adjustable person, you
get along well with others, and have a live and let live philosophy
that enables you to enjoy others whether or not they see eye to eye
with you; but you have one business associate who "gets on your
nerves." You don't like his ideas, his clothes, his laugh, his attitudes.
He "talks big"; he is eternally manicuring his finger nails; he tries
to patronize you; he interrupts you whenever you speak; he smiles

in a bored and superior fashion every time you mention your garden; he answers the telephone as though he were the president of the company; he calls his wife "the little woman"; he kids you about your rapidly increasing baldness; he brags that he "has a way with the women," etc.—in other words, he is the incarnation of everything that you dislike, he is anathema. Every night when you go home you have new evidence to recount of his stupidity, his crassness, his general hatefulness. What can you do? You'd like to knock him into insensibility; at times you would like to kill him; indeed, you enjoy pondering particularly painful ways of exterminating him. Your body gets you ready to carry out your primitive impulses; but the code of civilization inhibits you: the result is that he literally "makes you sick at your stomach," gives you a headache, is a "pain in the neck." He is blithely unaffected by your smoldering rage, but you are incapacitated by it. You can do one of two things: you can give up your job and so remove yourself from the source of irritation, or you can learn to be unaffected by him.

No one expects you to love him; but you can train yourself to be as unconscious of him as you are of the street cars that rattle past your home. When you first moved there, you were sure that the noise would "drive you crazy"; now you literally do not hear. Difficult as is the task of changing attitudes, it is usually easier and more feasible than removing or escaping the stimulus which brought about the attitude.

It is an interesting phenomenon that so many persons have mutually contradictory attitudes. Mr. G. is a sentimental advocate for the working man and verbally violent in his assaults on "Big Business"; yet each morning he reads the stock market report and starts his day happily or grumpily depending on the current status of his five hundred dollars worth of stock. Dr. S. is a careful research scientist, meticulously exact about his work and his statements; in any political discussion he refuses to be influenced by party loyalties; he arrives at conclusions along the path of calm, objective reasoning in every field—except religion. That he keeps in a hermetically sealed compartment of his mind (a logic-tight compartment), turns a deaf ear to any new information, and is nettled by any argument. Check on your own inconsistencies.

Whether these specific attitudes are mere trivia, adding color and contrast to your personality or are detrimental to the integrated functioning of your total organism depends on their intrinsic nature and the intensity with which they are felt. A single mosquito can keep you awake all night; a single immature attitude can keep you in emotional turmoil. Moreover, through irradiation the emotional tone which surrounds one specific attitude may be transferred to other situations and relations. For example, intense dislike of a particular person if brooded over long enough and felt keenly enough comes in time to include *all* of his characteristics whether or not they have any connection with the qualities which first aroused your antagonism. You know little or nothing about his race or his religion, but you hate them because they are his. You meet another person of the same group and it is easy to transfer your "feeling" about the first to the second. What started as a localized and particularized dislike is well on the road toward becoming a general attitude of intolerance.

You no doubt will have noticed that in this discussion of attitudes, we have often used the words "mature" and "immature," "healthful" and "harmful" as descriptive terms. Since the dawn of civilization philosophers have been attempting to decide the nature of "good" and of "evil." Our approach is the pragmatic, practical one of judging values in terms of results; and it is entirely apparent that some attitudes bear good fruit and others ill. The calm, objective, coolly reasoning, tolerant person who is aware but not overwhelmed by his and others' limitations, who is schooled to face facts instead of worrying about possibilities, and who is self-reliant is not only happier than is the person with opposite characteristics but he is also healthier. Just how attitudes can affect health will be discussed in the next chapter.

CHAPTER VI

TENSION

How the tension created because our bodies are not attuned to the demand of civilization that we postpone pleasures and meet dangers indirectly affects the autonomic nervous system and how it, in turn, overstimulates the various bodily organs to produce symptoms—*your* symptoms—will be the subject of this chapter. If you have some symptom which continues to distress you, despite your physician's inability to find organic basis for its existence and persistence, then you are probably the victim of tension and, paradoxically enough, are to be congratulated. Congratulations are in order because if you understand your symptoms—their origin, significance, and cure—and if you will *put what you know into practice* you can do three very remarkable things for yourself: (1) cure many of your symptoms; (2) greatly facilitate the efforts of your physician, when your disease is on an organic basis; and (3) prevent the development of additional symptoms.

As a background for understanding the "why" of symptoms we have pointed out seven important facts. (1) Man, like every other living organism, operates basically on the pleasure-pain principle, seeking to achieve satisfactions and to avoid dangers. (2) Man reacts to the environment as a total organism, his acting, thinking, and feeling being but different aspects of a total response. (3) To meet the demands of the environment man has, through a long evolutionary process, developed the involuntary and the voluntary nervous system, both being designed to enable man better to fulfill his basic drives. (4) Civilization has not only extended and complexed the satisfactions and dangers which man now seeks to obtain and to avoid, but it has also set up codes which prohibit or delay

53

direct satisfactions or escapes. (5) Consequently there is no longer the smoothly synchronized functioning of thinking, feeling, and acting present in simpler forms of life. We have seen further (6) how most of our so-called "thinking" is primarily emotional in nature and (7) how our established reaction patterns or attitudes operate to confuse our attempts at logical thinking.

Now that we turn to an explanation of tension symptoms, the pertinence of the foregoing discussion will become apparent. The word "tension" is used as a generic term to describe all those symptoms which are the result of the various body organs being bombarded by emotional stimuli which call for action—action which is not released. The word "tension" comes from the Latin verb *tenere,* meaning to pull or stretch, and that which is stretched is ready to spring or snap back as soon as it is released. An ordinary rubber band is an excellent example of this kind of resiliency. It can be stretched to many times its original length, and when released will resume its former shape and size. You can easily stretch such a band to the breaking point, or you can as surely though more slowly ruin its elasticity by using it to bind too large a package. In the second instance, the strain on the rubber, though slighter, is constant, and eventually results in deterioration of resiliency. Much the same kind of thing happens to human beings when subjected to strain from which there is no release. The body of man is amazingly resilient or adaptable; it automatically prepares to meet any and every situation which the mind of man apprehends. But you will remember two things greatly handicap this would-be automaticity: (1) civilization often demands that we postpone, or even permanently defer, the gratification of our impulses or desires, that we inhibit the expression of our fears and hates; and (2) our attitudes perpetuate and multiply the number of such "unfulfillable" stimuli in such a way as to keep our bodies and minds constantly "stretched," continuously under tension. Another analogy: a giant tree can be shattered by a single bolt of lightning just as the physical or mental health of a person may be wrecked by an illness or a strain too great to be borne. It is said that the myrtle tree dies if its perfect symmetry is marred; that is, if one large branch is destroyed, the whole tree dies. Most trees are neither destroyed by lightning nor do they require perfection as the *sine qua non* of their continued existence. They are more or less tall and straight, more or less gnarled and twisted, closer or farther away from the ideal strength and beauty which their species is capable of attaining, depending on the soil, the climate, the surroundings, the care, the storms to which they are subjected, etc. The analogy holds true for man: "as the twig is bent the tree's inclined." Obviously a cork tree can not be converted into an oak, nor a feeble-minded person into a college president. Whether an oak is, however, to remain a "scrub" or grow to ship mast proportions and strength is another proposition. You are never going to be entirely free from all the aches and pains, physical or mental, to which man is heir; but you can greatly reduce their number, you can at least approximate the ideal of a sane mind in a healthy body; and one of the most important ways is by recognizing the nature and operation, the cause and cure of tension symptoms.

Make a list of the things you wish and the things you fear—all of them, even the ones you will hardly admit to yourself. Granted that you have enough food for today and reasonable assurance that you will have sufficient for the days to come, granted that you are not in the presence of actual physical danger or fearful for your physical safety, what then? You get a Ford; you wish you had a Cadillac; you get a Cadillac, you wish you had a Rolls Royce. You get a Rolls Royce; if only you had an airplane—. You wish to be beautiful, to be handsome, to be popular, to be successful, to be brilliant, to be the center of attention. You are a traveling sales-man; if only you could go to your own little home every night! The same old street, the same old houses, the same old lawn to be mowed; if only you could travel! You are married to a person who obviously does not appreciate your superior worth; you think wist-fully of Jim or George, Jane or Geraldine and think how much happier you could have been, if only—. You wish you lived in another city, in another part of the city, in another house or apartment. If only you could be "free and easy" as Fred is when he meets strangers; if only persons would listen to the expression of your opinions with the same attention and respect that they give to Mr. M.'s words. Of course you love your family and everything like that; but if only you had had a different background, a better education, had met a different class of people.

Are you afraid of losing your job, of a destitute old age, of political or economic upheavals that will endanger your savings or wealth? Do you fear the prospect of lonely old age, the responsibility of rearing children: that they will not be healthy, that they may not "turn out well"? Are you afraid that some other man or woman is more attractive to your mate? Are you afraid to be alone, to be in crowds, to be on high places, of dirt, of illness, of death? Are you afraid of what others say and think about you, fearful about your own limitations and inclination? Are you afraid because your actions, your thoughts, or both are wicked and sinful? Are you afraid that you cannot measure up to what others expect of you or to what you expect of yourself? Are you afraid of being afraid? You smile when you hear of the woman who burst into uncontrolled weeping when the train on which she was a passenger crossed a bridge spanning a flooded river. Upon solicitous questioning from a train attendant she finally stated, "I was just thinking how dreadful it would be if I had a child and the child was ever drowned." And yet how many of our fears fall into just this category. We worry about the past which cannot possibly be relived, and we fear future eventualities which may never occur or if they do will be intensified rather than alleviated by our forebodings.

What about this host of wishes, this horde of fears? How do they affect us? If the tension they cause is not released in action designed to fulfill the desires or to escape the fears, then *symptoms* develop, symptoms which may be either primarily psychologic or primarily physiologic in nature. The psychologic manifestations of tension:

irritability, intolerance, hypersensitivity, anxiety, etc., are perhaps more obviously an expression of attitudes, but they are no more real than are the physiologic.

Physiologically what happens is this: the tension caused by the constant bombardment of desires, wishes, fears, anxieties, that is, by *attitudes,* stimulates the hypothalamus (see Chapter III). The overactivity of the hypothalamus, in turn, causes an excessive number of impulses to be sent down the sympathetic and parasympathetic nervous system. When these extra impulses reach the heart, the heart beats faster; when they reach the blood vessels, the blood vessels become spastic and the blood pressure is raised; when they reach the intestines, the intestines contract and cause spastic colitis, constipation, or diarrhea. *These physical symptoms are symptoms of tension.* The reader must remember that such symptoms may also be symptoms of organic disease such as infection, tumor, or inflammation, and that a physician's diagnosis is always to be sought. These tension symptoms are the end result of a general attitude which may seem to be far removed from the body.

Often patients in all good faith will deny valiantly that they are under any tension and maintain that they have no reason for being upset. It must be remembered that *just as our attitudes are habitual in nature so the tension created by them may be so chronic as not to be in our conscious awareness at all.* In dramatic or unusual experiences we are quite aware of tension symptoms in our bodies. You awaken from a sound sleep to hear stealthy footsteps in the next room. Your heart begins to pound, your throat is so constricted and your mouth so dry that you cannot utter a sound, you are stiff with fear. Or you come home after a harrowing day of just sitting in a hospital waiting room and you are as physically weary as though you had spent an equal number of hours at hard labor. It is easy in such instances to realize the intimate connection between the stimulating fear or anxiety and your bodily reaction; not so easy when the tension is the result of a life-long tendency to over-react to all situations. At the end of your anxious day of waiting in the hospital, the surgeon reassures you that the operation was successful and the nurse tells you that the patient is sleeping quietly. Your tension is released; the rubber band snaps back into place. But all your life you have been overly conscientious, overwhelmed by your inadequacies, intolerant of your failures. Your attitudes have kept your body under constant, though perhaps relatively mild, tension which is not released, and at last your tension begins to manifest itself in physiologic symptoms.

Mr. K. M., aged 37, had high blood pressure, a rapid pulse, and spastic colitis. These symptoms had been present for a number of years, but repeated physical examinations revealed no causative organic trouble. Alarmed by a sharp pain over his heart, Mr. M. again sought medical advice; and once more he was told that he had no organic pathology.

Mr. M. denied that he was under any special tension. He was working hard at his job but no harder than usual and no harder than others. He had a wife and three children of whom he was both fond and proud; his home was paid for and there was no need for concern over finances. He admitted feeling restless and discontent, but insisted that if he could just get rid of his distressing physical conditions, he would be all right.

In ensuing conversations, however, Mr. M. revealed that he had always been an overambitious and driving person. His father had been a shiftless ne'er do well, and as a child the patient had felt keenly not only the pinch of actual want but the social discrimination which the family poverty entailed. Early Mr. M. had decided to be a success, if hard work could make him so. No matter what goals he achieved, he was still dissatisfied, and forever with self-reproach measured his accomplishments with those of someone more successful. He not only worked with concentrated intensity when he was in his office, but he brought his business problems home with him and spent his evenings trying to devise new and more effective business techniques. He was irritated by the slowness and inefficiency of those who worked for him, irritated because his wife was not a "better manager," irritated by the controlling political party which was "ruining the country," and most of all irritated by his own inability to meet the impossible demands which he made on himself.

This patient was unconsciously suffering from tension symptoms. All his basic attitudes were conducive to a restless, overreacting, tense manner of meeting life. His tension expressed itself psychologically by his irritability and chronic dissatisfaction, and physiologically by an overactive hypothalamus and the peripheral symptoms of rapid heart beat, high blood pressure, spastic colitis, and the mild coronary (heart) spasms which gave rise to pain in the chest. The minor irritations of daily and ordinary life were sufficient to bring on new symptoms of tension without his realization of his susceptibility to these irritations and symptoms. His basic attitudes of tension responded almost reflexly and without his conscious recognition to each new irritation.

You will notice that every characteristic manifested by this patient is one which in itself is admirable; the danger and the harm lie in the degree. He was *unduly* ambitious, *excessive* in his demands upon himself, *hyper* critical of others. The other extreme of lazy, shiftless indifference is just as bad, and from the point of view of achievement even worse (though the person with the latter characteristics probably will not develop tension symptoms). Extremes —even of characteristics usually termed "virtues"—are in the end self-defeating. The cadaverous ascetic, no less than the glutton, is giving a place of undue significance to the relatively unimportant matter of food; profligate and miser alike reveal by their actions that they have no true sense of the value of money; and the person who can never make up his mind equally with the one whose code is iron clad and who regards his opinions as having the finality of the laws of the Medes and the Persians is a detriment to himself and to society.

Tension symptoms may also arise from the habit of *repressing* unpleasant memories. Particularly with pride or ego-wounding memories do we employ this mechanism; but the forgetting is rarely a true dismissal. Instead of actually ridding ourselves of the memory and all of its associated emotions we push it into the back of our consciousness where it festers and continuously breeds tension, the intensity of which is in direct proportion to our attitude toward the original stimulus. This repression or "dynamic forgetting" [1] accounts for the fact that tension symptoms often come to the fore in a situation which appears to have little if any potentiality for creating disturbance. The tension is there, seething, pent up, and needing only the slightest of stimuli to discharge it.

Miss G., aged 29, suffered from a persistent headache which felt like a constant pressure on her head. The pain had been present for four years and no medicine, diet, or other therapy had been effective for relief. She denied being worried about anything, and insisted that while her life was not ideal, she was getting along well.

Miss G. had wished to be a nurse, and had worked hard and saved her money to pay for the necessary training. With enough money saved to pay for her entire schooling, she entered a hospital and enjoyed her work even more than she had anticipated. Her father became seriously ill, and a major operation followed by months of nursing care were necessary to insure his recovery. The financial emergency demanded not only that the farm be mortgaged, but that Miss G. give up her plans and contribute her savings. She was devoted to her father and without any conscious sense of resentment left the hospital and sought work as a sales person. Thereafter she supported both her father and her mother. One day at work she fell and struck the back of her head. All examinations failed to reveal any injury, but the pain persisted.

Miss G. had a constant feeling of frustration over her work. She longed to go back to the hospital to continue her nurse's training and felt trapped because of the financial situation. She did not "blame" her father, but she was bitterly resentful of her pain; it was merely the stimulus needed to release her tension which hitherto had been unexpressed.

It is interesting that sleep does not necessarily release one from tension. The worries and fears which form the groundwork of tension continue to operate so that a person may: (1) sleep restlessly, (2) awake from a sound sleep with pounding heart and with a

[1] *Vide* p. 126.

sense of acute anxiety, (3) be disturbed by distressing dreams or nightmares, or (4) have aching muscles from having, during his sleep, clenched his jaws, his hands, etc.[2]

By now you no doubt are asking, "But why is it always my *head* that hurts?" or, "I can see why being in a state of constant apprehension makes one's heart beat faster but why after every meal do I feel as though I had a lump of lead in my stomach?"

The tensions present within the hypothalamus, activating as they do a central mechanism, *may produce symptoms in practically any portion of the body*. Persons under tension tend to be psychologically irritable, and physiologically overreactive. In most persons, however, one organ or system alone seems to be involved; and the immediate question arises as to why, when all the involuntary nervous system is stimulated, should one organ, as the heart or stomach, be selected as the major center for the nervous discharge. The reasons for symptom site determination may be classified as follows: (1) constitutional predisposition, (2) symbolism, (3) accidental selection, (4) focusing of attention, and (5) predisposing disease. Through all these factors runs the phenomenon of habit which, once a main channel of expression is started, tends to perpetuate the symptom in the organ involved.

The *constitutional predisposition* appears in many different forms. In some persons who suffer from "knots" in the pit of the stomach, sour stomachs, or peptic ulcer symptoms, there is a family history of stomach troubles of various sorts, and the patient seems to be carrying out the family inheritance. Other patients have a family history of heart trouble, or high blood pressure, of goiter, etc.; and when they become emotionally disturbed and their hypothalamus overactive the weakest or most susceptible portion of their organism seems to be that one which has a hereditary susceptibility. In similar fashion, once an organ has been diseased or has manifested symptoms from causes other than emotional ones, that organ remains less resistant to future illness; and in instances such as heart disease,

2 *Vide*, p. 117.

injuries to joints, or inflammations of the throat, any emotional disturbance of severity will, other factors being equal, tend to focus in rapidity of heart beat, aching of the injured joint, contraction of irritated throat, etc. In other words, the nervous system discharge which tends to flow into all channels to all parts of the body will have the greatest effect in the weakest organ, and will thereby produce the symptom which attracts most attention.

The *accidental* selection of the site of greatest sympathetic discharge occurs often. Thus some persons complain of marked throat irritations following the swallowing of a fishbone; and the general tension which was at a high level will be released by focusing attention upon the throat. The fishbone may have long since departed, and the superficial scratch in the throat long since healed, but the patient will continue to complain of the soreness in the throat and insist that the fishbone must still be there. In such instances the throat accidentally was seized upon as the site of nervous discharge. One patient complained of severe ear pains; and though all examinations were negative, the patient was "beside himself" because of the pain. This boy was under great tension because of a difficult domestic situation and a complete thwarting of his ambitions. Having given up his hopes and dreams of studying law, he worked as a janitor to support his aged parents; and, when one day a loud explosion occurred in the basement, his ears were left with the feeling of being stuffed. Soon thereafter the boy complained of his ears and, subsequently, his tension expressed itself through this accidentally determined site.

If for *any* reason a person's attention is *focused* on some particular organ he may localize his tension symptom there. Persons under tension, once they hear of someone suffering from heart disease, backaches, lung trouble, etc., will immediately complain of symptoms in similar parts of their bodies. In such instances, there are symptoms of tension in the part complained of, and once the attention is directed toward one area, the slightest emotional disturbance will be expressed in that part. Soon the element of habit takes over and the part responds automatically to tension under any emotional stress.

Symbolic symptoms will be discussed in detail in Chapter XI; but here it may be well to indicate that symptom site may be symbolically determined. One example will serve as illustration. Mr. E. K. was under great tension because of financial difficulties, estrangement from his fiancee, and an uncertain future. So disturbing were his problems that he felt himself "going mad." One day he was scratched by a dog, and immediately the fear arose that he would get rabies. His throat became parched (the sympathetic system in fear states prevents secretion of saliva, thus causing "dry throat"), and he was sure that this dryness was the first symptom of the disease. He complained constantly thereafter of throat constriction and his fear of rabies, even though the dog turned out to be normal and even though the patient received a course of antirabic vaccine. His fear of rabies and the accompanying constriction of his throat were symbolic expressions of his feeling of "going mad" over his personal problems.

Once an organ or body system has been selected as the main expression of general tension, then the *element of habit* enters the problem. The body is given to automaticity, and any response of the motor system—whether it be the muscles of the heart, stomach, blood vessels, or face—once initiated tends to recur even when the actual causative tension has disappeared. It is this element of habit which is so important and such an obstacle in the removing of many signs of tension.

One final word before considering typical tension symptoms as they appear in various parts of the body. The presence or the absence of symptoms, their relative mildness or severity will in the last analysis depend upon a total situation rather than upon any one single element of it. Thus the more constitutional predisposition, the less emotional disturbance will be required to initiate symptoms. In other words, not every person will respond in identical fashion to the same stimulus. The stress of the situation, the constitution of the patient, his physical condition at the time, his habitual patterns of response (attitudes), all are factors in the situation, and the importance of the rôle of each varies from person to person and within the same person.

CHAPTER VII

HEART SYMPTOMS

The heart, or rather the entire cardio-renal-vascular system, is highly complex in organization and amazingly efficient in functioning. It is one of the most elastic of human organs, and, designed as it was to meet widely varying conditions and exigencies, has remarkable ability both to adjust to, and compensate for, whatever demand is placed upon it or whatever abuse we may give it. Given half a chance, the heart will continue its efficient operation; but even the finest elastic, if subjected to constant and unrelieved strain, will eventually lose its resiliency. Like any other intricately designed and delicately adjusted instrument, the heart is particularly sensitive to all stimuli. This very sensitivity of response accounts for the widespread occurrence of heart symptoms; for the impact of emotional stimuli is felt and recorded immediately by the heart.

Tension symptoms involving the heart are not only common but particularly distressing. Everyone, however little he may know of anatomy and physiology, is aware of the tremendously important rôle which the heart plays in the total body economy, and consequently is inclined to attach particular significance to any heart symptom. Here, as elsewhere, "a little learning is a dangerous thing," and often a patient both prolongs and intensifies his heart symptoms by his panicky attitude about having heart trouble.

Whether a specific heart symptom is important or not depends on the condition which it reflects. *Don't attempt autodiagnosis.* If your heart beats too fast, if it skips beats, if you are short-winded after slight exertion, or if you have pains, consult a physician who can determine the presence or absence of organic pathology. If there is an actual disease process present, follow his instructions implicitly, for autotherapy like self-diagnosis is always foolish and often suicidal. If, however, you are assured that your heart is sound, that there is nothing organically wrong, then you must reduce the tension which is responsible for the distressing symptom. You can't by an act of will forget; but you can get rid of it. To say that pain is painful whether it be functional (without organic basis) or organic in origin sounds absurdly obvious, and yet it expresses a truth which the patient's would-be friends and advisors seem often to forget. Following the temporary relief that the patient feels when assured that his heart is in excellent condition, there frequently is a recurrence of the disturbing symptom. *The symptoms are bound to recur and to persist until their cause is discovered and removed.* The tension which caused the symptom in the first place is still there and still operative. The patient wonders why his heart should continue hurting if nothing is wrong. He consults another doctor and again is told to forget. But the pain persists. Then he becomes panic-stricken. Maybe his condition is beyond cure and they are too kind to tell him. His panic increases the tension, and his symptoms are increased in number and severity. Disturbed by pain and distraught by fear the patient becomes increasingly miserable.

Whatever your sypmtoms may be and wherever they may be located, whether they be mildly annoying or acutely distressing, remember these two things: (1) only a skilled physician is qualified to diagnose your condition and tell you whether your difficulty is functional or organic, and (2) if he assures you that there is no organic pathology, then you must undertake the arduous task of changing your attitudes and reaction patterns in such a way as to reduce or eliminate the overactivity of your hypothalamus; that is, release your tension.

THE HEART

Man's heart is a four compartment sac composed of a special type of muscle. Through a long process of evolution the heart has gradually developed from the somewhat thickened blood vessel found in reptiles until in mammals, such as cows, horses, dogs, and man, it has reached its present stage of perfection. Teleologically speaking, we say that the heart was developed for the purpose of distributing food, oxygen, and various catalytic agents to all the parts of the organism. The heart beats constantly, more slowly or more rapidly depending on whether we are resting or working. The more physical work we do, the more food and oxygen the body requires and therefore the more rapidly will the heart beat. The involuntary nervous system has close and intimate connections with the heart. The sympathetic nervous system tends to make the heart beat faster; the parasympathetic, slower. Because of the basic ability of the heart to continue to beat, the activity of the nervous system can rarely slow the heart below 60 beats per minute; and rarely, except in certain pathologic cases, increase its beat to over 140 per minute. Both of these rates are entirely compatible with a normal existence and occur without apparent damage to the heart. Emotional tension usually results in overactivity of the sympathetic system, thus causing an increase in heart rate. If the patient who has been assured by a competent physician that his heart symptoms have no organic basis will remember that nature has made the heart as nearly fool proof as possible, he will be saved much needless apprehension.

Palpitation, a symptom often complained of, means merely that the person is abnormally aware of a rapidly beating heart. When palpitation occurs one needs to rule out such conditions as fever, infection, hyperthyroidism, etc. That symptoms may *appear* to be identical and yet be totally different in origin and significance is illustrated by the following cases.

Johanna S., aged 34, complained of palpitation. She was worried and apprehensive, fearing that she had heart trouble and that she would "drop dead." Examination revealed, in addition to a rapid heart beat, marked hunger and loss of weight, despite the intake of large amounts of food, a large lump in her throat, and a basal metabolic rate of plus 35. The diagnosis was that of goiter (hyperthyroidism), and the palpitation cleared up when the goiter was removed.

Joan W., aged 19, had had a rapid heart beat (about 120 most of the time) and palpitation for many years. The clinical and laboratory examinations of her heart showed no signs of any damage. Joan has always been excessively conscientious. She worried about her school work, she worried about her sister, she worried about the fact that she was under weight, she worried for fear her father might lose his job. If there were no immediate troubles of her own she worried about what "might" happen; she even worried about the "heathen who would die unsaved." She was always tense, always restless, muttered in her sleep, and swallowed her food without chewing it. She cried easily and was never really happy. In all this behavior she imitated her mother, who incidentally was also subject to palpitation.

Joan's palpitation which had become her major worry was clearly the result of her emotional tension. This emotional tension produced physiologic tension in the sympathetic nervous system; and this tension in turn increased the rate of her heart beat, as well as giving her spastic constipation and other physical symptoms. The treatment of Joan was, among other things, to persuade her to get a job, to live away from her mother, and to change her basic attitude of overreaction and tension to every stimulus which presented itself.

In any given case of palpitation, the first step is to seek expert advice as to its cause. If the cause is physical, the physician will help you; if the cause is not organic, then the problem is to relieve the tension which you have, whether that tension be the result of chronically unhealthy basic attitudes, or of temporary tensions created by ambition, frustration, or any other worry. Rarely does palpitation resulting from tension lead to heart damage; so the sooner one stops worrying about this annoying but unharmful symptom, and the sooner he acts to relieve his basic tension, the quicker he will lose his symptom. To say that one would not be tense if there were no palpitation is to put the cart before the horse; for the palpitation is only a symptom, and the worry about this symptom is secondary to worries about other problems.

Heart jumps.—Heart jumps or extrasystoles, feel as though the heart skips a beat. This hesitation in heart action may actually occur from too much drug, such as quinidine or digitalis; from hyperthyroidism; from excessive smoking; and from any one of several other causes. A most important cause of skipped beats is chronic emotional tension, usually based on fears and anxiety which are not or cannot be expressed. From a technical point of view it appears that the parasympathetic portion of the hypothalamus probably acts to slow the heart beat for a fraction of a second, and it is this slowing which results in the skipped beat.

Mr. J. K., aged 39, complained of marked skipping of heart beats present at some times but not at others. Several electrocardiograms were normal and several showed the typical tracing of a skipped beat. Though all evidence pointed to a normally functioning heart, he was greatly concerned about his condition, made his will, and became increasingly despondent.

Mr. J. K. had grown up in this country, but he had relatives in Europe. When the Second World War started, his parents were caught in the maelstrom of refugees and disappeared. Then Mr. K. received threats that unless he desisted in his denunciation of the country of his parents' nativity, his parents who had been found would be deprived of food and sent to concentration camps. Occasionally he received from his parents brief appealing letters which seemed to indicate that the threats were not idle ones. He lived in a constant state of fear. During this entire time, Mr. K. was in a state of tension; and although he payed little attention to the palpitation which had occurred for several years, he became seriously frightened when the "skipped" beats appeared. It was difficult to get Mr. K. to adopt an attitude of determined resignation, to get him to feel that the lot of his parents would hardly be worse no matter what he did or didn't do, that the blackmail methods should they work on others as well as on him would eventually result in more misery for everyone, including members of his own family. Only when the tyrannical process became more evident, and he realized the futility of attempting to satisfy the insatiable hunger of tyranny, did he change his orientation from that of cringing fear to that of aggressive resolution to alter the situation as much as he could. Very gradually then did his extrasystoles disappear. The sensation of fear had produced a constantly overactive hypothalamus, and this in turn had produced the extrasystole; when the fear disappeared, and in its place was a reasoned and determined attitude which did not over react to every thought or stimulus, then the hypothalamus was not in a constant state of tension, and the symptom disappeared.

Heart pains.—Many pains over the heart are pseudoanginal, which is to say they are without organic basis as far as can be determined objectively; and many are the result of actual heart damage. Both are intensified by emotional stress. Anginal pains are apparently related to insufficient oxygen supply to the heart, a condition resulting sometimes from certain physical diseases, such as marked anemia, hyperthyroidism, coronary sclerosis, etc. Emotional tension, again operating via the hypothalamus, may, by causing a spasm of the blood vessels which supply the heart, reduce the oxygen supply to the heart muscle and thus give rise to heart pains, or increase the oxygen deficiency already existing from physical disease, and thus intensify symptoms caused by actual physical disease.

In many cases where careful physical examinations reveal no pathology, the patients continue to complain of their pains over the heart and insist that there must be heart damage. In such instances, the pain is the result of tension which interferes with the number of nervous impulses going to the heart; the mild pain is made the center of concern and becomes so magnified in the patient's imagination as to prevent him from going about his ordinary duties. needless to say, treatment of the heart, or even of pain about the heart is doomed to failure; for *the cause lies in the cause of the tension.*

Mr. M. N., aged 45, complained bitterly about his heart pains. He was sure that he had serious heart trouble and he found it difficult to continue working. The pain was so severe that the physician, knowing there was nothing wrong with the heart, decided to anesthetize the nerves of the chest over the heart, on the chance that there was some form of neuritis or other nerve damage. But the pain continued with increasing severity. The most disturbing element was not the pain itself, but the fear which the patient had over the possibility of dying of "heart trouble"; and in the paradoxical fashion characteristic of such persons he thought of suicide to escape from his worry.

Mr. M. N., the father of two children, was a quiet, conscientious, hard-working painter who had had fairly steady work so that he lived comfortably. He was an unduly conscientious, meticulous person inclined to worry over every little mishap. Unfortunately, his mishaps were real and serious; and his natural bent towards worry was given real food and his concern over these problems was much more intense than the ordinary person's. His youngest daughter had been suffering from a bone infection (osteomyelitis) for several years and there was a possibility that a leg would have to be amputated. His son, aged seven, was a behavior problem, a shy, sensitive, fearful boy who clung to his father. A month before his pain over the heart started, his wife suddenly developed a heart attack, and her physician cautioned her against too great exertion. The patient, who was devoted to his wife, grieved and worried all the more; and when this added weight fell upon his burdened shoulders, he felt that he could not bear up under it. After a strenuous night in which he was up caring for his ailing wife, his sick daughter, and his emotional son, he was painting and suddenly felt a sharp pain over his heart. He remembered what had happened to his wife, became very concerned, and rushed to a physician. On physical examination nothing could be detected, and electrocardiograms showed a normal heart. Though advised to return to work, the patient was sure that he was ill and stayed home. From that day he complained of pains over his heart, and despite repeated examinations by different physicians, and despite the constant reassurance that his heart was normal, he continued to be convinced that his heart was diseased, and that he was doomed to die. He was depressed, slept poorly, had no appetite, and was constantly tense and apprehensive.

This man was suffering from symptoms of tension. His cardiac pains resulting from mild vasomotor spasms and hypothalmic overactivity were entirely without significance as to pathology but were indicative of the tense emotional strain under which he was laboring. Treatment of this patient's heart pain was directed not toward the heart, but toward the emotional tension which was the origin of the symptom. It was practically impossible to change the situation: his daughter *was* ill, his wife *did have* heart attacks, his son *was* a problem. However, even though the patient could not change the situation, he could *alter his attitude* toward his difficulties; he could observe his difficulties more objectively and evaluate his misfortunes more with his brain and less with his heart; he could learn to be philosophical and calm, and the attitude of making the best of a bad matter would not only decrease his tension, but also make the other members of the family less emotional and better able to tolerate their troubles. There is nothing else more contagious than fear and depression; there is nothing else more communicable than cheerfulness and courage. It took much persuasion to induce Mr. N. even to attempt to adopt this new attitude, and much time elapsed before he began actually to "feel" this different way. After several weeks of discussions and efforts along these lines the patient's tension was lessened and his heart pains disappeared. They returned temporarily when disturbances in his home were intensified, but his general philosophy was sufficient to relieve his tension, and the pains eventually disappeared permanently. Not only were his symptoms relieved but his general personality attitude was so different that for the first time he began to enjoy life. Evidence of the pervasiveness of such changed attitudes was seen in the behavior of his son, who, though there had been no conscious or special alteration in his care, became much less sensitive, much less fearful, and far more happy in his reactions to his playmates.

HIGH BLOOD PRESSURE

It is interesting to note that relatively few Negroes or Orientals suffer from high blood pressure, which is so common a disease among members of the Western civilization. The difference may be explained in terms of the relative degree of tension felt by members of these groups; and that difference, in the last analysis, is to be understood in terms of differing philosophies and modes of living. The story of the Negro's explanation of why so few members of his race commit suicide has as much truth as humor: "The white man worries and worries about what torments him; and after a while he can't stand his worry no more and just kills himself. The Negro worries and worries, and then he just goes to sleep." Don Gophal Mukerji tells how as a little boy, living in a small village in India, he used to wonder why the Englishman who lived near him always rushed when he went to the store, the post office, and everywhere else. One day Mukerji asked his teacher for an explanation and received this illuminating reply: "He hurries because he thinks that there is an end to the road and an end to time."

If one conceives of life as being a matter of endless reincarnation, and if, moreover, the ideal life is one of withdrawal from active work and the serene contemplation of eternal, immutable, ultimate reality, then obviously persons reared in such a milieu will not have the restless, hectic, driving characteristics so common to our Western, "go-getting" world. Once more, the warning is against extremes. It is true that our hurried, crowded, noisy, and tense manner of living has countless concomitant and directly attributable evils; but it is equally true that the passive and fatalistic resignation of the Oriental has resulted in his being exploited and abused. It is possible to steer between Scylla and Charybdis and to live a life wherein ambition is a light, making clear the path to greater achievement, and not a holocaust; it is possible to do something other than "accept" life.

Throughout the following discussion of high blood pressure, there are two facts to be borne in mind: (1) whether the cause is organic or functional—the gravity of the disease and the severity of the symptoms are aggravated by tension; (2) the disease process is irreversible; once the harm has been done there is no undoing of it.

High blood pressure (hypertension) may result from many

causes: Bright's disease of the kidneys, arteriosclerosis or hardening of the arteries, an enlarged heart, hyperthyroidism, intercranial tumors, and other pathologic conditions. However, in many patients the cause of rise in blood pressure is emotional tension which operates via hypothalmic overactivity. In every case of hypertension, medical diagnosis must precede treatment.

The mechanism of blood pressure production is highly involved; but in that condition known as essential hypertension, where no demonstrable cause can be found, the cause of the elevated blood pressure lies in the spasm of the small arteries throughout the body. When these small arteries are spastic their lumen or openings are measurably reduced, and the heart has to pump harder in order to force blood through to the tissues of the body. This harder pumping results in a dangerous situation where blood vessels may crack and the heart may give away.

When a person is tense emotionally, the hypothalamus is overactive; and this overactivity usually tends to excite the sympathetic system. When this system is excited the blood vessels at the termination of the sympathetic fibers are in turn stimulated and contracted or spastic. It may well be that the vasoconstriction produces an anemia of the kidney, and experimentally it has been found that anemia of the kidney causes hypertension. Hence the rise in blood pressure under emotional tension. In some instances it is the parasympathetic system which becomes overactive, with the result that the peripheral arteries are dilated and a lowered blood pressure or hypotension is produced. The difference in reaction is probably based on different constitutions.

Temporary hypertension frequently occurs. It is a common experience to find an apprehensive patient's blood pressure higher by 20 to 40 points at the beginning of an examination than it is when the patient has been reassured that his illness is a minor one which can quickly be remedied. In ordinary physical activities such temporary hypertension is essential for effective functioning of the body and to furnish the proper supply of blood to the organs which need nutrition; but in most situations of our civilized existence, such elevations of blood pressure are not only not required but are even detrimental.

When a person who is susceptible to spasms of the arteries is constantly under emotional tension, the temporary rise in blood pressure tends to become permanent. Continuous irritability, constant fretting and worrying, states of fear and apprehension and their counterparts, states of dislike and hate all combine to produce a constant state of high blood pressure. When this state remains high for a long period of time permanent changes occur in the blood vessels; and the spasm which at first may be relaxed after each attack becomes fixed and irreversible and the blood pressure cannot be reduced. Accordingly, treatment of essential hypertension, if it is to be effective, must be given in the early stages of the disease.

Mr. E. D., aged 54, complained of dizziness, headache, irritability, and buzzing noises in the ear. Physical examination revealed no evidence of disease except a systolic blood pressure which was over 190. His symptoms were in large part the result of high blood pressure and the accompanying tension. Mr. D., partner in a large firm, was constantly harassed by business affairs and by friction with his partners. There were frequent arguments; and the constant flow of complaining customers, service men, and agents left him overwrought. He carried his troubles home and lay awake many nights fretting over what his partner had said or done, or anticipating difficulties. At home he was explosive in his irritability and frequently lost his temper to the extent of resorting to physical violence.

The constant emotional strain was sufficient to effect a constant rise in blood pressure, and the symptoms of dizziness and headaches resulted secondarily. In treatment it became important to: (1) remove him from the intensely irritating situation which could be done because the man was financially independent; (2) change his attitudes towards ordinary irritations so that he no longer responded with emotional outbursts, and this too could be done because the patient was both coöperative and intelligent; and (3) provide outlets for his energy in more congenial work, social activity, and recreation. When Mr. D. was seen six months after the first visit, he was well tanned from his frequent visits to the golf course, he spoke pleasantly of the work he was doing in his son's firm, and he had learned not so much to control his temper, as, by cultivating a feeling of tolerance and understanding, to avoid the production of emotional reactions in the first place. His symptoms had disappeared entirely, and he was really enjoying life.

If one is free from all the symptoms discussed in this chapter, the very absence of such signs argues well that he has avoided or conquered fear and hatred, intolerance and irritability, and all the other host of tension-producing attitudes.

CHAPTER VIII

STOMACH SYMPTOMS

Second only to the heart is the gastrointestinal system in its sensitivity as a recorder of emotional stimuli. The disturbances are numerous and the symptoms varied. One reason for the multiplicity of symptoms is that the gastrointestinal tract includes all those organs which have to do with the digestive process: stomach, intestines, liver, pancreas, gall bladder, salivary glands, tongue, and esophagus. Space limitations require that we discuss only a few of the most common and typical troubles. Of these symptoms and of all others, in whatever organ or portion of the body they may manifest themselves, two general statements always hold true; and your believing and practicing as well as your understanding the principles involved will facilitate a more efficient management of your body. In the first place, *any given symptom may be either organic or functional in origin.* If it is foolish for you, having obtained expert medical assurance that you are organically sound, to go on worrying that perhaps the doctor doesn't know or that he has not told you all the facts, it is no less unwise for you to decide that your persistent nausea is the result of your mother-in-law's prolonged visit! It may well be that it is; but find out. In the second place, whatever the cause of your disturbance, you can, by reducing tension, do much to mitigate the severity of your symptoms and much to facilitate your recovery. Obviously, cultivating a relaxed attitude can no more remove gall stones than it could put back in place a dislocated joint; but it can do wonders in shortening the postoperative convalescence and in preventing the recurrence of old or the development of new symptoms. Conversely, the most rigid following of a recommended diet will, in the case of peptic ulcer, avail little, unless the patient can, while carrying out his physician's orders, learn also to avoid nervous tension and thereby reduce the overactivity of his hypothalamus. In other words, the avoidance of tension by learning to cope with life and its problems in a reasoned, objective, tolerant, and relaxed fashion is always an asset and often the *sine qua non* of achieving and maintaining health and happiness.

One symptom which is almost always the result of emotionally induced tension is *pain at the base of the tongue.* This annoying condition results from excessive dryness of the throat following a slowing of the salivary flow, caused by overactivity of the sympathetic nervous system. Often there is an accompanying *difficulty in swallowing,* produced by the dryness of the mouth which prevents lubrication of food and also by the contraction of the muscles in the upper end of the esophagus and in the back of the mouth. These muscles, controlled partly as they are by the involuntary nervous system, respond by spasm when the hypothalamus is stimulated. Though the two symptoms just mentioned may appear singly or alone, it is far more common for the patient to have as concomitant disturbances such difficulties as a lump in the throat, palpitation, "knots" in the pit of the stomach, etc. You will understand why these troubles rarely come singly, if you remember that the sympathetic nervous system is a giant network connected with innumerable fibers to every organ and portion of the body. When such emotions as fear, anxiety, anger, and hatred assault the sympathetic nervous system, it may well be that a single organ [1] will feel the repercussions of the attack; but the vast majority of patients have many foci of disturbance.

Miss K. D., aged 32, complained of a pain in her throat, so severe as to interfere with her eating and to keep her awake nights. She was depressed, cried easily, and "didn't see how she could go on with her work—even though she knew she had to." She had spent all of her meager savings in consulting innumerable phy-

[1] *Vide* p. 61.

sicians, in an effort to relieve the pain in her throat. Every physical examination revealed a perfectly normal throat. Over and over she said, "I'm perfectly all right except for this one pain. If I could just get rid of it, I'd be fine."

Miss D. was the sole support of her elderly mother and a semi-invalid older sister with whom she lived. The mother's life had been one of frustration and unhappiness, and her attitude was one of endless complaining and self-commiseration. The sister, unhappy in her unmarried estate, played endless variations on the theme that "life was a gyp" and she the most misunderstood, miserable, and maltreated of mortals. During the day, the mother and sister occupied themselves with quarreling, recrimination, nagging, and whimpering; but in the evening they joined forces and vented their spleen on the sister whose chief crime was that she was their support. "Why didn't she get a better job?" "Why did they have to live in such a ratty neighborhood?" "Why couldn't they have a radio?" "Why should she waste money taking a course in night school?" "It's all right for you to spend your evenings with your nose stuck in a book; you go out every day and meet persons, and have a good time." And so on *ad infinitum*.

Miss D. came home from an eight-hour day of working for an irritable and demanding employer to be invariably met by a torrent of abuse and whimpering complaint. She had no men and few women friends, since she never felt free to invite any one to her home, and could expect increased vituperation from her mother and sister if she ever had the temerity to absent herself for an evening and thus deprive them of their audience.

One day Miss D. developed a cold, one symptom of which was a sore throat. After all other indications of the cold had cleared up, the pain in her throat remained and, indeed, became increasingly intense. Her throat showed no pathology; clearly, the pain was the focal expression of her general tension.

The patient's insistence that she "would be happy, and everything would be fine, if only her throat could be cured" was an uncon-scious misstatement of the real situation: that her throat would auto-matically be well, if the causes of her emotional tension were re-moved. The simplest solution to her problem, it would seem, would have been for her to get a more congenial position and to leave

home. Rarely, however, in actual life is one able thus simply to
meet his difficulties. Even though a burden must still be carried it
need not continue to be a galling, back-breaking load. Financial
stringency prevented Miss D.'s leaving her mother and sister, and
jobs were too scarce for her to give up what modicum of security
she had. She *could* do many things to make her existence less intolerable and to put some color and meaning into her hitherto drab
and futile life. She forced herself to participate in social activities
and made a deliberate effort to renew old and establish new friendships. She gave more attention to her physical appearance (it is
amazing what a new and becoming "hair-do" which elicits com-
plimentary comment will do for a woman's morale). On Sundays,
which had been particularly depressing and dreaded days, she vol-
unteered her services to a settlement house, and found increasing
joy in the affection of the little children with whom she worked.
Most important of all, she resolutely steeled herself against the carping criticism, the bitter fault-finding of her mother and sister. It
was not an easy task; but she learned to regard them without resentment or hatred, to be no more hurt by their cruel words than
one would be by those of a delirious patient. Under such self-
discipline, not only did her throat symptom clear up, but, to quote
her own words, she "was happier than she had been for years."
When she could no longer be reduced to tears by her mother's and
sister's nagging, when she no longer attempted either to defend herself or to strike back, they seemed to lose their zest for battle and
actually to become a trifle less acrimonious. Miss D. told laughingly
of how one evening when she was preparing some materials for
her settlement class, her sister had said, "For heaven's sake, let me
do that; you're as clumsy as an ox." Thereafter she always helped;
though it was months before she stopped her running commentary
on her sister's awkwardness and the stupidity of trying to do anything for ungrateful little "brats." This case has been told in such
detail not because it is in any way unusual or bizarre, but because
it illustrates so well that in apparently hopeless situations there is

always a way out, if the person involved is able to exercise a little ingenuity and is willing to make the effort.

The exact mechanism by which *chest pains* which have no demonstrable organic basis are produced is not known; but often they seem to be the result of emotionally induced spasm of the esophagus. The following case is illustrative:

Mrs. N. S. complained of constant pains in the chest. Physical examinations were negative. X-ray showed a constriction in the esophagus in the upper part of the chest. Such a finding is usually indicative of some pressure or scar; and the next step in diagnosis, an esophagoscopy, was performed. Again the findings were negative. When every known test had been made and no evidence of pathology could be found, it was concluded that the constriction in the tube from the mouth to the stomach was the result of spasm of the muscles, and that this spasm was the expression of emotional forces acting through the involuntary nervous system.

Mrs. S. was a young woman whose husband's tragic and accidental death had left her not only emotionally broken but in desperate financial straits, without any special training and with herself and two small children to support. She was forced to live with her husband's family who had bitterly opposed her marriage. Not for a moment was she allowed to forget how distasteful was her presence and that of her children; the food they ate was begrudged; the children were treated harshly; and the implication was constantly made that she was somehow responsible for her husband's death. When occasionally she was lucky enough to get a day or half a day of housework, she lived in an agony of fear as to what might be happening to her children and invariably returned home to find them in tears and to hear a detailed account of their "fiendish" behavior—"though what else could one expect with such a mother." Mrs. S. tried constantly to make peace, to be as unobtrusive as possible, to keep her children out of the way, and to maintain a brave front for her friends and acquaintances. It was against this background that her pain in the chest developed and continued.

To cure the chest pain two things were essential: (1) to alleviate the stress under which Mrs. S. was laboring, and (2) to inculcate new attitudes that would make it possible for her to live with some degree of happiness. The first was a practical problem in the solution of which a social worker was an invaluable aid. The children were placed in a well-run orphanage where they could be visited often; Mrs. S. secured a position as salesperson and was able to move to a room of her own. She enrolled in a night business school to study stenography, with the hope of obtaining a better position which would enable her to have her children with her. Such an improvement in her living conditions was of great help; but it was necessary for her to adopt new attitudes as well. She had to learn not to be a spiritual slave to her sorrow over her husband's death. She had had a few years of unusual happiness, the memory of which would always be a joy; but life must go on. She owed it to her perfect happiness to make the most of her present life, to get and to give as much joy as she could. In the same way she learned to forgive and forget her painful experiences while living with her husband's family. It had been a hideous nightmare while it lasted but it was past. It was important for her, as it is for everyone, to learn this attitude of not fearing and hating, of not feeling malice and bearing grudges, of not dwelling on past miseries and bygone cruelties and injustices; for fear and hate, whatever they may do to the person toward whom they are directed, invariably act as boomerangs to injure the person who harbors such emotions. This is not a sentimental plea that one kiss the hand that strikes or lick the boot that kicks; it is only hard-headed advice on the art of self-protection. Mrs. S. would have been foolish to continue subjecting herself and her children to the misery of living with her husband's family, once the way was opened for her escape. Just as certainly would she have militated against her own health and happiness and that of her children had she permitted the ravages of hate and fear, resentment and anger to continue in operation.

Within one month after she initiated the above changes, her chest pains had disappeared. Within the following six months, her symptoms recurred twice, both times when her children were ill.

For the past two years she has been symptom free and much more happily adjusted to life.

In both the cases cited, treatment was directed not toward the symptom but toward the basic, underlying cause. There are palliative measures for the relief of symptoms which are too intense to be borne; but they are at best temporary in value. Only when the true cause is discovered and corrected can one hope for permanent relief.

There is, as yet, no definitive answer as to whether *peptic ulcers* are actually caused by emotional disturbances; but that there is a relationship, seems incontrovertible. It is so generally recognized that peptic ulcer attacks can be both precipitated and intensified by emotional disturbances that practically all physicians attempt to correct the emotional life of the patient, as well as treat the ulcer symptom directly by medication and diet.

Several brain surgeons have demonstrated that patients and animals develop ulcers of the stomach when certain operations are performed at the base of the brain. It is at the base of the brain that the hypothalamus lies, and the implication that this portion of the brain has more or less direct connections with the stomach is strong. There are many evidences that stomach activity is altered by emotion. When one is angry the stomach stops its activity, the gastric secretion diminishes, and the digestive process is greatly impaired. Conversely, when one is relaxed and content, the motility of the stomach is excellent, sufficient digestive juices are poured forth to care for the food, and the entire digestive process proceeds normally. Countless experimental and laboratory proofs confirm an observation which is part of common knowledge: that to eat when one is angry and disturbed is unwise, and that the happier one is at the dinner table the better will his food digest.

By "relaxation," "happiness," or "contentment," we mean actual physiologic and psychologic states—not manners or appearances. Most fairly civilized persons feel that they have no right to inflict their moods and their displeasure on others, and so we have learned to be polite, to assume the manners which we think the occasion calls for, with the result that a person may, while inwardly seething with anger or "chewed up" with worry, be outwardly calm and superficially pleasant. We are not decrying the rôle of social amenities nor the value of self-discipline; we are merely emphasizing the fact that the human body is totally oblivious of such niceties and continues to react to the person's real feelings. One may fool one's fellow man, but one cannot fool one's body.

In persons who are under tension and who have some predisposition, the disturbed processes of digestion accompanying emotion will facilitate the production of ulcer symptoms; or if an ulcer already exists, will intensify the symptoms. The overactive hypothalamus will so interfere with the motility of the stomach that, to quote the famous physiologist Cannon, ". . . the stagnant food, unprotected by abundant juice, naturally undergoes bacterial fermentation, with the formation of gases and irritant decomposition products. These in turn may produce mild inflammation or be absorbed as substances disturbing to metabolism, and thus affect the mental state." [2] As a result of this physiologic change, food may remain in the stomach for long periods of time; and often food which should have been digested and out of the stomach in four to six hours will be found, after a vomiting spell of nervous origin, to have been in the stomach for twenty-four hours. The tension which produces this change continues even while the person is asleep, so that there is practically no relief from the emotional strain; nor can there be until the basic emotional cause is removed.

Ulcer symptoms include, among others, pain in the pit of the stomach occurring usually after meals. This discomfort is frequently associated with an irritable disposition, emotional outbursts, and chronic dissatisfactions. These emotional symptoms, which appear to be caused by the ulcer, in turn intensify the ulcer syndrome. A patient whose symptoms are controlled by medication and diet may suddenly have an acute onset of pain, though he has not violated

[2] W. B. Cannon: *American Journal of Medical Science*, Vol. 137 (1909), p. 480.

his physician's instructions. The reason for the flare-up lies in some emotional upheaval. Conversely, many persons go along for years without any ulcer attacks, and on investigation one will find a relatively stable emotional pattern for the particular person. The difficulty of the environment is not the most important element in the emotional production of symptoms; it is the reactivity of the person to the environmental irritation which counts. Different persons react in dissimilar manner to the same stimulus, and the same person may react to various stresses with differing degrees of intensity, the degree being determined not by the actual severity or mildness of the strain, as objectively evaluated, but by the person's "feeling" about it.

Mrs. P., aged 35, complained of severe pains in the pit of her stomach. These pains occurred 15 to 30 minutes after eating, and lasted for several hours. Fried foods intensified her pains; taking milk or baking soda relieved them. Her abdomen was tender, and she was continuously irritable, restless, and fault-finding. The physician's diagnosis, peptic ulcer, was confirmed by X-ray. The patient was given proper medication and diet, and her pains were lessened almost immediately. Within three weeks many of her symptoms returned; and despite the fact that she continued the prescribed medication and carefully followed the recommended diet, she continued to feel uncomfortable.

Mrs. P. was married and the mother of three children. Life at home was thoroughly unpleasant. He complained; she nagged; the children quarreled. Mr. P. earned a salary which should have enabled them to live not only comfortably but even to have some luxuries. He, however, was penny wise but pound foolish. He stormed about every expense incidental to the running of the house and acted as though his wife and the grocer were in a conspiracy for the purpose of bankrupting him. At the same time he was always following "a sure tip," investing large sums on the stock market, and invariably losing. She was sociable, enjoying both visiting and entertaining; he, on the other hand could not understand why "their house always had to be cluttered up with a lot of strangers" or "what was the use of their having a home if they always had to be running to someone else's place."

About a year before the onset of the ulcer symptoms, the situation was intensified by the fact that Mr. P.'s income was drastically reduced. Still convinced that he was a financial wizard, in spite of all evidence to the contrary, he plunged more heavily on the stock market, and her nagging increased in volume and intensity. The monthly sessions over household bills became a nightly checking up on the day's expenditures, always accompanied by accusations and reproaches. Hours of violent quarreling would be followed by periods of sullen silence.

Whether the ulcer symptoms would have developed anyway is not the question. The point is that the symptoms once initiated were, because of the prevailing tension, continued and exaggerated, even though proper medical therapy was instituted and carried out. The husband was so insulated in self-righteousness, so convinced that the fault was all hers and he the victim of a nagging, spend-thrift wife that it was up to her to work out her problem alone. Convinced that she could not change him, she gave up the effort, since her constant nagging in no way affected his conduct and only intensified her own troubles. She would have preferred to have a companion in her social activties, but the fact that she could not did not mean that she had to be a recluse. She devoted more time to her children; rejoined clubs; visited and had visitors in the afternoons; and, most important of all, learned to turn a deaf ear to her husband's tirades. By releasing her tension through interesting social activity and by her objective and dispassionate attitude reducing the amount of newly generated tension, she achieved a degree of relaxation that made it possible for her ulcer symptoms to be controlled by physical care.

Vomiting, the result of a reflex contraction of the stomach and associated muscles, is produced by anything which will cause the stomach to contract. Irritating foods, an irritating ulcer, an irritating tumor, and irritating emotions can all so excite the nerves leading to the stomach as to produce vomiting. Whether it actually occurs or whether the person simply feels nauseated or "too full' after a few bites of food, depends upon how irritating the stimulus is and upon how intrinsically irritable the stomach is. Thus, a mild ulcer, a small tumor, mildly toxic food, or a not too violent emotional disturbance may fail to produce vomiting; whereas, identical irritations acting upon a stomach already susceptible, because of some constitutional predisposition, or some previous or associated ailment, may readily cause vomiting. Hence, in pregnancy, the added pressure on the intestinal tract by the enlarged uterus is sufficient to increase the irritability of the stomach; and accordingly, when a woman is pregnant and at the same time under tension, the emotional irritation is more able to produce vomiting than at other times. In this condition as in all others involving tension symptoms, the symptom is usually the result of a multiple of factors.

Miss M. G. complained of severe headaches and of persistent vomiting spells. She had been given narcotics because of the severity of her symptoms; but as soon as the effects of the medication wore off, the symptoms recurred in full force. Since there was no evidence of physical disease in the stomach or elsewhere, she was sent for a complete neurologic examination. Again the findings were negative. Despite all forms of therapy, the disturbing condition persisted; the patient could not retain a meal and became steadily thinner and weaker.

Psychiatric examination revealed that this girl had had a disturbing emotional background. She had been orphaned early in life and felt keenly the lack of parental care and love. She had "put herself" through high school and with great difficulty and many deprivations had succeeded in taking nurse's training. She met a young man with whom she fell deeply in love, and in her association with him felt that for the first time in her life she had the affection and response she had always craved. However, the young man was deeply attached to and dominated by, his mother, who did not approve of Miss G.—or of any other young woman in whom her son showed interest. Though both dreaded and feared the mother, they secretly made plans for their marriage, and finally set the day on which to break the news. For a week beforehand, the girl was so fearful and apprehensive that she could neither eat nor sleep. On the appointed day, while they were eating dinner at the mother's home, the son broached the subject of their plans. They happened to be eating pumpkin soup which was new and slightly distasteful to the girl. The announcement produced an eruption of volcanic rage, which concluded with the mother demanding that her son "choose" between "that worthless, no account girl, who never would have gone into such a profession if she had been decent" and "his poor old mother who had sacrificed everything and worked her fingers to the bone for him." The girl saw that her future husband was giving ground before the wrath to which he had always submitted in the past. The pumpkin soup which she was eating came up violently, as did all the other contents of her stomach. From that day on she vomited, no matter what she ate or in what small amounts though all tests showed her stomach to be normal.

The vomiting was the physiologic expression of her tension, the particular form being accidentally determined by the presence of a mildly nauseating stimulus occurring simultaneously with the culmination of her emotional stress.

In similar fashion, the condition termed *spastic colitis* is the result of continuous tension. Spastic colitis is characterized by general tenderness of the abdomen, diarrhea alternating with constipation, and cramps. There may be such additional tension symptoms as: belching, abdominal distention resulting from gas formation, and loss of appetite, X-ray examination often reveals that the intestine is marked by spasms. Rough foods and uncooked fruits and vegetables are often intolerable, and only the blandest diet can be managed.

That the symptoms are not imagined is proved not only by the subjective feeling of pain and cramps, but by the diarrheas and the X-ray findings. These real symptoms are the result of a real change in the activity of the gut; but the cause of the change lies in the spastic contractility of the intestinal musculature, which in turn results from the general state of tension. As a result of such general tension, the entire intestinal tract is overreactive; so that not only do spasms start spontaneously, but food which would ordinarily be easily digested becomes highly irritating and causes spasm. Treatment of spastic colitis, therefore, must be directed primarily at its cause; and diet and medication are merely temporary and palliative measures until the general emotional tension is relieved.

Spastic colitis may be the result of reflex impulses arising from disease of the gall bladder, duodenum, appendix, etc., or from such conditions as tumors, adhesions, etc., but even in such physically originated spasms, emotional disturbances or emotional calmness can serve to accentuate or to diminish the muscular irritability.

Mr. H. R., aged 41, complained of abdominal tenderness, occasional diarrhea, and cramps. He was an industrious person, holding an excellent executive position; he was happily married and had many friends; and his manner was one of poise and admirable self-confidence. Physical examination did not show any evidence of disease other than the abdominal tenderness; but the X-ray revealed definite claustral markings, indicative of intestinal spasticity.

Mr. R. was a rather typical successful business man. Yet the very qualities and attitudes which made his success and popularity possible were also the basis for his gastrointestinal disturbance. Whatever he did he did "hard." He was capable and ambitious, as evidenced by his rapid promotions in the company for which he worked. But he was not content with a day's work well done; he brought his business problems home with him. He was constantly planning new schemes, more effective devices, so that his mind was constantly preoccupied and he gave himself little relaxation. Even when he played, he maintained the same attitude of being satisfied with nothing less than perfection. He took golf lessons to improve his game, and was exasperated with himself when he made a poor shot; he took bridge seriously, determined to learn and to apply all the rules; he never relaxed at his own parties because as the perfect host, he was always conscious of his guests and exerted himself to be sure everyone had a good time. He was just as strenuous in his rôle of guest, never forgetting his social obligation to be amusing and entertaining.

Mr. R. needed to learn that he could accomplish the same goals with less expenditure of nervous energy; the time he took out for quiet reading would not be time stolen from his business; for when he was less tense, he would work with even greater efficiency and accomplish as much or more. At first, he worked as hard at trying to *make* himself relax as he did in all his other activities, and of course thereby defeated his aim. Very gradually, however, he retrained his basic general pattern of driving ambition; and as he learned to be really relaxed, the overactivity of his hypothalamus was reduced and his symptoms of spastic colitis disappeared.

Mucous colitis is but a more intense form of spastic colitis in which not only is the muscle of the intestine involved by the excessive nervous stimulation, but the glands which secrete juices are excessively stimulated and, accordingly, secrete mucus. In some cases, there is an occasional stool covered with mucus; in patients with severe disturbances the stool is continuously covered with mucus. The cause of this condition, as well as the treatment, is the same as that of spastic colitis.

The fact that the body tries to adjust constantly to any abnormal state accounts for the alternation of diarrhea and constipation. When a state of constipation exists for a long period, the body attempts to remedy the quiescent condition by producing an active state of motility of the intestine; but instead of stopping at the point of normal function, the body overreacts in the opposite direction, and diarrhea results. To compensate for this condition, the body then turns to constipation; and so the circle continues. (The tendency of the body to overreact from one extreme to the other is often characteristic of the patient's personality. If, for example, he cannot get his way by stormy protest, he will retreat to sullen silence; if he is given a reducing diet, he will literally starve himself for a few days and then go back to his excessive eating; etc.) Though there may be this alternation between diarrhea and constipation, the latter is the rule and usually prevails.

There is no other symptom more commonly found than *constipation*. Sometimes it is a single presenting symptom; often it has many associated symptoms; it seems almost, indeed, to be the inevitable accompaniment of civilization. The fault lies not with civilization, but in the manner in which persons react to it.

The normal evacuation of intestinal contents tends to occur automatically. In infancy, when the lower bowel is distended by excreta, the reflex contraction results in evacuation. As the child learns to walk, however, he learns to control this reflex impulse; and whereas the small child finds it necessary to go to the toilet as soon as he feels the impulse, he learns to inhibit the impulse longer and longer until he can actually forget it.

Normally, when food is eaten the resulting stimulation of the stomach end of the intestinal tract is sufficient to stimulate the entire intestinal tract; hence the tendency to have a bowel movement after meals. This tendency should be taken advantage of by patients with constipation.

Although the training is somewhat difficult to establish, the intestinal tract is subject to habit formation; for the fundamental tendency of all visceral activity is to operate automatically and without need for conscious interference. This automatic activity is established by conscious direction, but one cannot simply say to the intestine, "You start your peristaltic (rhythmic) waves at such and such a time," and expect to get results. One orients the body in the desired direction, going to the toilet at a given time each day. One must not be in a hurry; a given time should be allowed. Each day this routine should be followed; and, under ordinary circumstances, the intestinal activity will soon be so regulated as to result in an established habit. It should be remembered that if one is excessively concerned about his symptom his anxiety will increase tension and therefore prevent desired results. It is also important to remember that training our viscera takes time and patience.

Eating a normal, well-balanced diet is a valuable aid. Cathartics should be avoided, except under a physician's direction, for the irritation caused by the cathartics often increases intestinal spasticity.

In our civilized life, the person arises hurriedly, and rushes to wash his face, brush his teeth, and gulp down a cup of coffee before rushing to the office. If the desire for elimination occurs, the person squats upon the toilet seat for a moment, and obtaining no results rushes on. Throughout the day, he has no time to be relaxed; and in the evening, particularly if he is a chronic worrier, he is too tense to sit long in any one place. Consequently, the intestinal mass, remaining so long in the rectum, becomes hardened and dried as the fluid is absorbed, and when bowel movements result under pressure of great straining or of cathartics, the movements are hard and doubly irritating. This irritation acts as a factor to make the person avoid further movements, and thus a vicious cycle is created.

An additional cause of the prevalence of constipation—and it seems amazing in view of our much vaunted disregard for other senseless taboos—is the false prudery which masquerades as modesty. Women in particular are oversensitive about ordinary body functions, and will refuse to respond to the reflex irritation of the colon when they are away from home or when there are guests present.

These symptoms of the cardiovascular renal and the gastrointestinal (heart and stomach) systems have been dealt with in some detail because so often even if they do not form the major complaint they accompany the more immediately distressing symptom. You will remember, however, that emotional overstimulation of the hypothalamus may express itself in any portion or organ of the body (via the involuntary nervous system); and in the next chapter will be mentioned at least some of the more frequent tension symptoms to be found in persons whose habitual way of thinking and "feeling" is such as constantly to overstimulate the hypothalamus.

CHAPTER IX

OTHER SYMPTOMS

The fact that *every* organ of the body is, via the involuntary nervous system, closely connected with, and responsive to, the hypothalamus, means that *any* organ can become the focal point at which hypothalamic overactivity may be expressed. Presence of tension within the organism almost certainly guarantees that sooner or later symptoms will appear, the certainty being dependent upon both the chronicity and the intensity of the tension. Location of the symptom is usually determined by three factors: (1) constitutional predisposition; (2) presymptom personality; and (3) the nature of the specific precipitating stress. The actual symptom may not appear until all three factors are present in proper proportion; though in many tension conditions, a single one if sufficiently intense will suffice to bring symptoms to the fore, irrespective of the mildness of the other two causative elements. Which factor is most important will vary from case to case; but their close interrelationship must be remembered both for diagnosis and for treatment.

The tension symptoms dealt with in the following pages, though by no means all-inclusive, are both common and typical. The reader who understands their mechanism can apply the same principles to other symptoms not specifically mentioned.

THE EARS, EYES, AND NOSE

The eyes, ears, and nose are often involved in the production of tension symptoms. "Noises" may originate from such physical causes as inflammations or Ménière's disease, but also from emotional tension acting by changing the blood supply, causing contractions of muscles attached to the small bones of the middle ear, or closing the Eustachian tube. Changes in circulation probably interfere with the normal operations of the internal ear; as a result ear function is disturbed, and noises produced. Similarly, the small tube (Eustachian) connecting the ear and mouth may become spastic, with a consequent disturbance of air equilibrium, which facilitates production of abnormal sounds. Or, the small bones in the ear, which conduct vibrations from the tympanic membrane to the inner ear, may become tensed by muscle spasm and thereby produce sounds. Whatever may be their production method, these noises (usually high-pitched, insistent and comparable to the sound of escaping steam) are apparently caused by emotional tension. Such noises are not the result of actual sounds, but of mechanical irritation of the endings of the hearing nerves. Since hearing is the only impulse this nerve can conduct, noises *seem* to occur.

The disturbed emotional state caused by these noises is often intense. Since the noises are present constantly, patients become irritable, have temper outbursts, find it difficult to sleep, lose their appetite, and often become highly suspicious. Though many of these noises originate in emotional tension, the very constancy of the symptom serves to intensify the patient's emotional reactivity; and a vicious circle is thus initiated, the added emotionality increasing the tension, which in turn increases the noise.

It is often necessary to utilize medication to decrease the added emotional irritability, until the person learns to remove the basic causes of tension. The patient must learn to steel himself against the noises and to engross himself in attention diverting activities. Minor inflammations of the ear may be the origin of these noises; and, once an outlet for tension is found, continues to be used long after the initial cause has been removed.

Mr. L. B., aged 41, complained of having had noises in his ear for several years. He had been to local physicians and to many clinics, the diagnosis always being that the noises were without organic basis. The noises were present most of the day, were worse when he arose, and especially disturbing when he retired. He gave up work, stayed home most of the day, was depressed, wept on occasion, was easily fatigued, could not eat much, and had a restless, disturbed sleep. The patient was an intelligent and successful business man; but no one seemed able to do anything for him, and he was equally powerless to do anything for himself.

Mr. L. B., a personally kind and socially responsible person, was extremely interested in both world and local affairs. He was head of the United Charities in his home town, influential in the Jewish Temple, and considered one of the most public-minded of citizens. When the depression of 1932 came on, and with it the rise of anti-Semitism both in the United States and in Germany, he felt deeply disturbed. He felt that by being an exemplary citizen he could in some measure mitigate the racial intolerance in his own community; but the deliberate, cultivated, and rapidly spreading hatred continuously bombarded him with feelings of helplessness, insecurity, and fear. Often he would waken in a cold sweat over a nightmare involving personal and group persecution; and during the day he was tense, disturbed, and restless. He could not concentrate on his work, and although he redoubled his efforts to aid local causes, found little satisfaction or relief. He developed headaches, and lost his appetite, but he forced himself to continue working.

In the spring he developed a cold, with the usual symptoms of coryza: a running nose, a feeling of fullness in the head, listlessness, and a sensation of blocking in the ears. After the acute symptoms had disappeared he still had the feeling of blocked ears, and in addition a ringing noise, which was high-pitched, shrill, sounding he said as if "steam were escaping from the radiators." The noise continued; the patient became alarmed and sought medical advice. When it was explained that occasionally mild inflammations in the middle ear give rise to ringing noises he was not satisfied, and sought advice elsewhere. The noises became more intense; the worry about his ears more disturbing; the tension already present from concern over world problems was multiplied by his concern over his ear noises, thereby producing intensification in the noises. The patient slept more restlessly and finally gave up his work.

Two major factors were responsible for this man's illness: (1) an initial mild inflammatory process in his ear, and (2) a general state of tension, created by his concern over the growth of intolerance which augmented his ear symptoms and gave rise to other general symptoms. Treatment of his condition was directed towards the primary causes: (1) building up his general physical resistance by diet, exercise, and medication to cure whatever inflammation might remain; and (2) removing his tension. His tension was the result, not of imagined troubles, but of real ones. The source of these troubles lay in the activities of persons beyond his control. Mr. B. could not change the situation, but he could change his own attitude. If he wished to rid himself of his troublesome symptoms and to ameliorate the situation he so deplored, then he must learn not indifference or meek resignation but to discard his paralyzing fear and to plan a course of action, directed along positive and constructive lines. First, he must really *understand* three things: (1) that anti-Semitism was not the result of his behavior, or for that matter, of the conduct of his fellow Jews; (2) that persecution is a mechanism of tension release, a form of vicarious anger, a technique, often unconscious, for venting personal misery upon someone else; and (3) that only by curing the general want, misery, and unhappiness of the world can we hope to eradicate the, "symptom" of intolerance. Secondly, he needed to realize that understanding does not mean fatalistic acceptance of a situation as inescapable or irredeemable. He alone could do relatively little to solve so gigantic and so desperate a problem; but that little he could and must do. He could help foster allegiance to the spirit of the American Constitution, aid the victims of the aggressors, and utilize his powers in behalf of the democracies. In essence, this man learned to redirect his emotion-engendered energy into new and external channels.

After one month of discussion he had resumed his full time work and was engaged in many socially constructive activities. His noises were present only briefly when he arose and when he retired; but his attitude toward them had so changed that he could regard them as being annoying but not alarming.

The *eyes* are subject to such different tension symptoms as: blurred vision; unusual "tiredness" after short periods of reading; hypersensitivity to ordinary light; concern over "spots" before the eyes, spots without physical basis; tubular vision (ability to see only as much as one could through a telescope); etc. One of the most difficult situations to deal with occurs when, though the glasses are expertly made and fitted, the person under tension is so disturbed in visual ability that no adjustment of the glasses will correct his eye difficulty, although repeated attempts are made. The nose may be involved in much the same way, but space does not permit elaboration of the specific symptoms.

SPEECH

It has been estimated that over one million persons in the United States have some such speech difficulty as stammering or stuttering. "Cures" have ranged all the way from putting pebbles in one's mouth, as did Demosthenes, to the use of witchcraft, voice training, and hypnotism. The major limitation of all these therapies has been that the *cause* has but rarely been understood or dealt with.

Speech, a recent acquisition in the animal kingdom and present only in man, is dependent upon the fact that man can so control his speech muscles as to make a relatively wide variety of sounds relatively distinctly. Most animals bark or cry in only a few different notes or patterns of notes, and cannot vary from this pattern. Since they do not have the ability to perform the intricate muscle movements required to make different articulate noises, they cannot speak.

If we closely observe the actual mechanism of speech, we may see that articulating a single letter involves many steps. Try saying "B." Say it strongly. Notice what happens. The lungs are held relatively stationary so that one momentarily stops breathing. One closes his lips, and forces air outward so that the closed lips are distended. Notice the tightness and constriction in the throat which serves to form a narrow channel for the air to follow and represents contraction of the vocal cords and throat muscles. One then opens his lips, and at the same time places the tongue so that it is held tense at the floor of the mouth. The teeth are held a definite distance apart and then closed. While this complicated process is going on, the soft palate is held against the nasal air passage to prevent the escape of air. In short, numerous movements, in exactly the right position, duration, and flexibility, occur; and these complex movements must succeed each other rapidly, with great flexibility when one makes the various sounds which form a word. When one observes a deaf child learning to speak the manner of forming sounds seems a painful effort; whereas in the well-trained adult, the various muscle movements proceed so smoothly as to be almost effortless. The entire structure of speech is dependent upon muscular flexibility which permits rapid alternation between tension and relaxation of the muscles involved.

One can readily see that any process which interferes with the facility of muscle contraction and relaxation will interfere with speech. This interference occurs most commonly in those whose general tension is sufficiently great to cause tension in the vocal cords and associated speech muscles. Stuttering children, for example, almost always are more serious in their reactions, more intense in their activity than are other children. Anything which creates tension may be the cause of stuttering. Whether the tension is produced by chronic feelings of inadequacy or inferiority, by love or hate, by an intense sense of guilt, by excitement, irritability, fear, or by excessive fatigue, the result is the same.

There are different types of stuttering, called by different names; but whether spoken of as stammering, stuttering, respiratory tics, or grimacing, any involvement of speech without pathologic organic basis is the result of tension as described above. Tension so fixes the small muscles that they cannot relax with sufficient rapidity to make normal sounds. Each sound is prolonged because the speech muscles will not relax to permit the formation of the next sound; or else, the muscles are so fixed and tensed that when they are momentarily relaxed and again contracted, only the same muscles contract, and consequently the stutterer repeats the same word over and over.

Some persons with speech difficulties may, because of chest muscle tension, hold their breath before emitting a sound, which when produced is normal. Others, because of facial muscle tension, will grimace before emitting a sound, which when uttered is normal. Some emit "broken" words resulting from tension within the actual speech muscles. Others are psychologically so tense, that they cannot think of the right word, and have to use a substitute, which when spoken may be perfectly formed. Still others may have a combination of these different types of stuttering. But all suffer from the same difficulty: tension.

Habit plays an important rôle. Once a pattern of speech difficulty has been started, it tends to continue. Many persons, however, notice that when they are calm and relaxed, or so interested in what they are saying that they completely forget about themselves, their speech returns to normal.

The personality of the stutterer is almost uniform. These persons are usually serious and conscientious; ambitious; socially or morally minded; and intense about what they do. Not infrequently they are rather seclusive, being intensely ashamed of their affliction and feeling greatly inferior. This feeling of inferiority is based primarily upon their tension and is merely accentuated by their difficulty in expression, instead of the situation's being the reverse, as most patients claim. The infrequent stutterer, who is shiftless rather than hard-working, usually has a strong sense of guilt or unworthiness which he may try to allay by drink, boasting, or belligerency.

Successful treatment of stuttering can be accomplished only when the basic tension is diminished. Many forms of treatment are temporarily successful because there is something either in the technique or in the person giving the therapy which instills confidence in the patient and thus diminishes tension; but the most effective therapy is that which goes directly to the source, and corrects the personality defect which the symptom reflects.

Mrs. A., aged 23, had stuttered most of her life. She felt shy, rarely went among strangers, and when she did, did not know what to say. She was self-conscious, sensitive, and easily hurt by the not too severe criticisms of the mother-in-law with whom she lived.

At the age of 4, the patient, who had spoken well till then, was seized by a young hoodlum of 15 and carried to a woodshed and assaulted. Ever since she had been in constant terror; and not only did she dream repeatedly of the incident, awaking terror-stricken but during the daytime, she was fearful, shy, and tense.

Only by reorienting her conscious attitudes, by retraining her socially, by teaching her how to be relaxed "inside," was it possible so to release her general tension that her symptom of stuttering could be removed. Her tension was so chronic that the process took almost a year.

Mr. J. K., aged 27, stuttered badly and had since early childhood. He spoke rapidly, slurring most of his words and hesitating painfully for the right word.

Mr. K. was a conscientious person, who because he was unskilled could not find work. He did odd jobs, and was distressed when he was idle. His father was an alcoholic, who regularly squandered his pay check on Saturday night and beat his wife Sunday morning. The fright in the home disturbed all the children; and the patient, the oldest, was frequently beaten as he attempted to interfere.

In both these cases, the fundamental effort in curing speech difficulty lay not in discussing the speech, nor in vocal exercises, but in removing the underlying tension. This change was wrought not so much by altering the environmental situation, as by changing the person's attitude from that of tense overreactivity to a calmer, less emotional objectivity. In some instances this change is relatively immediate; in most, because of the habit element, several months are required to effect sufficient personality modification to affect the speech.

RESPIRATORY SYSTEM

Among the many symptoms involving the respiratory system—symptoms which may result from, or be aggravated and prolonged by, tension are: sighing, shallow breathing, inability to take a deep enough breath, persistent coughing, clearing the throat, hiccoughs, and asthma.

Many persons state that they have "had trouble in breathing all their lives." Usually such symptoms as *shallow breathing* or continual *sighing* indicate a habitual tendency to overreact to all situations. Teleologically expressed the explanation is somewhat as follows: whenever man prepares to meet danger, he begins to breathe more quickly in order to get more air for his fight; in tension conditions, he is, in effect, constantly preparing to meet danger—hence the rapid shallow breathing. However, when man is engaged in actual fighting, the muscles, in burning up more oxygen, generate excess carbon dioxide which must, by rapid breathing, be blown off through the lungs; whereas in states of tension little added carbon dioxide is generated, and rapid respiration consequently blows off too much of the normal amount. Since a certain amount of carbon dioxide (in combination) is essential for the blood stream, and to keep respiration going, when too much carbon dioxide is blown off, the person stops breathing for a moment (apnea) and then has to take a deep sigh or breath to make up for his lack of breathing. Moreover, excessively rapid and shallow respiration indirectly increases the excitability of the nervous system and is thus a factor in increasing emotional instability. The tension state makes this breathing condition worse by making the breathing center more irritable, thereby increasing the rate of breathing.

Here again, the problem is not so much one of how to make

the breathing slower and deeper, but rather how to decrease the tension. *The cause of the tension must always be dealt with.*

Constant hacking coughs, clearing the throat, and hiccoughs frequently are intensified if not actually initiated by emotional tension. *Coughs* usually start with a sore throat, or mild bronchitis, but persist long after the irritation has disappeared. A cough is a reflex, spasmodic contraction of the chest and lungs, and is usually brought about by some mucus or foreign body in the air passages acting as an irritant to the nerves of the lung mechanism. The irritated nerves reflexly contract the chest muscles in such fashion as to expel the mucus or foreign substance. If this reflex action is controlled, there is no cough; and in good tuberculosis sanitariums, patients with mild infections, and therefore with minimal irritations of the air passages, are taught to control their tendency to cough.

When patients are laboring under great tension, the occurrence of an accidental, physically predisposing site provides an outlet for pent-up tension; and the reflex cough which ordinarily would cease with the disappearance of the irritation, continues because of the hyperirritable, habit-determined nervous reflex. Once such a cough or clearing of the throat is initiated, the patient's attention is focused and he begins to worry. Such worry increases his tension, which in turn makes the cough worse.

Mr. N. M., aged 27, habitually cleared his throat and made grunting noises. Despite repeated failure to find any physical cause for his malady, the patient was tireless in seeking a cure. Strangely enough, he was always better when he was in the presence of strangers; but at home or at work he would clear his throat and make grunting sounds continuously. He tried hard to desist, but seemed unable to do so.

Mr. M. was married, seemingly happily; had two attractive children; his home was modest but he had only a small mortgage on it; and he had a steady position. There seemed to be no cause for tension.

Closer investigation revealed that Mr. M. had had these symptoms at irregular intervals for about fifteen years. His father was a drunkard who made the boy miserable. There was a constant feeling of inadequacy, irritation, and unhappiness; so that the patient had run away from home at the age of thirteen. He was always excessively timid; and the fact that he mustered enough courage to leave home indicated how wretched he was. A year before leaving home, he had had a sore throat, during which time there had been even more family arguments than usual. The clearing of his throat started then; and although he would be better at times, the symptoms had never entirely disappeared. He never forgot his unhappy childhood; and the tension thus generated expressed itself through the throat noises. In the presence of strangers he was so ashamed of his symptom that he was usually able to inhibit the habitual reflex; but restraint could be maintained for only a short time and the symptom would then come to the fore.

Presence of strangers increases tension in the average patient and so aggravates the symptom; and Mr. M. was but one more proof that the exception proves the rule.

In similar fashion, *hiccoughs* are reflex, spasmodic contractions of the diaphragm, just above the stomach and below the lungs. Hiccoughing can be produced by anything which irritates the diaphragm: inflammations, tumors, reflex irritation from stomach disturbances, and emotional tension. As in tension coughs, though there may be some initial organic cause to start the hiccoughing, the symptom is continued because of the increased excitability of the nervous system resulting from general tension. Sometimes the diaphragmatic contractions continue until the patient becomes actually exhausted. Indeed, the symptom may be so severe that it must be stopped by an anesthetic; but in every case, the force which perpetuates the non-organic hiccough is general tension.

Asthma may be bronchial, cardiac, or allergic in origin. Asthma results from spasms of the thin, smooth muscle which lines the tiny bronchioles or air passages in the lung. Associated with this muscle spasm which decreases the size of the bronchioles is edema (swelling of the cells lining these tubes) which further narrows the air passage. This narrowing of the air tubes makes it difficult for air to enter or leave the lungs; breathing becomes difficult; and as the patient strains for breath, his heart pounds. In severe cases, the physician must inject adrenalin, a substance which dilates air tubes.

Commonly, asthma results from sensitization to some substance (protein) which is foreign to the body. Pollen, dirt in the air, feathers, certain foods, and many other substances may be so irritating to the body that the body will overrespond by contracting the smooth muscles, particularly those in the lungs. In most instances asthma tends to stop when the substance to which the patient is sensitive is removed; hence many persons have asthmatic attacks only during the summer when certain pollens fill the air, and by going to places free from these pollens they can rid themselves of asthma.

Not only the sensitizing protein but constitution and the general state of tension must be considered in any case of asthma. In many persons these last two factors are minor, and the sensitization is major; in others, the reverse is true. Often patients with asthma are intense, driving, industrious, and successful in daily affairs, persons who have not learned how to relax inwardly, although they may be able to present a calm exterior. The cure of asthma is greatly facilitated by relieving the patients' tensions and by changing their attitudes toward life.

Mrs. J. S., aged 48, suffered from acute attacks of asthma. Sensitization tests proved that she was allergic to the pollen of ragweed which grew profusely in her neighborhood. However, her attacks always began much sooner, lasted longer, and were more severe than were those of anyone else living in the community. She had tried everything: sedatives, desensitization procedures, medication of all kinds, even living during the summer months in a different locality. Adrenalin would sometimes bring temporary relief; but otherwise she choked and struggled for breath from early spring until late into the autumn.

Mrs. S. was a quiet, unassuming, well-liked person, who contributed generously of her modest means to all community causes and who was indefatigable in her efforts to help others. Her husband, who had died a few years previously, had left enough money so that by careful management she was able to live fairly comfortably. Her life was certainly neither luxurious nor exciting, but it seemed to be as satisfactory as most and more comfortable than many.

Mrs. S. eventually revealed the source of the tension which was intensifying and prolonging her symptom of asthma. Her childhood had been one of bleak loneliness, both of her parents having died when she was very young. She was reared in an orphanage where she was not mistreated, but where she was never shown any particular affection or tenderness. She had gone to work at sixteen and, being untrained, had had to accept whatever jobs were available. She married the first man who asked her, and happily anticipated her first real home. Mr. S. was a good provider, but he was dour, taciturn, and completely undemonstrative. When their child was born, Mrs. S. for the first time had someone on whom to lavish her care and affection. The child became the idol of her heart, and all her thinking and planning were centered around him. She scrimped and saved to make his professional training possible and dreamed happily of the years they would spend together. As he developed new interests and plans of which she was not a part, she was sure that "as soon as he was settled, everything would be different." News of his entirely unsuspected marriage arrived at a time when she was suffering from a mild attack of asthma. The new daughter-in-law, jealous of the mother's possessiveness which amounted almost to worship, managed so that her husband saw increasingly little of his mother. Mrs. S. was too "proud" to complain, but brooded incessantly over her disappointment and sense of injury. Her attacks of asthma increased in frequency and intensity until her life became little more than a struggle to breathe.

It was necessary for Mrs. S. to learn not only with her head but with her heart—to "feel" as well as intellectually to realize that it was right, normal, and desirable that her son should lead his own life, that no parent should expect to be the center of his child's mature life. To break the habit of years was far from easy;

but as she learned that ownership and love are not synonymous and as she sought and found new outlets for her great capacity for devotion, her asthmatic condition improved until it could be well controlled by medication.

GYNECOLOGY

The female generative tract is subject to many tension symptoms. Most of these symptoms center about the menstrual function; and since the menstrual function is so intimately related to the function of the endocrine glands, it is extremely difficult to differentiate emotional from endocrine dysfunction.

Menstruation, which begins at about the fourteenth year, and ceases at about the forty-fifth year, is indicative of the childbearing period; for before the age when menses begin and after the age when menses cease, pregnancy is relatively impossible. The actual process of menstruation consists of the shedding of the lining of the uterus or womb; this lining is discharged with a small amount of blood, and a new lining is immediately formed. Menstruation usually occurs every thirty days, with many individual variations. Any radical variation from the normal should be thoroughly investigated.

Although menstruation itself is the result of changes in the uterus, its actual basis lies in endocrine activity. The gland which has most to do with menses is the ovary, which undergoes characteristic changes just before and after menstruation. The ovarian gland itself is greatly influenced by many factors, the most important being the pituitary gland. The pituitary gland, lying at the base of the brain, secretes a hormone which stimulates the ovary; and when the pituitary gland does not function correctly, the menstrual process is disturbed. Since emotional changes act upon the hypothalamus, and the hypothalamus is connected directly (via the supraoptic hypophyseal stalk) with the pituitary gland, one can see how *anatomically* emotion may influence the menstrual function.

Many physical factors may disturb menstruation: tumors of the uterus, diseases of the ovaries, lesions of the pituitary, weakness, general sickness, pregnancy, fatigue, anemia, etc. Such conditions must be ruled out before a diagnosis of emotional causation can be made. However, long after their physician is convinced that all physical causes have been adequately dealt with, many patients continue their distressing symptoms, and it is these patients who suffer from tension.

During menstruation, many women have mild disturbances: a vague sense of pressure in the lower abdomen, backache, cramps, a general feeling of tiredness, and a state of mild irritability. These disturbances vary in intensity; but not infrequently the emotional state of tension so aggravates the symptoms that the first two days of the menstrual period must be spent in bed. Very mild disturbances are usually the result of physiologic changes; intense disturbances are frequently the result of emotional tension.

When women are tense or upset their menstrual symptoms are intensified; when the emotional difficulty is resolved much of their menstrual difficulty disappears. In many cases no specific cause for emotional disturbance is apparent, although many other symptoms indicating general tension are present. Treatment of such cases is all the more difficult because of the habit element, the dysmenorrheal symptoms tending to continue long after the causes of tension are removed. However difficult the task may be, only a thorough change in the emotional attitude will suffice to bring about a complete cessation of symptoms.

Miss R. H., aged 24, a musician, complained of severe dysmenorrhea. For three days out of each month she remained in bed, and during this time suffered greatly. For several days before and after the period, she was irritable, could not concentrate, and in such pain that she could neither teach nor practice. Thorough physical examination revealed no disease or malformation; and even injections of ovarian substance, which often help such patients, brought no relief.

Miss H. maintained that she was not disturbed about anything. She was teaching at a musical college, living at home, had many friends, and a pleasant social life. "No," she insisted, "there is no reason for me to be tense."

In further conversations, however, Miss H. told of many disturbing elements in her background. She had been reared by a domineering mother and a weak, vacillating father. The mother was extremely irritable, continually making life miserable for herself, her husband, and her children. When the patient was 18, she wished to study nursing, but her mother violently forbade this step, insisting that she continue her studies in music. So unsatisfactory had been the mother's own sexual experiences that she always spoke of men, marriage, and sex with bitter loathing. Miss H. grew up with warped and distorted views of all human relations and with a shamed disgust at her own impulses and desires. All her reaction patterns were those of an emotional, tense, sensitive, extremely prudish person. When some years earlier she had "gone out" with a young man and fallen in love with him, she was put into an almost hysterical state of terror when he attempted to kiss her. She literally ran away from him, and refused to see him again. Her mother became fairly apoplectic over this new evidence of the lustfulness of men, and more violent in her tirades against the vileness of sex. The conflict growing out of her desire to see her friend and her feeling of disgusted fear became more and more intense, resulting at last in the patient's conscious gratitude to her mother for protecting her against such an awful degenerate, and unconscious hatred of her mother for depriving her of her one love. The tension which this girl had always had became even more intense; and simultaneously her menstrual cramps, which had always been annoying, became unbearable. It took many months for her to develop a more tolerant and understanding attitude towards men and sex, and to become emotionally independent of her mother; but as she succeeded, not only were her menstrual difficulties relieved, but her whole life became easier.

The tension producing menstrual disturbances is so often associated with actual endocrine changes of a purely physiologic nature that treatment of these conditions is usually one of combined therapy. Again, generally speaking, one may say that if the specific symptom is but one expression of underlying problems, it can be permanently removed only when the entire personality structure is so remolded that it functions more efficiently and less emotionally.

Pregnancy.—Nowhere else is the influence of emotions on the function of the generative tract more obvious than in the menstrual delay experienced by women who either fear pregnancy or eagerly desiring children are sure they can never have one. Often a woman who because of limited resources or for any other of countless reasons, fears having another child will when her menstrual period is a few days delayed come with great anxiety and apprehension to the physician's office. Fear of pregnancy is often the basis of sexual maladjustment, the woman's apprehension causing her either to avoid conjugal relations altogether or making her, when such relationships do occur, tense, irritable, and unresponsive. After each such experience, there is tense and anxious waiting for the onset of the next menses to indicate that "nothing has happened." This very tension has an inhibitory effect on normal functioning, with the result that there may be actual delay. It is interesting to note how reassurance that there is little cause for such alarm will frequently bring such relief from tension that the overdue menses will occur almost immediately.

Many other women so ardently long for children that they dread every menstrual period, are sorrowfully disappointed when it occurs, and start hoping for "better luck next month." It apparently makes little difference whether the inhibiting tension has its origin in fear of or hope for pregnancy; for in both instances, it operates in such a way as to interfere with the normal menstrual process and causes delay. Countless cases have been recorded of women who solely on the basis of their intense desire for a child have experienced a menstrual delay of several months' duration.

Exactly how tension delays regular uterine function is not understood; that it does is incontestable. It is probable that the tension stimulates the hypothalamus, which is so intimately connected with the pituitary gland. Since the pituitary secretes a hormone which stimulates the ovary, inhibition of the pituitary means that the ovarian hormone is inhibited, and menstrual delay occurs.

GENITO-URINARY SYSTEM

Frequency of urination is a rather common symptom. The bladder, an elastic, muscular sac, may operate automatically when the nerve supply to it is destroyed; so that when it becomes full, the urine will overflow. Normally, the bladder is innervated by both the sympathetic and parasympathetic systems so that when the bladder is stretched by the inflow of urine from the constantly acting kidneys, the nerve endings in the bladder wall are stimulated and a reflex occurs by which the bladder muscle contracts and the sphincter (closing) muscle relaxes, thus permitting the fluid to escape. In infants this process occurs automatically. As the child matures, the impulses from the nerves in the stretched bladder wall go not only to the lower reflex center, but also up the spinal cord to the brain. The brain inhibits these impulses, so that the reflex action does not occur. When the person can go to a urinal he no longer needs to inhibit the impulses, and the reflex center operates automatically to empty the bladder. The brain is so trained from earliest childhood, that even when one is asleep the nervous impulses are inhibited and urination does not occur.

This normal state of affairs has many exceptions. Many persons can inhibit bladder activity for only relatively short periods of time. The primary reason for this frequency, in the absence of any determinable physical disease, is that when a person is in a state of tension, his brain is more ready to discharge than to control stimuli, and the impulses which come to it are intensified rather than inhibited. When persons are in a temporary state of acute excitement, there may be an almost unconscious emptying of the bladder; when persons are under emotional pressure for long periods of time, this lack of cerebral control (often misnamed "increased bladder irritability") enables the lower reflex center to empty the bladder automatically when any urine is present. When one is asleep, tension often continues and thus one may wet the bed.

This symptom of diminished urinary control illustrates well the fact that symptoms in themselves are unimportant, that they have significance only as indications that a disturbance exists. The symptom itself may give rise to such embarrassment and annoyance that the person may feel that he could well put up with the tension if only the bed-wetting would stop; but generally speaking one has no more chance of curing isolated tension symptoms, than one has of killing weeds by just picking off their leaves. As long as the cause still lies at the root of the matter, symptoms of that cause will continue. Symptoms are really nature's warning that something is wrong with the total economy of the organism, and our curative efforts must be directed toward that cause.

SKIN

Heart pains may be more terrifying and gastrointestinal pains more excruciating, but few symptoms are more annoying than those involving the skin. The polysyllabic names—psoriasis, pruritus, eczema, neurodermatosis—give no comfort; the skin continues to itch and burn, to look blotchy and unsightly. Many persons suffering from tension symptoms can conceal their true feelings, are able to wear a mask of poise and control; and the very fact that skin disturbances are an outward and visible sign is undoubtedly one element in the particularly annoying nature of skin symptoms. Moreover, the very obviousness of skin lesions makes it difficult to believe they are caused by emotional factors; they are so localized, so definite, that it seems there must be specific and immediately discernible causes. As a matter of fact, there often are. Irritating or chafing clothes, general allergic states, physical disease, and many other causes may bring about skin disorders. Naturally, if a man's neck is chafed from wearing too tight a collar, what he needs is not a change of attitude but a change of collar size. On the other hand, it is equally obvious that if all external irritations have been removed and organic causes ruled out, and the skin symptoms persist, then it would be wise to scrutinize general reaction patterns and attitudes. The three main factors present in most tension conditions are usually found here also; namely, some actual *physical agent* acting on an organism whose *constitutional predisposition* is intensified by *emotional tension*. Thus a person with constitutionally thin and fine skin may, when he is under undue emotional strain, develop a certain type of neurodermatosis as the result of eating a particular food. At other times, the same food will have no effect.

The skin, which acts not only as a covering but as a mechanism by which heat can be more or less rapidly lost, is supplied with countless nerve fibers, blood capillaries, sweat glands, etc. It is the changes secondary to alterations in blood flow, and to irritability of nerve endings that bring about most emotionally determined disturbances in skin sensation as well as changes in skin color and texture. Emotionally created changes may be precipitated by physical changes in the general chemistry of the body or by direct irritation to the skin; but the actual determining mechanism is alteration in nerve tone or capillary activity, secondary to hypothalamic excitability from emotion.

About fifteen seconds after the skin has been stroked firmly with a fine but blunt instrument, there will appear a white line which indicates spasm of the capillaries and an absence of red blood; if the stroking is done more firmly or with a sharper point, a red streak may—because of an accompanying dilatation of the deeper blood vessels—appear over the line drawn; if the line is drawn still more heavily, and the person is susceptible, a raised welt will appear over the part stroked, indicating escape of some blood fluid from the capillary wall so as to form a thin wall of fluid.

Such experiments will help make understandable the blushing which comes to many persons when they are embarrassed. Emotional tone, acting inside the body in a fashion similar to that of the physical agent acting from outside, will cause the blood vessels to dilate and thus give rise to blushing and to the frequently seen splotchy necks. Curing this type of flushing should not be attempted, as has been suggested, by cutting the involved involuntary nerves but by removing the stimulation to the hypothalamus.

As the skin may become red from dilatation of the blood vessels, and increased blood flow, so it may become pale when there is spasm of the blood vessels. This spasm, with its decrease in blood flow, often affects the hands and legs, which, because there is less warm blood and therefore less heat, become ice-cold. Many conditions will cause this peripheral spasm of the blood vessels and the associated cold hands and feet, but the most common cause is the relatively mild state of tension so characteristic of modern civilized life. This tension may result from suppressed excitement as well as from frustration and fear; but its very existence is indicative that the person has not learned adequately to release tension.

When persons are constitutionally predisposed, or when some physical agent acts to determine the site of least resistance, then emotional stress may produce actual lesions of the skin. These lesions are real and observable; and although the associated physiologic changes are not clearly understood, it is generally recognized that changes in blood supply brought about by spasms of blood vessels constitute one of the most important elements.

A garment worker, spending her days cutting and sewing suits, developed marked dryness of the skin which was soon followed by cracks and fissures in her finger tips. No physical or allergic cause could be determined, but it was observed that she was in a continuous state of emotional stress. She labored to support her family, though she was 55 years old. Her two married daughters could not live on their relief allowances, and she felt it incumbent upon her to aid them. She lived with one and found it difficult to bear the continuous wrangling between her daughter and son-in-law, who with his pride wounded and bitter at his inability to find work and support his family resorted to abuse and resentment against even the mother-in-law who helped support him. The tension was not so much intense as chronic; and physical infirmities of age plus the difficulty of sustaining continuous effort added to her tension. The skin, already susceptible because of age, and irritated by the continuous handling of rough garments, was further injured by the tension-produced spasm of the blood vessels. The cracked skin resulted from all these causes in combination.

Psoriasis is another skin symptom common to tense persons. The condition usually develops slowly and often areas over the elbow and knee are red for years before a real patch of scaly skin appears. Since in these patients tension tends to be chronic, it follows that therapy must be a long term alteration in personality. Not infrequently it is possible solely by medical measures to accomplish cures; but either these cures are temporary, or it becomes necessary to raise to abnormal heights the threshold of skin resistance. Sunlight or ultra-violet rays often benefit psoriasis, but the moment light therapy is discontinued the psoriasis returns. Moreover, the tension which still exists will appear in some other symptom so that the patient as a total unit is no better off.

Mr. F. H., aged 29, married and divorced, had a severe case of psoriasis. All forms of therapy had failed. Mr. F. H. had been reared by an adoring foster father who gratified all the boy's desires and whims. The father planned to send F. H. through law school but died shortly before the boy's graduation from high school. So limited were the funds left that instead of going to college F. H. had to go to work. He hated work, resented having to arise early, and lost position after position. His foster mother who cared greatly for him was willing to continue supporting him; and being selfish and undisciplined he lay about the house. Gradually he drifted into bad company, started gambling and stealing small change from his home. His gambling was not an expression of a drive for thrills and excitement, but a simple though inadequate way by which he hoped to obtain money easily. Mr. F. H. was disappointed in himself as much as his foster mother was; yet it was so much easier to go on in his shiftless manner. He was tense and irritable because of his losses and his laziness, but was unable to muster sufficient energy to change. There seemed no future for him; and he could not bear the prospect of remaining a low salaried "slave." He started drinking, more to forget his difficulties than because of any taste for liquor. He noticed over each elbow a red area, about the size of a dollar. In summer, under the influence of the sun, these areas disappeared; but in winter returned. With each succeeding year, the areas grew larger, and they lasted for longer and longer periods of time, not clearing up quite so readily in the summer. These symptoms intensified as he married, had a child, and was divorced for nonsupport. At the age of 29, he was a "nice fellow" to whomever he met, but he refused to work, drank frequently, and gambled whenever he had the opportunity.

Therapy of this person was extremely difficult because of his deeply ingrained habits of laziness, inactivity, and irresponsibility. Only when he was persuaded to enter a trade school where he learned to be a machinist and when he secured a position which flattered his ego, inasmuch as he supervised several workmen who had less training, did he begin to accept the responsibilities of an adult. Yet even before he had finished his course as a machinist, his psoriasis had almost entirely disappeared.

Eczema, of the hands particularly, is subject to similar considerations. In eczema, there is often a marked sensation of itching, and the accompanying scratching produces a secretion which is like the exudation from the capillaries under a welt. There are so many different variations of eczema, and the association to allergic states is so strong, that one needs careful physical check-ups to determine whether the symptom is on an organic or an emotional basis.

Itching of the skin, likewise, is a not infrequent symptom of emotional tension. Skin sensitivity may stem from allergic conditions, but usually marked tension is also present. Sometimes, the tingling produced by cold weather will suffice to start the itching; sometimes the tightness of the clothes; sometimes a particular soap. One frequently observes men twisting their necks in an effort to diminish the irritation from a shirt collar which in actuality is adequately large. The itching in such instances is merely a focal expression of tension within the organism; and when tension disappears, the itching ceases.

One of the most common forms of itching is anal pruritus. The precipitating cause may well be the irritating nature of the material which passes by the skin at this point; but the fundamental source of the itch is the patient's tension.

It is well to repeat that one cannot judge whether a person is tense, simply by the way he looks or talks at the moment. In cases cited above, many, on first appearance, and even on first discussion, seemed quite calm and manifested no evidence of so-called nervousness. One person often says of a second, "I wish I were as calm and relaxed as he," when in reality the envied person, despite the mask he wears over his face and voice and the control he exercises over his actions, is tensed to the breaking point. Poise of manner is no guarantee of internal peace.

HEADACHES

One may say with almost literal truth, that the causes of headaches are innumerable. Headache is a symptom; its cause may vary from a brain tumor to eyestrain or constipation. A most common cause is emotional disturbance. The person who, mentioning some unpleasant circumstance, says, "It gives me a headache," is speaking the truth. Emotional tension usually does cause one's head to ache. The great difficulty with most persons is that they worry about their headaches instead of doing something about the worry which caused the headache in the first place.

It has been found in operations performed on conscious patients for the removal of brain tumors, that the brain tissue itself (at least the outer cortex) and the covering membrane (dura mater) are insensitive. The sensitive region lies in the blood vessels which enter the brain, and the pain travels via nerve fibers in these vessels through the intercranial branches of the fifth cranial nerve. Consequently, whatever dilates the blood vessels (or constricts them) will stimulate these pain fibers and thus give rise to headaches. Even constipation apparently causes headaches primarily by reflex nervous action on these blood vessels. Since we know that emotion constricts blood vessels, we can assume that emotional headaches are produced in the manner described above.

There are all sorts of headaches: pain over the eyes, usually associated with eyestrain but also existing on an emotional basis; pain over the back of the head and neck; and the type often described as "My head feels as if it would burst," or, "There is pressure on top of my head pushing down."

There may be areas of tenderness over the scalp; and occasionally patients complain of actual "scabs" forming over these tender areas. Occasionally there are "shooting" pains along the temples, pains without any determinable physical origin, temporary, sharp pains which disappear when tension is removed.

Often headaches prevent clear thinking. Such headaches differ in degree and somewhat in character from migraine headaches, but are often almost equally incapacitating. Effectiveness in treating headaches is determined in large part by the coöperativeness of the patient, the severity of the emotional disturbance, and the removal of all possible physical factors.

Mrs. A. R., aged 45, had continuous headaches, generalized over her entire head. Thorough physical examination revealed no pathology, though her headaches had been present for years.

From earliest childhood she had been pampered and overprotected, and at the same time insecure. She married against her will and at the insistence of a stern father. She was unhappy, discontented, and had headaches which at first were worse during the menstrual period, but which soon became chronically severe. After the birth of her third child she became a semi-invalid, remaining in bed most of the time, presumably because of her headaches. This patient was under constant emotional tension.

INSOMNIA

One of the most common as well as one of the most distressing tension symptoms is insomnia. The term covers a multitude of miseries. Some persons have great difficulty in falling asleep, tossing restlessly for hours or for minutes that seem like hours; others fall rather immediately asleep, only to awaken shortly and spend hours in a vain attempt to recapture sleep; others sleep an adequate number of hours, but their sleep is haunted by distressing dreams, broken by nightmares; still others awaken more weary than when they went to bed, their jaws and hands aching from having been clenched so tightly during the hours of their supposed relaxation.

The hours of night can seem endlessly long when one is in physical pain or mental distress. Situations which by the light of day seem relatively minor disturbances are in the long dark hours of night magnified and distorted into insurmountable difficulties. It may be that we carry over as part of our social heritage memories of the night as an actual danger, a time when we were in actually greater physical danger from animal and human enemy alike; it may be only that during the day we are able with countless activities to crowd out of our minds those problems, fears, and unfulfilled longings which, held in abeyance all day, are ready as soon as we lie down to pounce upon us and take possession.

If insomnia is a concomitant of the toxic state frequently found following operations or accompanying chronic illnesses, then obviously treatment must be directed primarily toward removal of the toxin-source. Much more often, however, sleep difficulties have their origin in personality problems of the one so tormented; and then the problem of therapy becomes one of retraining the basic attitudes. Many problems are imaginary and of our own concoction; they should be recognized as such and dismissed. Still others are real and demand solution. Worry never has and never can find the answer; only by logical, unemotional, and "cortical" reasoning can we hope adequately and successfully to meet and surmount difficulties. There are many first aids which we can employ in establishing good sleep habits (the habit factor plays an important rôle). Retiring at the same time every night; warm, relaxing baths; the avoidance of excitement or overstimulation prior to going to bed: these and many other devices may help in establishing the desired routine. In the last analysis, the best guarantee of restful, relaxing, recreating sleep lies in our ability during the day to meet major and minor irritations in a calm, dispassionate, and objective fashion. Our bodies have never learned "to tell time"; and the tension generated through successive days of overemotional, over-reactive response will take its toll, if in no other way, in sleepless, rest-disturbed nights.

ACTUAL PHYSICAL DISEASES

When a man becomes ill, he is still a man—a man who is ill. He is not just a housing for a disease process; nor does he react as one. Depending upon his personality, he will accept his painful or discomfiting ailment with equanimity, with hysterical fear, or with some modification of one of these attitudes. When one becomes ill not only does his body suffer, but his routine of living is interrupted, his very necessities may be cut off, his pleasures and desires are checkmated. If one is desperately ill, he may not be able to think or even feel anything about these factors; but if he is chronically ill, all these problems must be considered.

If, under ordinary circumstances, a man is barely stable enough to maintain an averagely calm existence, the advent of illness may be sufficient to disturb him emotionally to the degree that many tension symptoms will come to the fore. If he is ordinarily calm and stable, physical disease will do little to alter his personality reaction. If a person becomes tense while physically ill, the actual changes in nervous and vascular activity may prevent recovery or prolong the illness. Many persons who constitutionally should quickly recover from pneumonia, sore throat, pregnancy, etc., maintain lingering illnesses, primarily because of a continued state of tension. In such instances the patient must help the physician by doing everything possible to reduce tension and to avoid emotional disturbance.

Mr. M. G., aged 25, developed a carbuncle on his neck. His temperature ran to 104° F., and he became acutely ill. He was hospitalized, and large incisions had to be made to provide adequate drainage for the abscess. After a week he began to improve, his fever subsided, and the diseased area was healing nicely. Although Mr. G. made a good recovery up to a certain point, he did not seem to improve thereafter. He complained of weakness, inability to think clearly, insomnia, and loss of appetite. He often burst into tears, had palpitation, and developed aches and pains throughout his body. All these symptoms appeared after his temperature had returned to normal and when the wound was healing. It was feared that there might be germs in the blood stream, that abscesses might have formed elsewhere, that the high temperature had exhausted him, that he had insufficient vitamins, etc. But as test after test came back normal, as the blood sedimentation rate proved normal, the white cell count normal, the urine normal, the temperature normal, the basal metabolism normal, etc., it was suspected that factors other than those of a physical nature must be involved.

Mr. G., a prominent real estate owner, was known as a successful and financially sound person; he had a pleasant home and there was no apparent reason for his emotional difficulty. But after his confidence had been won, he revealed that he was under great tension because of his business affairs: he was not so successful as persons imagined; he managed to "put up a front," to live in an expensive home, and entertain lavishly, in order to attract wealthy clients; in actuality, he was only "one step ahead of his creditors." The tension produced by financial worries came to the fore during his illness, when, feeling miserable from his physical ailment, he was more susceptible to the tension from his life situation.

In similar fashion *any* physical disease may be intensified by emotional stress. Chronic diseases, such as diabetes, arthritis, and rheumatic heart disease are often greatly aggravated by the patient's tension. There tends to be increased sugar in the blood of diabetics, more pain in the joints of arthritics, more pain and more rapid heart beat in the rheumatic disease of the heart, when the person is under emotional tension. It is therefore most important in these organic diseases that emotional stability be secured and maintained.

Mrs. E. W., aged 48, had been suffering from diabetes for many years. Most of the time by the use of insulin and by diet she kept her condition under control; but frequently, for no apparent reason, she would develop a high blood sugar and on occasion actual coma. During these periods of aggravated symptoms she had not changed either her diet or her insulin intake.

Mrs. E. W., a highly nervous and chronically nagging woman, with seven children and a neurotic husband, was in a constant state of tension. Though their financial situation was comfortable, she eternally complained of inadequate funds; when her neighbor moved to better quarters, she complained of the miserable two story home they owned; when her friend was elected head of the local book review club, she felt intensely insulted over "being passed up." On the slightest provocation she became enraged, and either had fits of crying and temper or took to her bed and sulked. It was at these times that her blood sugar rose.

It may well be that in this discussion of typical tension symptoms the one that troubles you has not been touched upon. However, whatever your symptom may be you can do much toward its alleviation, if you will bear in mind and put into practice the principles which we have sought to demonstrate and illustrate. First, seek competent medical advice and have all necessary physical and laboratory examinations. Second, follow implicitly your physician's advice and recommendations. Third, by cultivating an unemotional, reasoning attitude, reducing the tension under which you live, get your body into the condition which will make it possible for your physician most adequately to help you and which will speed your recovery. Fourth, in the absence of organic disease, take over the job of managing your life—your thinking-feeling-acting total organism—and use it for your own enjoyment instead of letting it use you. You need not be a puppet made to execute a painful and grotesque dance, jerked this way by painful memories and that way by the irritations of the day, yanked bolt upright by fears of possible eventualities or laid low by your limitations and inadequacies.

CHAPTER X

PSYCHOLOGIC MECHANISMS

Solely for the sake of clarity we make a distinction between physiologic and psychologic mechanisms; but you will keep constantly in mind the fact that man is a totality, and that his acting, thinking, and feeling are merely different aspects of a total process. Man is determined to find pleasure and to escape pain; and he has evolved a fearful and wonderful set of techniques, or mechanisms, by which to obtain his goals. Some are good, some are self-defeating. If they make for health, happiness, effectiveness, then obviously they are good, and vice versa. Psychologic mechanisms are devices by which man attempts to meet his problems in a world of pyramided wishes and countless, intangible dangers; and, as you would expect, they fall into two major categories: (1) defense mechanisms, and (2) pleasure substitute mechanisms. Previous chapters have shown you how our wishes and fears, as expressed by our attitudes, can act as a boomerang to produce physical symptoms; this chapter will focus on another aspect of the same picture: harried man defeating his own quest for health and happiness by utilizing "mechanisms" which are inadequate or even harmful.

An important factor which has been implied, though not specifically stated, is our concept of "time." We live not only in the immediate present but in the past and future as well. Thanks to our memories and to our creative imagination we have greatly expanded the scope of our actual experience. These two abilities: to remember and to look ahead are powerful assets, for without them we could neither learn from past experience nor plan intelligently; but like every other good thing they are subject to abuse, and can become hindrances rather than helps. If one makes a stupid mistake and as a consequence suffers, memory of his experience can be harmful or helpful, depending on how he utilizes it. He can analyze the situation, see wherein he was wrong, and in the future avoid repetition of the same folly; or he can brood over his mistake, develop feelings of inferiority, blame others, find excuses for himself, etc. In like fashion, our ability to look forward can either serve to establish goals or become a lazy substitute for effort. There is a vast difference between dreaming of the future and planning for it. Even worse than the idle dreamer is the gloomy prophet. The old men—whatever their chronological age—dreaming wistfully of "the good old days" and the wild-eyed visionaries painting glowing pictures of future Utopias are of little value to society; for both are (often unconsciously) defeatists who, overwhelmed by the magnitude of today's task, seek refuge in the past or the future.

Our misuse of memories and anticipations gives rise to most of our harmful psychologic mechanisms. Everyone reading this book, to say nothing of the countless millions who are not, has hosts of memories: some joyous, some painful. You have had good fortune you did nothing to deserve; and you have had more than your share of trouble. You have been insulted, hurt, misunderstood; you have had traitorous friends and fine plans that collapsed; you have worked hard for every penny and there are precious few of them; you have lost all your money or you never had any to lose; your father was stern and domineering or he didn't care what became of you; you were so overprotected that you can't cope with life; or you had responsibilities too heavy for young shoulders to bear; you have had to work so hard you've never had any time for fun, or you have followed every momentarily enticing detour so that you have made little progress along the main highway; you have made fool mistakes, you have failed time and time again, etc. *Well, what of it?*

This question is not rhetorical nor meant to minimize the reality and poignancy of your suffering. It is a question calling for an honest answer and on your ability so to answer it depends much of your future happiness. One fact is certain: we can neither re-live nor un-live the past. Mourning for past joys, excoriating our-selves or others for past miseries will profit us nothing; and they may cause us infinite trouble and pain. Do you find either heroic or admirable the king who, because he lost his son "never smiled again," or anything but silly those ghostly nineteenth century heroines who wistfully devoted their lives to pale sorrow? Remem-ber Schopenhauer's statement "suicide is too mild an antidote for the grim business of living," and realize that there are many kinds and degrees of suicide. Whatever handicaps and cripples, whatever frustrates and defeats our ability to manage our present lives—if it is a matter within our control—is suicidal. So we repeat the ques-tion, *Well, what of it?* and the "it" refers to any experience, past or future, to which you react as though it were in the immediate present. We *can,* by recalling past mistakes, our own or others', avoid repetition, as we can build new successes, modeled after earlier ones. Many of our memories are valueless; they should be discarded with the same finality with which we discard outgrown clothing. The useless trash with which other persons store their attics and basements never ceases to amaze us; but the most clut-tered storeroom would be an orderly and barren place compared to our memories, crammed as they are with multitudinous useless and often harmful recollections. If you wish a text: "Sufficient unto the day is the evil thereof."

What do memories have to do with psychologic mechanisms? Just this: psychologic mechanisms are techniques by which indi-rectly we attempt to meet present situations; their form and sub-stance are determined by our attitudes, our general habits of reac-tion and they, in turn, are an expression of our adjustment to previous and past experiences.

Habits, if indulged in long enough, become unconscious, take on a quality of primary certitude, and are difficult to recognize, much less correct. It is easy to realize that Mrs. R. "always finds excuses for whatever she does" (rationalization); Mr. S. "dreams of the 'big things' he is going to do, instead of trying to pay his bills and take care of his family decently" (phantasy formation); and Mr. T. "tries by 'lording it over his family' and always speaking in loud tones to 'make up' for his small stature" (compensation). Our own psychologic mechanisms defy detection; they are part of us; we "have always been that way." Understanding *why* persons act as they do helps us be more tolerant of their shortcomings or failures; understanding why *we* act as we do should be merely the first step in effecting whatever changes are necessary for a more adequate way of life. It is impossible blindly to hate anyone whom we really understand; for understanding casts out fear, and in the last analysis hatred is but a form of fear. Understanding ourselves, however, carries with it the moral obligation to *do* something; otherwise our understanding soon degenerates into mere excuse-making.

Four further general statements should be made about the psychologic mechanisms before we consider specific techniques. First, more often than not, we are so habituated to our psychologic mechanisms that we are entirely unaware of them. A persistent physical pain demands and gets attention; we attend it ourselves and expect our long-suffering friends to be equally solicitous. A hypercritical, faultfinding, and nagging person, however, rarely applies these adjectives to himself; he is aware not of his own habitual attitude but the faults, failures, and mistakes of others. Secondly, the particular mechanism evoked in a given situation will be determined very largely by the ingrained habit of response characteristic of the person. Third, rarely does a person employ a single mechanism to the exclusion of all others.[1] Often a patient has one particularly distressing symptom on which he focuses most of his attention; but usually has many other minor symptoms stemming from the same source. In the same manner, a person may use one particular mechanism more obviously or more consistently than he does any other, but at the same time have recourse

[1] *Vide* p. 78.

on occasion to countless others. Finally, everyone utilizes these mechanisms at one time or another, and desirably so. Here, as elsewhere, extremes are dangerous and should be avoided. The carping critic is no worse than the person whose mind is so "open" that nothing stays in it long enough for him to make a judgment; the man who broods over and magnifies every mistake is as immature as one who blithely refuses to assume responsibility for his own actions; one who rivets his attention on his inadequacies is meeting his problem as inefficiently as one who refuses to face facts and overcompensates by aggressively domineering whenever he can. The social implications differ radically; but so far as proportioned integration of personality is concerned there is little difference between martyr and inquisitor, Uriah Heep and Hitler, Pollyanna and Jeremiah. It matters little whether it is·to right or to left that a boat lists; to make safe passage it must keep a steady keel.

Psychologic mechanisms fall roughly into two categories: (1) those which are primarily defensive—defense may be either aggressive or a matter of avoidance or retreat—and (2) those which serve as pleasure substitutes. Once more you will notice how the pleasure-pain principle is the basic, motivating power behind all our actions. No attempt will be made to give an all-inclusive enumeration of psychologic mechanisms; but this discussion of the more typical forms may enable you more adequately to interpret and modify some of your own thinking. You will notice that often the difference between mechanisms is one of degree rather than of kind, and that a particular mechanism may be utilized both as a defense and as a pleasure-getting device.

DYNAMIC FORGETTING AND REPRESSION

One of the most common defensive mechanisms is *repression* or, to speak paradoxically, *dynamic forgetting;* and it, like so many other weapons of defense, frequently acts as a boomerang rather than as protection. Everyone, however insignificant he may seem to others, is tremendously important to himself. Check your own conversation and see how often the personal pronoun "I" and the possessive pronoun "my" appear. *My* house, *my* car, *my* dog, *my* work, *my* son, *my* friend, *my* country, *my* god; *I* said, *I* think, *I* wish, *I* do, *I* know, *I* went, etc. We are inclined to interpret everything in terms of how it affects our own welfare; we even take it as a kind of cosmic injustice if the weather interferes with our holiday plans! We have so expanded the meaning of "self" that we need satisfy not only our physical wants but our spiritual or psychological wishes as well. We want food when we are hungry; we also wish fame and recognition. We seek protection from physical blows; we also wish to have our opinions respected. There are countless ways in which we build up, fortify, satisfy, and aggrandize our ego; there are multitudinous ways in which this same self can be endangered or hurt. Nobody else feels the same tender solicitude for your ego that you do, so it is inevitable that you have ego-wounding experiences.

From within as well as from without will come the "slings and arrows of outrageous fortune." We hurt ourselves, betray ourselves quite as often as we are wounded by others. We are petty, mean, ignoble, stupid, unkind, selfish, stingy, cruel; and our ego suffers as a consequence, the intensity of suffering being in direct ratio to our degree of sensitivity. Or we are the victims of pettiness, ignobility, stupidity, unkindness, selfishness, stinginess, or cruelty. What happens when *you* have such experiences (and you are going to have them so long as you take the trouble to stay alive)? There are several things that you can do. You can learn not to take your caprices, whims, and minor wishes with any greater degree of seriousness than you do those of your friends and acquaintances; then you won't be hurt so often. You can correct many of your mistakes, provided your false pride does not prohibit you from admitting you were wrong. You can learn from past performance and avoid future repetition. You can steel yourself against the inescapable—and there are many inescapable pains. You do not stand in a cold November rain, shivering and wishing that you were warm; you seek shelter, get under a roof, behind walls, light a fire if possible. You label as "idiot" the person who does not have sense enough to come in out of the rain; and yet how many persons fancy they have a kind of spiritual superiority, because they have "always been so sensitive," and are "so easily hurt." All these things you can do, and they are all truly defensive.

Many of our experiences, whether we were villain or victim, must be simply forgotten. But forgetting is not simple; and here is where *repression* comes in. True forgetting implies actual abandonment and loss of all emotional overtones and nuances of emotion associated with the experience. Forgetting does not necessarily mean inability to recall, or that life is just the same as though the disturbing event had never occurred; but it does mean that you do not respond emotionally to past events as though they were in the actual and immediate present. You know that it happened—yes— but you know with the same emotional detachment that you know countless other things: your telephone number, the date of Waterloo, the number of children your next door neighbor has, etc. Perhaps such an impersonal attitude is too much to expect, but the more closely you can approximate it, the happier you will be. Recall some of your most embarrassing moments. When you were fourteen, arrayed in your first real party dress and armored with the secret conviction of your charm, you went to your first big dance. You slipped and sprawled flat in all your crushed white organdy, and pride. You longed to die; but being disgustingly healthy, you were not even bruised. Your "life was ruined"; you "could never show your face again," etc. Now, that experience is one of your best stories. Why? Because you have lost not the memory but the anguished emotion which overwhelmed you at the time. The ability to forget; that is, to see a situation honestly and clearly and then to dismiss it, is an invaluable asset. What too often happens, is that persons refuse to think about their ego-wounding experiences and at the same time refuse to dismiss them; they push them out of conscious awareness, store them away in the hidden recesses of the mind where they fester and frequently multiply. To use an unsavory and completely inelegant analogy, we might say that it is a good deal as if one refused to have a dead cat in the living room and so tossed it into the dark hall closet along with a lot of other useless or worse than useless trash.

Two things happen when we repress painful memories. Because their associated emotional tone is still operative they continue to live and are constantly being evoked, whenever any stimulus penetrates the layers of unawareness with which we thought to conceal them. How many times have you heard; "I could die of mortification, every time I think of it." "I won't let myself think about it; but every time I remember what he did I hate him as much as I did when it happened." "The very thought of it makes me sick." There has been no true forgetting, merely a damming up, a holding in abeyance. The second thing that may happen is perhaps even more harmful. If we succeed fairly well in pushing these "hurting" memories quite far back into our consciousness, then the memory itself may not so readily be evoked; but the emotional tone associated with the experience—an emotion which has been neither expressed nor dissipated—must find release and so gives rise to other psychologic mechanisms which are detrimental to happiness and health.

Miss H. S., aged 24, was deeply hurt when the man with whom she was in love suddenly married her best girl friend. Miss S.'s friends had taken it for granted that she was engaged; so added to her genuine grief was the wound to her pride. She found pity and curiosity equally unbearable, and refused to discuss the situation with anyone. To her family she said, "Don't ever mention either one to me. I've forgotten all about them and you'd better do the same." She continued her teaching, but refused all social engagements (withdrawal). She refused to "have anything to do" with men because "they are all fickle" or with women because "they are all treacherous" (irradiation). In her schoolroom associations she became increasingly irritable and strict, the especial object of her almost sadistic cruelty being small blonde girls. She spent her evenings alone, either reading voraciously detective or horror stories or going to movies of the more lurid type (compensation). She was annoyed by her family's concern about her, and had "good reasons" (rationalization) for everything she did. "Why on earth should she spend her time gadding around with a lot of persons, when she preferred to be alone?" "If she was a strict disciplinarian it was certainly for the children's own good."

Far from having forgotten the injury to her feelings and her pride, she had let it crowd out every other thing. She did not deliberately wish and plan to become bitter and disillusioned; she did not consciously say, "I'll make life as miserable as possible for every blonde-headed kid in my class, because that snake of an Edythe who stole my Tom has yellow hair"; she was not aware that in her reading and her theater-going she identified herself with persons who get direct revenge for their injuries nor did she admit that her withdrawal from social relationships was motivated by fear of being hurt again.

Whether repression will cause such drastic changes will be determined by the severity of the wound and the type of personality involved.

Everyone is somewhat subject to a mild form of repression, a "dynamic forgetting" which enables us to put out of consciousness things which are mildly disturbing or disagreeable. It is easy to forget to return the borrowed book or umbrella—particularly if it is a good book or if we have no umbrella, thanks to someone else's having conveniently forgotten to return ours! Children *really* forget to sweep the sidewalks, empty the wastebaskets, and write their themes. Men really forget "they were told two weeks ago that the party would be formal" and they really lose the hats they don't like. (Losing Christmas tie atrocities is more difficult!) Women really forget dreaded social engagements and more easily lose their ugly handkerchiefs than their pretty ones. This forgetting and losing are not deliberate or even conscious; they are almost as automatic as is brushing away an annoying fly. The person who has thus dynamically forgotten or lost will assert valiantly that it was pure accident; and so far as any conscious willing is concerned he speaks truly. The extent to which this mechanism is utilized determines whether it is within normal range; though usually excessive use indicates a tendency to repression and repression inevitably militates against the ultimate happiness of the person who thus inadequately seeks to escape pain.

To face painful facts or memories is not easy; far from it. It is, however, in the long run, less difficult and less painful than coping with all the complications and additional troubles that are bred by repression. Have you ever jabbed a splinter under your finger nail? It hurts—sickeningly. Removing the splinter and applying iodine give additional pain, but a pain slight in comparison with that experienced if the splinter is not removed, an infection sets in, and gangrene develops.

WITHDRAWAL

Often *withdrawal* is the best possible mechanism with which to meet a given situation. We withdraw from a flooded area or the brink of a precipice; we withdraw from burning sunshine to find rest and refreshment in the cooling shade; we withdraw from associations which we find harmful or profitless. Every human being needs places of quiet, havens of refuge, temporary escapes from the noise and confusion, the work and the worry of the day. The word "temporary" is important. We sleep, we listen to music, we walk under the stars, we take vacations, or do any one of dozens of other things not as a *substitute* for the arduous business of living but as a meaningful and helpful part of it. We work better after a night of deep and relaxed sleep; we enjoy companionship more, if we have some time alone; we return to work with renewed enthusiasm after vacation. Such temporary withdrawal is excusable, desirable, even indispensable. The danger lies, once more, in extremes, in overuse.

When withdrawal is used as a permanent escape and when it is grounded in fear it becomes dangerous and detrimental. The hermits, the recluses, the dwellers in ivory towers have in effect admitted that life is too much for them. One who feels the urgency and poignancy of the world's heartbreak finds it difficult to see much "saintliness" in the lives of men who retire from the world and all its problems and give themselves over to contemplation of the mysteries of ultimate reality.

Withdrawal may be physical or psychological. Physical withdrawal varies from the natural shyness of adolescents, which makes them uncomfortable in the presence of strangers, through the asocial behavior of adults who refuse social contacts and reduce to the inescapable minimum all other personal relations, to the pathologic withdrawal of schizophrenic patients who first refuse to stay in the room with others and later so completely withdraw as to be unaware of the world of reality.

Mr. H. R., aged 25, was an expert and high salaried accountant. He was shy, retiring, and resisted all attempts at friendliness made by his office associates. He ate alone, and consistently refused participation in office parties or celebrations. He was as withdrawn in his personal as in his professional life. He had no friends; refused all invitations; and whenever guests called, made an excuse to leave the room.

In high school he had been the star of the football team and ringleader in all social activities. When he was seventeen, he had to have a leg amputated, as the result of an automobile accident. He learned to manage his artificial limb well; but his sense of being inadequate, of being a cripple, haunted him and he developed a deep sense of inferiority. He "couldn't bear pity"; he "wouldn't be a drag on everyone else"; he "had no right to inflict his deformity on others"; etc.

Such physical withdrawal is, of course, a reflection of psychological withdrawal—an attempt to escape the pity, scorn, criticism, contempt, or any other of the intangible dangers with which modern man has multiplied his possibility of being hurt.

Though physical withdrawal always stems from, or is accompanied by, psychologic withdrawal, the reverse situation does not hold. Most persons stay in the world, participate more or less in human activities, have friends, do things, go places, and yet withdraw psychologically.

Psychologic withdrawal is grounded in fear: fear of being hurt, fear of being disregarded, fear of the unknown, fear of that which is different, fear of the future, fear of reality.

Withdrawal is an attempt to negate actuality or feared possibility by refusing to admit into consciousness anything even potentially disturbing. This mechanism stems from desire to avoid hurting one's ego; and many have set their ego at such a level that they regard expression of differing opinions as equivalent to attacks. Do you know persons who refuse to read anything they think will be disturbing? Do you know others who get their feelings hurt if you disagree with them? Are *you* willing to listen to the other side? How do you *feel* when someone expresses an opinion utterly at variance with some cherished notion or belief which you hold? Incidentally, have you ever tried to distinguish between your notions and your beliefs? What do you think about concentration camps abroad or chain gangs at home? Or do you find it too painful to contemplate what countless thousands of your fellow men are called on to endure? What facts do you refer to as "propaganda"—facts which you have thoroughly investigated, or merely those which irritate or terrify you because they differ so radically from what you already hold to be true? Are you ever troubled about the disparity between your everyday conduct and your Sunday morning and Fourth of July "confessions of faith"? This list of questions, honest answers to which will reveal the startling degree to which we all withdraw, can be multiplied indefinitely and in every realm of human affairs.

The tragic chaos of the world is all the more tragic because it is unnecessary. Man has sufficient intelligence to deal with the problems confronting the human race, but he refuses to face the facts of the situation, refuses to learn from past experience, refuses to subject what he wishes and feels to the revealing and illuminating light of all available knowledge. Our concern, our anxious solicitude about our own precious little egos would be laughable were it not for its tragic implications. Perhaps even more true today than when they were first uttered are the words, "No man liveth to himself and no man dieth to himself." The welfare of each individual person is so inextricably bound up with that of the world, that to think one can be "disregardful in what state God's other works may be," is as futile and as doomed to failure as it would be for one in a burning building to congratulate himself because the fire had not yet reached his room. If we are to be saved at all it must be through our coöperative efforts; we must open our minds to all the wisdom available and be willing to modify or even discard our preconceived ideas, our inherited notions.

REGRESSION

Regression, a reversal to an infantile level of behavior, occurs when an adult faced with disappointment, annoyance, or frustration acts like a spoiled child. In cases of senility and other pathologic instances, regression may include inability to control physiologic functions so that the patient has to be cared for as would an infant. There may be temporary regression, as in the case of convalescent patients whom nothing can satisfy. Though the whole family dances attendance, he feels abused. The pillows are hard; the room is draughty; the light shines in his eyes; his friends don't visit him, or if they do they stay too long; nobody knows or cares how much he suffers; it would, no doubt, be a relief to everyone if he just died, etc. If such whining, unreasonable petulance is out of character, the family can take his spoiled child performance as a sure sign of returning health; for no actually ill person has the strength for such complaining.

The spoiled child has two favorite techniques by which to control his environment and assure gratification of his caprices: temper tantrums and sulking. Too often families, like nations, wish for peace at any price and so give in to the child. A child learns rapidly which members of his family he can "work" and which remain impervious to both his shrieking and his sullen pouting. Going to school often offers salvation to such children; for in the classroom and in the playground there are too many other egos demanding attention and seeking expression for little Sammy or baby Susie to have much chance to dominate the scene, no matter what technique is used.

Distressing as such behavior is when displayed by children, it is infinitely worse when encountered in chronologically adult persons. Do you know women who use the via lachrymosa to get new clothes? Do you know men who sulk and feel unappreciated unless they are constantly commended and praised? Do you know persons who enjoy bridge only when they are winning? Do you know women who indulge in "baby talk?" Do you know women who dissolve in tears or men who resort to rages in order to win an argument? Do you know persons who refuse to speak when they are angry? Do you recognize some of your own performances as being childish, immature, and regressive in nature?

Temporary regressions caused by physical illnesses or unduly severe stress need cause little concern; for when the precipitating factor is removed or ameliorated, the condition clears up automatically. Sometimes, however, the person may become fixated at an infantile level.

FIXATION

Fixation is a psychologic mechanism wherein a person rivets his attention and focuses his emotional force on some one idea or action, or at a given level of adjustment. Some (though probably not so many as the Freudians would have us believe) men have a mother fixation, and so prolonged and intense was their dependence upon, and devotion, to their mothers that they disparagingly measure every other woman by the mother-standard, and consequently find it impossible to find happiness away from "mother's apron strings." One with a racial fixation feels that all members of a given race are entitled to honor, homage, and adulation, or conversely, that they are a pestilential scourge to be destroyed. Fixations imply a basic immaturity, a lack of self-reliance. There are, of course, countless exceptions to every generalization; but it is interesting how often persons who have a racial fixation, glory in their race to the discredit of others, and feel they are entitled to special considerations and privileges have achieved little in their own right. The man who has really wrought mightily— whether he has composed a symphony, written a sonnet, built a bridge, discovered a cure for a disease, or merely done his day's work well and lived happily—does not need to bolster his pride by invoking the greatness of his group. If he *is* superior he need not *prove* his superiority to himself or anyone else. The harm of this psychologic mechanism lies in its quality of excessiveness. To love one's mother, one's family, one's neighborhood, one's country is natural; to be proud of them is highly desirable. It is only when love of one's own becomes exclusive and leads to suspicion, distrust, and hatred of outsiders that it becomes destructive and eventually self-defeating.

Man's ability to adjust to environmental demands, to adapt himself to changing necessities, is one of the major elements in his survival; and the great trouble with fixations is that they reflect rigidity and inflexibility which are bound to be self-defeating, since change is forever characteristic of life itself. Our bodies change; our ideas, ideals, customs, modes of life change from generation to generation and within each lifetime. Becoming fixated on masturbation is wrong, not for any ethical or metaphysical reason, but because such fixation makes impossible the enjoyment of normal, adult sex relations. Similarly, it is wrong to become fixated on an infantile level of behavior, because not only does the person shirk his responsibilities as an adult, but he also misses the rewards of maturity: a sense of poise, of control, of being at home in the universe.

Ability to change and modify, to discard the old and assume the new does not connote an amorphous, vacillating formlessness of character; indeed, the reverse is true. We live in an ever-expanding universe; beauty, goodness, and truth are all relative and not absolute terms; and to be happy in such a world we must be capable of *growing*—*not* only physically, but mentally and emotionally as well.

DISSOCIATION

We avoid contact with persons whom we find disagreeable, "dissociate" ourselves from them; and in the same fashion, we may dissociate from our conscious awareness ideas or emotions which we consider unpleasant or disturbing. Dissociation differs from repression in that while the latter is an attempt to forget, an unwillingness to face that which is painful, the former (dissociation) is actual (though unconscious) *denial* of the existence of those attitudes, qualities, or actions which we possess but of which we do not approve.

Judy H., aged 4 and an only child, had an imaginary playmate called Sally. Sally was "an ever present help in time of trouble"; for it was she who spilt the milk, broke the glass, forgot to close the door, wouldn't let Judy come when called, wouldn't let her pick up her toys, etc. Sally was the perfect scapegoat and enabled Judy to deny all responsibility for her childish misdemeanors or mistakes.

Such whimsical make-believe is amusing and charming in a four-year old; but such refusal to face facts is neither charming nor amusing when displayed by an adult. Have you ever noticed how often a person will criticize sharply some fault in another which you have been acutely aware of as being characteristic of the critic?

Miss W., a school-teacher, had a nervous habit of continually clearing her throat. She amazed her colleagues one day by saying of a student: "I don't see how Catherine will ever get, much less keep, a job. The way she is always clearing her throat would drive any employer crazy."

Make a list of the characteristics you most dislike and the actions you most heartily disapprove of. Now quite honestly ask yourself how many of these attitudes and actions are really your own, though ordinarily unadmitted even to yourself. Do you, for example, dislike intolerance to the extent of being intolerant of it? Despite your "sensitivity" do you condemn "self-pity" in others? Do you criticize Mrs. M. because "she is always finding fault with everyone?" Do you excoriate Mr. A. as being a "tight wad"—you who are more than a little cautious in your expenditures? It would be rather devastating for most of us "to see oursel's as others see us."

Explanation of the universality of dissociation lies, no doubt, in the fact that each person represents a plurality of selves; no man is wholly consistent and single-minded. We surprise ourselves alike by our capacity for goodness and its opposite; we sometimes show judgment, wisdom, kindness, and generosity beyond our usual wont; sometimes, the reverse. Everyone has an ideal concept of himself, makes certain demands upon himself, and has certain expectations as to what he will do and be. Being imperfect man can never more than approximate his ideal, and rather than face failure, he simply denies the existence of the affronting idea, attitude, or action. Rarely is cleavage of personality so dramatic as that of Dr. Jekyll and Mr. Hyde; but we all know persons whose hearts bleed for humanity but who do nothing to make life easier or happier for anyone; persons who talk eloquently about economic justice and underpay their own employees; persons who rail against vice and immorality, yet enjoy books of pornography and dirty stories. Such inconsistencies, dissociations, hypocrisies, or whatever you may wish to term them are easy to observe in others; but our own are for the most part unrecognized as well as unacknowledged.

PROJECTION

Closely allied to dissociation is another mechanism: Projection. Projection, like dissociation, is a technique for dealing with those aspects of our own nature which we are unwilling to acknowledge as ours; but it represents a further step. Not only do we refuse to accept feelings or desires which we consider wrong, but we attempt to rid ourselves of them by ascribing them to others. It is more than seeing in others our own unrecognized faults and limitations; it is literally a hurling away (*pro,* meaning forward and *jacere,* to throw) from ourselves those attributes and actions which our ego finds it intolerable to acknowledge. The jealous man, knowing that jealousy is childish, and secretly realizing that admitting such an emotion is tantamount to acknowledging the possibility of superior charm, ability, or worth, denies that he is jealous, but projects his feeling by accusing his wife of being possessive and distrusting. Similarly the person who accuses his mate of infidelity is often by his accusation projecting his own suppressed (or unsuppressed) desires.

Crusaders against vice, who find in the theater, books, dancing, and even in the innocent activities of young children evidence of lust and sex vileness, are often repressing their own sex drive, projecting their desires by ascribing them to others, and simultaneously deriving vicarious compensatory thrills from being able at least endlessly to *talk* about sex. They will not acknowledge having such "sinful" desires, but both their desires and their secret sense of guilt are so strong that they must somehow be released: hence, the roundabout, indirect projection and accusation. Were it not for the unfortunate effect on others, such accusations could be disregarded; but they actually wreak much harm, creating in otherwise normal minds a leering and even sadistic conception of a normal function which needs normal control.

Mr. C. T., aged 57, the chief pillar of his church, was blatant about his God-fearing piety and vehement about being the archenemy of sin, sin and sex being synonymous, in his mind. He led a movement to stop the showing of movies on Sunday, and would have been delighted could he have "blasted the whole nefarious industry from the face of the earth." He successfully opposed dances in the community hall of his church. He haunted public bathing beaches and, "horrified" by the "indecencies" apparently attempted in his subsequent diatribes to approximate the "lewdness" and "filth" he had witnessed. Short skirts, slacks, parked cars, coeducation: anything and everything even remotely connected with sex was fit subject for his denunciation. That he considered sex sinful, filthy, and to be abhorred was obvious; that the subject preoccupied him to the exclusion of all else was equally apparent. There was a certain sardonic fitness about the manner of his death; for he was found shot to death in the arms of another man's wife—shot by the irate husband.

The moral of this rather melodramatic case—and life often manages to be more melodramatic than the wildest fiction—is not that everyone who preaches is necessarily himself prey to the very evil he attacks, but rather to indicate two things: (1) violent denunciation and accusation are often evidence of projection, and (2) projection, like other psychologic mechanisms, seldom proves to be a satisfactory method of meeting a problem.

Projection works in yet another way: "the wicked flee when no man pursueth." If the sense of guilt is intense enough, one may simultaneously proclaim his innocence and be sure that others are accusing him. Schizophrenic patients actually "hear" such accusations, even though they are alone when the "voices" are heard. Persons suffering from persecution mania are usually projecting their own feelings of guilt or inadequacy in such a way as to believe that others are attempting to bring about their downfall. The harm of dissociation and projection, as of all the other defense mechanisms, lies in the fact that they do not really protect. Danger can sometimes be escaped by retreat, but usually it must be met and overcome. It can never be adequately handled by evasion. Fear is the inevitable concomitant of danger; and so long as danger is not faced and overcome fear, that most prolific of all breeders, continues its destructive work.

NEGATIVISM

Negativism is a normal, though thoroughly exasperating, phase through which most children pass. It may be *passive*, a refusal to do what is requested, or *active*, an insistence on doing the opposite of what has been asked. It is easy to understand why a child (particularly easy, if it is someone else's child!) should go through the stage of negativism. A child passing from wholly dependent infancy begins gradually to have some dim conception of himself as a person, with rights, wishes, and powers of his own. His contrariness is merely a childish and ineffectual attempt to assert his personality, to establish his importance. As he matures he learns more adequate techniques of self-realization and expression and passes out of the negativistic phase.

In many adults, this childhood level of reaction is never transcended; and such persons are obstinate not because they have contrary convictions or ideas but because by such refusal to conform or comply they hope to convince themselves and others that they are just as good as the next fellow, no one can "lord it over" them, and what they wish is just as important as what anyone else wants. This conscientious refusal ever to agree or coöperate can go to such extremes that the person will forego something he really desires or do that which is in actuality distasteful to him rather than give in.

It might be well to note that probably no one is entirely free from this negativistic attitude. There are persons whose *ex cathedra* manner of speaking, dogmatism, or cocksureness are so irritating that we automatically disagree. There is, however, a difference between being consciously contrary (childish though such "revenge" may be) and being defensively negativistic in an attempt to give false superiority and courage to a basically insecure and wobbly ego. At the opposite pole from negativistic opposition is spineless acquiescence. Both are expressions of immaturity and insecurity, and both are ultimately ineffectual and self-defeating.

DISPLACEMENT

Displacement is the term applied to another protective mechanism, used primarily to release emotional tension built up by repressed memories or immediately irritating circumstances. *Emotion,* whether smoldering and controlled or flashing and unrestrained, *must be released.* There is a close analogy between the operation of steam in a boiler and emotion in the human organism. In both instances, safety or escape valves must be provided. If the pressure of steam, or of emotion, is increased or if the valves are blocked, the outlets of emotion repressed, and other vents not provided, an explosion is bound to occur. Sometimes there will be an accidental opening which will temporarily serve as escape valve. You have seen steam escaping through a seam or a small rust hole in a boiler; in the same way, wives, husbands, children, and other domesticated animals often serve as escape valve for "displaced" emotion. Mr. A. cannot, much as he would love to, tell his employer in words of one syllable just what he thinks of him; so Mr. A. damns his employer silently, dams his emotion, and when he gets home releases his pent-up feeling by "taking it out" on Mrs. A. Mrs. A. has had her own troubles, not the least of which was the fact that not she but Mrs. B. was elected president of the Garden Club. Being a lady, Mrs. A. congratulated Mrs. B. with just the correct degree of simulated cordiality. When Mr. A. declaims, "It does seem to me that instead of gadding around all day, you might stay home once in a while and prepare a decent meal," does she, much as she would love to, break a platter over his head? Instead, a few minutes later she sends Junior dessert-less and weeping from the table, when she discovers that once more, "after she has told him a million times," he has not washed his hands. Junior, unpracticed in the art of rationalization can find no legitimate outlet for his sense of outraged dignity and stomach. He does know that he cannot with impunity bite his mother's hand, much as he would love to; so instead as he stumbles from the room, he kicks the unoffending cat.

A man, finding his business about to fail often displaces his emotional concern by blaming the reds, the political party in power, or some competitor. We all are guilty, upon occasion, of "snapping at" another for some trivial, inconsequential thing which he has said or done—not because we even momentarily consider his word or deed important, but because it gives us an opportunity "to let off steam."

Displacement is not bad, *per se*. Tension created by suppressed emotion or by the irritations of everyday life *must* be released; but it behooves us, both for our own personal good and for the welfare of society, to find constructive and creative channels through which to express this excess energy. Hobbies, participation in sports or civic enterprises, avocations, and enthusiasms offer as adequate release for pent-up emotion as do hates, prejudices, temper outbursts, and substitute revenges. Obviously, digging your own flower beds is more profitable than yanking up flowers from the city parks, because you are annoyed at the corrupt city government, your employer, or your wife; similarly if you are wrought up about the world's tragic condition, releasing your energy through coöperation to effect changes in the detested situation will profit you and the world more than will hating the enemy, or displacing your hate to some other focus.

IRRADIATION

Irradiation is displacement raised to the nth degree. In displacement, the person usually chooses *a* target other than that which is the original source of his emotional turmoil; in irradiation, he permits his irritation to become at once so intense and so diffuse that it affects *all* of his relationships, all of his contacts until everything and everyone are targets. Like concentric rings spreading over the entire surface of a pool into which a stone has been thrown, so irritability, starting from a single repressed memory or from a particular immediate disturbance, can so irradiate as to color all reactions and attitudes. One who is chronically irritable and over emotional in his responses usually excuses himself in terms of his multitudinous troubles and worries; but upon analysis one finds that the many expressions stem from a single source.

PLEASURE-SUBSTITUTE MECHANISMS

The psychologic mechanisms so far discussed: dynamic forgetting and repression, withdrawal, regression, fixation, dissociation, projection, negativism, displacement, and irradiation are all techniques —for the most part abortive and unsuccessful—designed to ward off danger and to protect the ego (at whatever level it may have been set) from injury. Another group of mechanisms, closely related to, and often appearing in conjunction with, the above, stem from the positive pole of the pleasure-pain principle and have as their purpose flattering or supporting the ego or providing vicarious pleasure. Pleasure-substitute mechanisms tend to fail, as do the defense techniques, and for the same reason. There is an immediacy and an urgency about our fears and our desires which demand direct answers, definite solutions, specific satisfaction. There is little relief and there may be disaster for a nervous driver who finds looking at the slippery road too upsetting and so contemplates the beautiful scenery along the road; and reading the cook book does not appease the pangs of hunger! Most psychologic mechanisms imply basic immaturity, because they are all grounded in the inability or the unwillingness unflinchingly to face actuality and then to summon all one's resources of knowledge, skill, and ingenuity for ameliorating, changing, overcoming, or accepting the situation.

RATIONALIZATION

Probably no other mechanisms is more universally employed than is rationalization, a process of self-justification which is called into play whenever any cherished belief, opinion, or action is challenged.

Rousseau was perhaps unduly emphatic, as was his wont, when he said that the archenemy of mankind and the first criminal was the man who first used the word "my"; but certain it is that the possessiveness which that word connotes is the source of national and personal acquisitiveness and ruthlessness alike and also that it is responsible for most of our excuse-making and our self-justification. The minute a thing—a material possession or an idea—becomes "mine" and its worth is questioned, rationalization begins its operation. To be satisfied or pleased with what one has is a desirable attitude and certainly more conducive to happiness than the opposite of always feeling that the grass in the farther meadow is greener; but, carried to an extreme, this attitude leads to intolerance on the one hand and unwarranted self-esteem on the other.

Look at your beliefs and opinions. Where did you acquire them? For the most part we unconsciously absorb them; and just because we have "taken them over" rather than "worked them out" they have a quality of obviousness which precludes our examination and arouses our resentment when anyone else does so. Mr. Trotter in his essay, "Instincts of the Herd in Peace and War," has summarized this kind of unquestioning acceptance of ideas.

When we find ourselves entertaining an opinion about the basis of which there is a quality of feeling which tells us that to inquire into it would be absurd, obviously unnecessary, unprofitable, undesirable, bad form, or wicked, we may know that the opinion is a non-rational one, and probably, therefore, founded upon inadequate evidence.[2]

If our inherited and "taken for granted" beliefs and opinions were adequate; i.e., if they really sufficed to meet the demands of our personal and communal life, there would be no necessity for

[2] William Trotter, *Instincts of the Herd in Peace and War* (Macmillan), p. 44.

discarding, changing, or even examining them. But they don't. Necessities, demands, difficulties, dangers, and satisfactions are so constantly changing that many of our traditional concepts and ideas are as worthless as medieval armor would be in present-day warfare.

If you find yourself responding emotionally—with irritation, distrust, dislike, aversion, etc.—to the expression of opinions at variance with your own, you have a danger signal warning that you are not really thinking but merely being defensive. It is not the idea or opinion to which you are giving such intense but misplaced loyalty but your own self-esteem: the idea has value to you primarily because it is *yours*. In a world such as ours, the only constructively intelligent attitude that we can hold with reference to any idea or belief is a *tentative* one. We must be willing to say, "This is what I believe *today* in the light of *all* the information which I can get. If tomorrow new truth necessitates the modification of what I now believe, I shall accept the new information and make whatever change is called for." Incidentally, never forget that values are not weakened by scrutiny nor destroyed by being tested by experience. Indeed, your analyzed and tested principles support you; whereas your uncritically accepted beliefs are constantly calling for your support.

The process of rationalization is carried on not only with reference to our major concepts but in all the minutiae of daily life. Since we are human we are always making mistakes; but to acknowledge our mistakes, to face our limitations would wound our pride, injure our ego. Falling below our self-set standard, and finding admission of failure intolerable, we set about excusing ourselves, justifying our action. Do you rationalize your stinginess by telling yourself that the beggar would undoubtedly spend your dime at the corner saloon and that he probably has more money than you do anyway? Do you rationalize your extravagance with high-sounding phrases about keeping money in circulation? Do you stir up trouble among your acquaintances and justify yourself by saying that "everyone has a right to know what is being said about him by persons who pretend to be his friends"? When a clerk gives you too much change, do you figure that the store certainly has made enough profit on you in the past? Do you consider your disregard for the feelings of others honest frankness and similar frankness in another, intolerable rudeness? Do you rationalize your acquisitiveness into enterprise, your stubbornness into firmness, your cruelty into justice, your maudlin sentimentality into tenderness, your restlessness and desire for excitement into liberal philosophy, your reactionary tendencies into sound conservatism? Are you a failure because you are too lazy to improve your condition or because you "never had a chance," or are "unwilling to descend to the methods" of your successful competitors?

Not only do we find excuses for the faults, inadequacies, limitations, and mistakes which our ego is unwilling to claim; we are equally adept in finding "good" excuses for doing whatever we wish to do. You know that she is vain and thinks about nothing but clothes; she will tell you she has to keep up her appearance to hold her job, her husband, or whatever. You know that his driving a Cadillac is an ostentatious display of his wealth; he will tell you and himself that he prefers a smaller car, but his position makes certain demands upon him. You'd like to live your own life for a change and have a rest from responsibility; so you send your children to camp. Why? For the true reasons given above, or because "they will learn team work, become more self-reliant, etc."? Such questions and observations are only samples. One can almost categorically make the statement that any human being, granted that he wishes anything long enough and hard enough can, by the process of rationalization, get to the place that he not only feels that he has a right to gratify his wish but also that it is right for him to do so.

Mr. J. G., married and the father of two small children was a maestro in the art of rationalization. He always had the best of reasons for everything that he did, things which his family and friends judged and his own experience proved to be impractical and foolish. He had an excellent position, but was unhappy in his work because he considered it beneath his ability. His "boss" was "a bully"; his co-workers "nothing but clods." Since he was entirely innocent of any practical business knowledge or experience, his dreams of what he could accomplish if he "were on his own" were entirely rosy. "If he were in business for himself," his children could go to a private school, instead of having to "mix with riff raff." "His wife could have a maid and dress in style." He would be happy because he would be doing real work instead of following the dictates of a "little Hitler." He could "put his elderly father on easy street," etc.

He resigned, after giving himself the satisfaction of telling them all what he thought of them, took his savings and those of his father, and launched into his venture. Undoubtedly he worked hard; but his efforts were doomed to failure not only because of his lack of experience but because his "pride" made it impossible for him to accept advice from anyone. As the inevitability of failure became increasingly apparent, Mr. G. marshalled his new rationalizations. He was failing—yes. Why? His wife had never believed in him and helped as she should. His employees were inefficient and lazy, concerned about nothing but their pay checks. The persons he had taken into his confidence turned out to be traitors. And when all other excuses failed, there was always "the cut throat administration in Washington" to fall back on.

Maybe Mr. G.'s venture would have succeeded had it been in the hands of another; but the important thing is that Mr. G. did not honestly face the facts of either his factory job or his projected scheme. He justified his actions at every turn; he substituted wishful thinking for intelligent planning; he refused to admit, much less profit by, his errors.

COMPENSATION AND SUBLIMATION

Compensation and sublimation are alike in that both are positive rather than negative techniques and both are in the nature of substitution. Compensation, as the word implies, is largely a matter of balancing, of "making up" for some lack; whereas sublimation is primarily concerned with redirection.

One of the simplest examples of compensation is found in the auditory acuity of persons whose vision is impaired. We depend so largely upon visual imagery for recognition and identification that only under necessity do we to any great extent develop our other sensory abilities. The blind make up for, compensate for, their visual deficiency by increasing both their auditory and their tactual sensitivity.

You will recall from childhood reading how almost always one wicked fairy was present at the christening of the prince or princess so that no child was born wholly fortunate. Certainly the same is true of all the children of men: some seem and are more fortunate than others; but all have limitations and handicaps. The wise man "compensates" for his deficiencies by building up his assets. If a door is closed, one does not stand indefinitely battering upon it and refusing all other entrance to the room in which he wishes to be; he seeks other openings or even creates new ones. It would be interesting to know how much creative and inventive genius would have remained undiscovered had it not been "housed" as it was. Recall Steinmetz with his deformed body and his magnificent inventive mind; deaf Beethoven composing immortal music; or the tragically distorted Van Gogh able to pour sunshine into his pictures.

In less dramatic and spectacular fashion we all compensate for our own limitations. Mr. S. has compensated for his lack of college education by bending every energy toward making a financial success, determined that even if he cannot take his family to the University Club they shall have everything money can buy. Miss W., from whose christening the "fairy of beauty" was conspicuously absent, has deliberately cultivated the art of conversation. Mr. P., crippled by infantile paralysis and never, consequently, able to participate in sports prides himself on his chess game. Our pride, the level at which we have set our ego, our disinclination to admit our inadequacies, make it easy for us to "play up" our abilities or virtues; and this mechanism used intelligently and in moderation is a very definite asset. *Over*compensation, like all other excesses, results in disproportion and distortion in personality development. If one is too keenly and painfully aware of his handicap or liabilities, he is prone, out of resentment and injured pride, to go too far in the other direction, to magnify his own importance in a particular realm and discredit those qualities or abilities which he does not himself possess; and to take out on others his own hurt feelings. Very often the bully on the schoolground is a child who at home is dominated and harshly treated. Not strong enough to cope with his own situation he revenges himself by making life miserable for those who are defenseless in the face of his greater strength. Have you ever noticed how many small men, painfully aware of their short stature, have loud and booming voices and a strutting walk, and how many "hen-pecked" men are office tyrants?

Mr. S. W., an instructor in a small college, is feared by his students and avoided by his colleagues. He prides himself that his word is law, and delights in ridiculing or humiliating his students. In association with other teachers, he never relaxes his effort to demonstrate the superiority of his own erudition and his amazement over the abysmal ignorance of everyone else. He utters casual opinions with an air of finality, and quotes obscure poets that he may be "pained" by the "illiteracy" of his audience. His whole attitude is that of a great and superior intellect whose sad fate is to waste its greatness on oafs and yokels. He rationalizes his unpopularity as being the "envy" of stupid and ignorant men. About the kindliest epithet he ever gets is "conceited ass"; but he is, in reality, a tragic victim of overcompensation.

Picture a small boy always on the outside fringe of every play group: a rather grimy and poorly dressed child, in a school in which the majority of children came from more than comfortable homes; the only child of his race and religion in a smug and tight minded community in which anything or anyone different from the accepted pattern was looked upon with disfavor and distrust; an undersized and slightly hunchbacked child, unable to take part, let alone excel, in sports. The set up is perfect for the development of a thoroughgoing sense of inferiority. Early in his school life, S. W. discovered that the one thing he could do was learn his lessons; and right then the pattern of his future development was established. In school, he was always at the head of his class (a fact which did not endear him to other children); he won scholarships; he earned fellowships; he took degrees with honors. In other words, he used his one ability not to break down the cruel barriers which separated him from others but as a wall behind which to hide his loneliness and his pain: he overcompensated to the degree that today his erudition has no value other than the doubtful one of insulating him in synthetic self-esteem.

Compensation, if grounded in an honest and objective facing of one's limitations and special assets and expressed by overcoming the former and wisely utilizing the latter, is a psychologic mechanism of great value; if used as an escape technique it will eventually prove harmful.

Sublimation is one of the most valuable psychologic mechanisms, for by it we achieve positive good from situations which are potentially harmful. Sublimation concerns itself with the direction of energy, energy which unreleased would increase the activity of the hypothalamus and thereby produce tension symptoms. We have noted the way in which energy is produced within the body to enable it to meet dangerous situations and to achieve satisfactions; and we have seen the inhibitory effect which civilization exerts upon the free release of this mobilized energy. The inescapable tensions, the countless frustrations, the necessity for performing disagreeable tasks and for postponing our satisfactions: all are energy-producing. The analogy of the steam boiler is in point. Steam produced by boiling water, if properly channeled, is capable of gigantic operations; if not, it is useless; and if pressure is increased and no adequate provision is made for the utilization of the increased volume of steam, destructive explosions are certain. Our civilized lives call for the expenditure of less than all of our natural energy; and every worry, every "insult" to our ego, every

anger, every irritation (present or remembered), every disappointment, every primary or secondary fear or wish inadequately dealt
with increases our store of energy which if unexpressed results
in such overstimulation of the hypothalamus as eventually to manifest itself in tension symptoms.

What do you do if you plan to have strawberry shortcake for
dessert only to discover that the market has no berries? Do you
mourn and say, "Well, we just will have to do without dessert";
or do you change your plan? If you discover that the route you
planned to follow is under repair, don't you choose another highway and go along toward your destination?

Every life inevitably is marked by grief and sorrow; every life
has its disappointments and frustrations. No man escapes trouble;
no man "has it all his own way." What are you going to do about
it? You can shrink away, cravenly refuse to face facts—repress,
dissociate, project—or you can sublimate in such a way that what
could have destroyed you becomes instead the source of new strength
and power.

Dr. and Mrs. S., financially successful and socially prominent,
had one son in whom they centered their pride and joy. In addition to everything his family could give him, Jim had everything
else; he was handsome, brilliant, popular, a fine athlete, and an excellent musician. During his sophomore year in college, he was
killed in a freak football accident. His parents were prostrated with
grief; and their friends wondered how they could "carry on," now
that the mainspring of their lives was broken.

Being courageous, generous, and intelligent, Dr. and Mrs. S.
realized that to give their lives over to futile regrets and devastating sorrow was poor tribute to the memory of their son. They en-
dowed a scholarship in the name of Jim, and took in their home
and treated as though they were their own, boys who would not
otherwise have been able to attend college.

Of course, these other boys did not and could not take the place
of their own son; but they did offer comfort and pleasure and they
did furnish an outlet for grief and a new channel through which
to express a great capacity for love and devotion.

Not only the person involved but society as a whole is benefited by this process of sublimation. Much of what is most valuable— art, music, social reform, invention, etc.—is the result of man's ability to rechannel his energies, to use constructively and in new ways that excess energy which unreleased would have been useless or harmful.

PHANTASY FORMATION

Phantasy formation is daydreaming which has become an end rather than a means toward an end. Daydreaming, building castles in the air, envisioning the "alabaster cities undimmed by human tears": all these can be a source of pleasure to the dreamer and of, incalcuable worth to society, *provided* they are used to furnish goals and to spur effort toward achievement. In daydreams we per-mit our wishes free rein; all obstacles are easily hurdled; the world is the "Land of Heart's Desire"; all is "forever young, forever fair." Such daydreaming serves a twofold purpose: it softens our disap-pointments and rests us from the weariness of the day; and, in the second place, it sets a goal toward which we can strive and furnishes clews as how best to realize our dreams. Those who have "achieved greatly and wrought mightily" have been at heart dreamers; but their dreams have served not as feather beds into which to snuggle for ease and comfort but as springboards from which to dive into new and often terrifying experiences. The doer without the dream is a mere robot; the dreamer who does not at least attempt to actualize his dream is a mere escapist.

One of the signs of old age is the inability to dream "big dreams." One reason for the retardation of social and economic progress is that too often the governing classes have become so habituated to customs, so enslaved by tradition, that they can no longer even imagine a newer and better procedure. Too often men shudder away from schemes which they term "crack-brained" and which, though perhaps impracticable, nevertheless contain elements of a dream for the improvement of distressing conditions. If men would only dream more, compare their dreams, and then set about actualizing their dreams, civilization would become civilized.

Dream of yourself as popular, a welcomed addition to every group, a much sought-after and well-liked person; but then learn how to be: listen sympathetically, consider the rights and wishes of others, believe the best instead of hoping the worst about your friends, take your own minor disappointments lightly and those of your friends seriously, etc. Dream yourself illustrious in your profession; but then bring your dream to pass by getting the best training possible; seizing every opportunity, no matter how arduous; working persistently and imaginatively, etc. Dream of a world of peace and justice, wherein every child born will have adequate opportunity for self-realization and fulfillment; but do something besides dream: check your own impulses of intolerance and hasty generalization; respect the personality of others; refuse to take unfair advantage, even when you can do so with impunity, etc.

Our personal and our social problems are concrete and call for practical solution. In our daydreaming we fashion the design for our lives; but that design is worthless unless we set about the practical task of weaving the pattern.

IDENTIFICATION

Identification, which may be the superficial aping of external manner or the deep and meaningful merging of one's personality with the aspirations and ideals of another man or of a "cause," is a psychological mechanism capable of achieving great good or of wreaking great harm. Whether hero worship is good or evil depends largely on: (1) the basic worth of the hero selected for imitation and identification, and (2) whether personality is lost or fulfilled in such identification.

The little boy wearing a brightly colored, feathered headdress, skulking behind a tree, and emerging with deafening shouts is identifying himself with his Indian hero. The fourteen-year-old girl, torturing her hair into fantastic shapes and assuming a languorous air is identifying herself with her favorite movie heroine. The captain refusing to leave his ship is identifying himself with the tradition of the Sea. We not only imitate the manners of our heroes, but as nearly as possible appropriate their characteristic attitudes and ideas. It is through this process of identification that we come to assume pride in, hope for, responsibility for, our family, cur race, our religion, our country, or any other group of which we feel ourselves a part. Why is it that when you meet a person from your home state, you feel a special warmth for him? You may willingly or even gladly have left the state of your birth; and yet anyone coming from there seems somehow to "belong." The experience is even more vivid if you happen to be traveling or living in a foreign land.

Identification which is more than mere imitation is grounded in creative imagination which enables us actually to think and feel with another. A parent actually suffers the pain of his child; and a person though himself well fed actually feels the pinch of hunger that another experiences. Most of our charitable and humanitarian organizations owe their inception and continuation to this ability to identify ourselves with the needs of another, this capacity for imagining how it would be to occupy the other person's shoes. It works the other way also: we are able not only to help but to be helped. A man in the uniform of his country, one of a group, is able through absorption of group purpose and group strength to perform feats of bravery and courage which would be beyond his individual power. Men can struggle and suffer beyond their individual might when their efforts are given meaning through identification with a purpose which they consider to be more significant than their own immediate comfort or desire. The person who has thus identified himself has not "lost" his significance and importance; indeed he has expanded and enlarged his ego to exactly the proportions and value of that of which he is a part.

It is easier to identify ourselves with a person, to follow a leader, than it is to devote ourselves to a cause; for the human mind, as a rule, needs to seize upon some concrete object; and only the better trained, the more mature, the farther-seeing mind can be adequately motivated by an ideal. The great religions and ideologies which have persisted have done so because they were based upon enduring principles and values independent of personalities. And so despite the advent and temporary triumph of Alexanders, Caesars, Napoleons, and Hitlers, men have been and still are willing, glad, and proud to live for and if need be die for (the former is often more difficult than the latter) an ideal world of justice and kindness. The identification of man with ideals which are inherently beneficial to all mankind rather than to individual or closed group aggrandizement is one thread in history that is unbroken, regardless of how at times it is twisted and snarled.

The dangers inherent in the process of identification are apparent. If one takes a gangster as his ideal or identifies himself with the aims of a petty, ignoble, self-seeking cause then obviously those harmful and destructive attitudes become part of the identified personality. In the second place, it is easy for the immature mind to be "possessed by," rather than identified with, the person or the cause that commands its allegiance. There is a vast difference between conscious, directed, and deliberate devotion which a mature mind gives to a cause and the blind subservience which leads to a person's becoming a tool, a mere puppet. Finally, you will remember that earlier in the chapter we spoke of our social and humanitarian organizations being dependent on our ability to put ourselves in the other person's place. That oneness of feeling, that ability to suffer with another has its value *only* if it is followed up by intelligent effort to ameliorate the conditions. To agonize over the troubles of our friends or over the heartbreak of the world degenerates into nothing more than maudlin, masochistic sentimentality unless we transmute our awareness into action. To weep over the plight of children living in tenement districts avails little for them or for you. What you can do may seem tragically little as compared with either the need or the ability of others to help; but do the little you can. To stay awake nights torturing yourself by picturing the horrors of concentration camps will not bring about their abolition, nor do you any good either. Limited though your sphere may be, within it do all you can meaningfully and actively to identify yourself with those groups and organizations which have as their purpose the establishment of a world order in which there will be no place for, nor tolerance of, organized cruelty.

CONVERSION

Conversion is a psychologic mechanism wherein repressed, emotionally toned ideas are expressed indirectly in the form of symbols; and these symbols appear as disturbances of bodily functions. If a person has seen a horrible sight, one which affected him deeply and personally, and he is unable to face the situation, he may suddenly lose his sight; i.e., he symbolizes the repressed, emotionally disturbing idea which he cannot face, by not being able to see it. Such blindness is not organic but merely a *conversion* of underlying disturbances into symbolic bodily illness. Usually such conversion symptoms are easily cured when one discovers the emotional basis for the symbol. Inasmuch as this group of symptoms is extremely interesting and rather common, the entire next chapter will be devoted to its description.

CHAPTER XI

SYMBOLIC SYMPTOMS

Symbolic symptoms, like tension symptoms, are induced by environmental or attitudinal stresses and appear in the absence of organic pathology. Often patients presenting symbolic symptoms have tension symptoms as well; and not infrequently a single symptom may express both tension and symbolism. The picture presented by symbolic symptoms is not so clear-cut as that of the tension group, primarily because they are predominately ideational and therefore not so easily subjected to objective analysis and interpretation. However, if you will bear in mind several concepts already discussed, the significance of symbolic symptoms will become apparent.

First, recall the difference between the voluntary and involuntary nervous systems. The autonomic nervous system is not under conscious control; its function is to coördinate bodily activities so that there is smooth, harmonious action in waking and sleep, in rest and action, in peaceful work and fight. The "brain" of this autonomic nervous system is in the region of the hypothalamus where most of the autonomic impulses are received and whence most of the autonomic impulses are released. This system is involved in the production of *tension* symptoms; and these symptoms are *real* reactions of the body, (rapid heart beat, rise in blood pressure, spasm of the intestines, etc.), even though the ultimate cause of the overactivity of the hypothalamus is merely a disturbed emotional state.

In man, superimposed upon this "lower" system, is that part of the brain which "thinks," controls conscious movements, and appreciates sensation. This overlaid portion of the brain (corticospinal system) has marked *indirect* influence on internal organs because conscious thought can stimulate the "lower" hypothalamic "brain"; whereas the autonomic system responds almost wholly in reflex fashion. The corticospinal system is more concerned with conscious feeling, thinking, and acting. Movements are made by the cortex of the brain; sensations are appreciated by the cortex; vision, hearing, memory, thinking are controlled by the cortex.

Thus, when a person is disturbed his total organism is involved; and there may be not only signs of tension resulting from stimulation of the hypothalamus, but also disturbances in the functions controlled by the corticospinal, or "higher" brain.

Remember also the operation of the two psychologic mechanisms: dissociation and conversion. By the former, one is able to deny the very existence of whatever seems too acutely disturbing or ego-wounding. Denial, however, does not mean disappearance of the original irritation, and even though the person may have so perfected his technique that he is not aware of its operation, the energy created by such repressed memories must still seek an outlet. Conversion is often the means by which such outlet is found; that is, the person who, refusing or being unable to face and overcome some distressing or disturbing experience, has "dissociated" himself may express the dissociated irritation through the medium of some physical symptom. What happens is that the person "turns away from" (L-con, meaning away and vertere, to turn) the basic trouble and transposes his suppressed desires or fears and his repressed memories into symptoms, which at first sight seem to have little or no connection with the true cause.

You will remember, also,[1] from the discussion of the nature and use of symbolism, that we learn to read associated meaning into words or objects: meanings not necessarily apparent to one with a different background of experience. That in addition to the many symbols we hold in common, everyone has his own particularized associations or symbols is one element of difficulty in properly interpreting and dealing with symbolic symptoms.

[1] Vide p. 31.

In the fourth place and finally, remember that *man reacts as a total organism,* so that you will understand why symbolic symptoms, though primarily ideational in origin, may yet express themselves by means of what would appear to be physical disturbances.

Symbolic, or dissociated-conversion symptoms, though fantastic or unreasonable to an outsider, are to the patient *actual* and distressing. Among the more common are *nonorganic* paralysis of the hands or legs; inability to feel any sensation; inability to see, hear, talk, or remember. Some persons deliberately pretend or assume symptoms but in the vast majority of cases of persons suffering from symbolic symptoms there is honest conviction that the trouble is exactly as they feel and represent it to be. To tell such a person that "there is nothing wrong"; that "it's all in his mind"; that he can see or walk or hear does not help so long as he *feels* that he cannot. That he has conversion symptoms indicates his inability to face the initial difficulty; and so it is unlikely that he can face the fact that his trouble is purely ideational in origin. In addition, the continuance of strongly irritating, though suppressed, memories provides sufficient unreleased energy so that some outlet must be provided, and his symptom provides some tangible problem about which to complain, or try to do something, or focus his attention.

Sometimes the symbolism in a symptom is readily discoverable.

Mr. N., who had a dissociated-conversion symptom of muteness, was symbolically expressing his remorse over the violent quarrel which he had with his father on the morning of the latter's accidental death.

Miss G. barely missed being struck by the body of a suicide who leaped from a window above the walk along which she was hurrying to work. She did not, however, miss the horrifying sight of his mangled body. She developed a dissociated conversion symptom of inability to see, whereby she attempted, unconsciously, to shut out the distressing memory.

Miss C. was painfully hypersensitive about her scarred face (she had been in a bad automobile accident). She dreaded seeing her old acquaintances; and even more, meeting new persons. She developed the conversion symptom of paralysis of the legs, expressing thereby her unwillingness to leave the house.

Sometimes the symbolism in a symptom is extremely involved and difficult to find. The important thing about discovering the initial repressed or suppressed cause is not simply that the casual relation be· established but that the patient face the situation objectively and thereafter *retrain* his whole orientation so that not only can he rid himself of the immediately distressing symptom but avoid either recurrence or the development of new symptoms springing from dissociation, which is an outgrowth of the person's inability adequately and maturely to deal with life's problems.

There are two major categories of symbolic symptoms: (1) those obviously the expression of distorted ideas, such as phobias, obsessive-compulsive ideas and the like; and (2) those equally ideational in origin, but manifested in physical dysfunction.

Of the symbolic symptoms none are more obviously ideational in origin than the *phobias,* or intense fears to which mankind is subject. The word "phobia" is used not to describe the natural fear any man feels in the presence of actual danger, whether it be a tornado or the loss of one's job, but rather those intense and apparently groundless fears about which the person will often say, "I know it's unreasonable, but I can't help feeling that way." Phobias may stem from actual experiences which were particularly distressing; they may be purely symbolic; they may represent a combination.

Mrs. S. H. suffered intensely from claustrophobia (fear of being in an enclosed place). She would not ride in a subway; closed-in elevators terrified her; she "could not bear" to be in a room if both the windows and door were closed; she would never lock a door unless she was leaving. She traced her intense fear to a childhood experience when she was for several hours locked accidentally in the attic of her home and was unable to make any of her family hear her cries. Interestingly enough, her claustrophobia did not manifest itself until many years later, when, unhappily married, she felt herself to be "trapped." The mother of three small children and untrained to make a living she felt that she *had* to remain with her husband, though he was abusive in both action and language and though she longed to be free.

You may be interested to know the impressive sounding names given to phobias; so a partial list follows. In each instance the word is made of a prefix designating the name of the object feared plus "phobia." Thus agoraphobia means fear of open spaces; mysophobia, fear of dirt, sickness, or contamination; anthrophobia, fear of men; zoöphobia, fear of animals; syphilophobia, fear of syphilis; pyrophobia, fear of fire; etc.

At the basis of every phobia there is some unresolved conflict, some inadequately dealt with situation which, even though dynamically forgotten, still continues to operate. One with syphilophobia, who despite many negative tests is still tormented by fear that "maybe the tests are wrong," "maybe the doctor isn't telling the truth," is often a person troubled by intense sex desires which though inhibited are an ever-present source of concern. In the same way, a person faced with the necessity of making a decision and unable to come to a definite and final conclusion often pushes aside the immediate problem and symbolizes his emotional turmoil by a fear of "going crazy."

More frequently than not there is associated with the emotional turmoil symbolized by the phobia an intense guilt feeling. Our desires run counter to what we have been taught to believe is right; and yet the urgency of our wishes is so much stronger than our theoretical conviction that we give in and then feel guilty because we have. For example, children of overprotective parents are torn between their desire to be free, live their own lives, and think their own thoughts and belief that their parents' hovering concern is motivated by love. They are chafed by the restraining affection, and galled by their sense of guilt over being "ungrateful" or "disloyal." If only parents could learn the difference between direction and domination, between mothering affection and smothering possession, between helping and coddling, children would have an infinitely better opportunity to develop some genuine self-reliance; and far from loving their parents less, would be able to give freely that which can never successfully be demanded: respect, companionship, love.

Another source of guilt feelings which often result in symbolic symptoms is the discrepancy between our teachings about sex and the nature of our needs and desires. This problem is discussed in the following chapter; so suffice it here to state that whether a person has been inculcated with the Calvinistic conception that sex is sinful and abhorrent or with the romantic notion that love is all moonlight and roses, he is in for a bad time if he tries to make either jibe with his actual feelings or experiences.

Sometimes a phobia may result from a single devastating experience, the unresolved emotional tone of which is permitted so to irradiate as to color the entire life of its victim.

Mrs. R. S. was a devoted wife and mother, her life bounded by her garden walls and centered in her home. She had no interests exclusive of her family; she was inordinately proud of her husband's achievements, and equally exultant when one of her children brought home good report cards. Bill, her youngest child, became ill during a typhoid epidemic. Night and day, Mrs. S. nursed him with agonized care and devotion. His death brought inconsolable grief; and she tortured herself with wondering whether this, that, or the other thing might not have been neglected. If only she had watched him more carefully, boiled all his drinking water, not let him buy ice cream cones, etc. Though her husband, her doctor, and her friends did all in their power to convince her that she was in no way to blame, her grief turned to self-blame, and she developed a full-fledged case of mysophobia (fear of dirt). Her life became one unending warfare against "germs." She insisted that all meals be eaten at home, using no food except that which she had herself prepared. When she baked bread or pastry, she covered it with sterile cloths while it was cooling; she boiled drinking water and milk; dozens of times daily she scrubbed her hands, and used a disinfectant in the dish water. She even got to the place where she would serve raw foods only after they had been soaked in water containing peroxide to "kill the germs." That she made life miserable for herself and her family goes without saying.

The obsessive idea or phobia may be the focal point through which a whole series of emotionally disturbing and unresolved experiences finds expression.

Mrs. A. D., aged 24, lived in constant fear that she would kill or harm herself or someone else. Three years earlier, kneeling in church, she had felt an intense desire to scream. Though she controlled her impulse, the experience frightened her; for she said she had no reason to scream. Shortly thereafter, she began to develop her fear of hurting someone. If she were out walking, she would retrace her steps to reassure herself that she had not knocked somebody down or choked someone. She knew her fears were silly, but she just had to make sure. At first, she experienced these fears as attacks, and was able to laugh at her own foolishness; but soon the attacks so increased in frequency and intensity that she refused to leave the house. She refused to see friends, for fear of what she might do to them, and insisted on sending her baby away to "be out of danger." Her fear manifested itself in countless ways: she would not light a cigarette for fear she would set fire to her dress; was afraid to enter the bathroom for fear she might drink iodine; would awaken her husband several times and insist that he check to be sure that she had turned off the gas, etc. She had fears of brain tumor, of cancer, of paralysis, etc.

Mrs. A. D.'s mother had died when the child was three. Her father, who alternated between harshness and indifference to his little girl, remarried twice; and while both stepmothers had been scrupulously "just" in their treatment of the child, neither felt any particular affection for her. She saw the petting other children had, missed it sorely, and dreamed of the time when she would have someone of her own to love. When she was old enough to go out with boys her father and the current stepmother were judge and jury as to her companions. For reasons they never troubled themselves to explain some boys were deemed "all right" and others were forbidden. One day her father brought home with him a young man who was "just the right one for her." At her father's insistence she gave up seeing her other friends; and later at her father's direction, married Mr. D.

Mr. D. had all the major virtues and none of the minor vices (which can be very endearing). He worked hard. He wanted to make his home "the prettiest one on the block." He made good wages which he held in a joint account with his wife, whose expenditures he never questioned. He "never so much as looked at another woman"; and even complimented his wife's cooking! In other words, Mrs. D. "had everything in the world" except the one thing she most desired: tenderness. Mr. D. was a good man, but dull and unimaginative, inarticulate, and knew no way in which to express affection save by "working hard to give her everything she wants." She was bored and frustrated and at the same time felt guilty. She wished to find a job, but Mr. D. was adamant in his insistence that no wife of his should go out to work, so long as he had two good hands. Her friends with their interminable talk about their babies and their domestic problems bored her as much as did her own life. She longed for gaiety, excitement, romance. When she knew she was going to have a baby, she thought everything would be different. Instead, she felt even more trapped; for now she merely added to the general monotony the equally dull routine of making the baby's formula, washing the baby's clothes, changing the baby, feeding the baby, and then washing more clothes, and once more making the formula. To her guilt-feeling about finding her husband, in spite of all his goodness, almost more than she could endure, she now added a new sense of guilt because she took no joy in her baby and found his care to be nothing but a chore. The baby was only one more chain binding her to a life she found unbearably dull.

Her desire to scream was symbolical of her whole general attitude of protest against her way of life; and her fears were symbolic of her deep though unconscious wish to be rid of her husband, her baby, and everyone else who represented restraint, boredom, and the frustration of her desires.

In addition to the phobias, there are many other obsessive ideas; in fact, any idea which preoccupies a person and which is not subject to modification by reason or experience may become an obsession. Convictions are scientifically arrived at conclusions; whereas obsessions are "fixed ideas," grounded in emotion, resistant to reason, and because of their very intensity and immutable nature harmful to their owner.

At the opposite pole from obsessive fears, are obsessive desires. Pyromania, the love of fire which is so strong as to make its victim disregardful of property value or rights; kleptomania, the intense desire to steal, irrespective of economic need or of either the value or desirability of that which is stolen; nymphomania, the neurotic and insatiable desire for sex contact are examples of the unreasonable and unreasoning desires which sometimes obsess mankind. Let it again be stressed that good and bad are never absolute but always relative terms; any virtue carried to extremes becomes a vice; and every attitude or act must be evaluated in terms of its individual and social effect. There are, for example, healthful fears, or rather there is such a thing as valuable awareness and appreciation of danger. The research doctor who so appreciates the danger of cancer that he devotes his best ability to discovering its cause and cure is an asset to society; the neurotic who is so afraid of cancer that every slight bruise is the source of agonized concern, and who is constantly "feeling for lumps," accomplishes nothing by his fear save the impairment of his own health and happiness. Frank Lloyd Wright's healthful fear of earthquakes and tornadoes —a fear which led to the construction of buildings capable of withstanding earthquakes is a praiseworthy fear; the senseless worrying and apprehension which some persons feel at the first clap of thunder or the first zigzag of lightning eventuates in nothing but distress. If love of one's country results in attempting to exemplify its finest ideals and correct its faults, such loyalty is of great worth to both patriot and country alike; if it leads to smugness, bigotry, intolerance, and exclusiveness, it is detrimental.

Not only ideas but mannerisms may be obsessive or compulsive in nature and the symbolic representation of some deep-seated emotional fear or wish. Samuel Johnson used to retrace his steps, if he failed to strike a single post with his walking cane; whenever Mr. V. is in a crowd, he *must* take off his shoes; though Mrs. J. "knows" she has locked the door, she *has* to go back many times "to check just to be sure"; Mrs. F. washes her hands dozens of times each day to wash off imaginary dirt or germs; Mr. R. "can't bear" to sit anywhere else except on the left-hand side of theater, church, or train. Almost invariably persons with such "compulsions" will readily admit that they are "silly"; but nonetheless, feel tense, unhappy, disturbed if unable to do whatever they have the "must" feeling about. It is often easier to discover the situation from which the symbolic symptom arises than the exact and specific content of the particular symbol involved; but always the important problem is to get and cure the fundamental cause.

Phobias, manias, and other obsessive-compulsive states are quite obviously ideational in character; but we turn now to a group of symptoms which are equally the result of the dissociation-conversion process but which at first glance appear to be physical rather than mental in origin.

DISTURBANCE OF THE FUNCTION OF MOVEMENT

It is not uncommon to find persons suffering from what appears as paralysis of the legs, when there is no organic involvement of the nerves or muscles. During war, it is common to find uninjured soldiers who are unable to walk. The basis of this functional disability is fear; fear of being hurt, fear of being killed: fears which, though often unrecognized and unadmitted, are common to us all. It works like this. The soldier wishes to avoid active duty; he fears death. To admit his wish or fear would brand him as "yellow." The level at which he has set his ego makes him unable to acknowledge his fear; so he represses and dissociates the emotion. He is not consciously afraid; but the charge from his emotion even though repressed and dissociated must be released and so is converted into the symptom of inability to walk, a symptom as definitely symbolic as Mrs. D.'s fear of harming her baby. It is readily understandable that such symptoms should come to the fore in soldiers torn by the conflict between what they have been taught to believe is courage and manliness and the spectacle of wholesale murder; but the same phenomenon appears in young and old, men and women, in times of peace as well as war.

Mr. H. M., aged 65, suddenly developed complete paralysis of both legs. Complete physical examination was made and when no organic damage could be discovered, a diagnosis of hysterical paralysis was made. The problem was to find the cause of the dissociation-conversion mechanism.

Mr. M., a thoroughly disagreeable and domineering person, had for years lived with his son and daughter-in-law. The latter heartily disliked him, but put up with him because of his paid-up $5000.00 life insurance policy in which her husband was named as beneficiary. That policy was the whiplash Mr. M. used to get his own way. On the day Mr. M. developed his paralysis, his daughter-in-law, snooping through his possessions, found the box in which the old man kept his "valuable papers." She found that all the cash value had been withdrawn and the policy cancelled. All of her pent-up dislike and suppressed anger was unleashed, and in a furious tirade she ordered him to leave the house. He did not know where to go for he had no friends who would or could keep him; so he collapsed. Revived, he found he could not stand and had to be carried to bed. He was sure he had had a stroke, caused by the cruelty of his daughter-in-law. His paralysis was, in reality, a conversion symptom and was his way of symbolizing his fear of being sent to the poorhouse.

In similar fashion there may be dissociated-conversion paralysis of the arms or hands.

Mr. C. W., aged 32, complained of an inability to use his right hand. A year and a half earlier he had noticed that he needed to support his hand when he was writing, else his hand would turn to the left. When he was shaving, his hand would jerk and go in the wrong direction. After a few months, his symptoms had so increased that he was unable to hold a pencil. It was suspected that he might have a brain tumor; but all examinations and laboratory findings were negative. His paralyzed hand was his most distressing symptom; but he complained also of tightness in his throat, difficulty in swallowing, poor appetite, sleeplessness, and a constant feeling of fatigue.

Mr. W. worked for a large firm. When he accepted the position at a low salary it was with the understanding that if he made good, his advancement in position and salary would be rapid and certain. He worked hard and effectually; but though his superior officer often complimented him, the increases in salary were negligible and there was no advancement in ranking. Mr. W. saw man after man advanced over him. He made no audible complaints; but he seethed with a sense of being unjustly treated and of being blocked in his ambitions. All the other men made out their reports on office time; but Mr. W. sat up late into the night to prepare his. It was while making one of his monthly reports and as he was reproaching himself for "being fool enough to go on working like a slave, when obviously his boss had it in for him" that he first noticed the trembling of his right hand.

Mr. W.'s "paralysis" of the hand was a conversion symptom by which he symbolized both his sense of futility and his resentment. He had allowed his unexpressed and repressed irritation to become a source of tension symptoms and eventually dissociated to the extent that he had no realization of the connection between his mental attitude and his inability to use his hand.

SENSORY DISTURBANCES

Sensation itself may be involved in symbolic symptoms. In organically sound persons there may be one or more anesthesias (inability to feel) so that in localized portions there is no response to external stimulation. Those parts may be stuck with pins, pinched, or even burned without the person's feeling any pain. In such instances, the mind is so oriented that the stimulation of the pain fibers in the skin is simply not given any attention when the sensation is received in the brain. Among the more common anesthesias are: "glove anesthesia," the hands being unresponsive to stimulation; "stocking anesthesia," involving the feet and lower leg; and "hemianesthesia," which renders one whole side immune to sensation. Psychologic anesthesias offer amazing proof of the ability almost completely to dissociate from reality; and furnish excellent examples of conversion symptoms involving the use of symbolism.

Miss K. A., aged 35, complained of headache, pain on opening her eyes, and complete anesthesia on the right side of her body. Two years earlier she had suffered a skull fracture from which she had recovered. The onset of her symptoms had been sudden. Though all tests were negative she could not feel pinpricks anywhere on the right side of her body; when the skin was pinched, she had no sensation; nor did she feel anything when the hairs on her right arm or leg were pulled. It was possible to touch the right eyeball without the patient's even winking. In other words, though there was no evidence of organic disturbance, her entire right side appeared utterly devoid of sensibility.

Miss A.'s life was, and always had been, one of misery, poverty, and sordidness. Her own father had died when she was a baby and her stepfather was little more than a hoodlum. He was shiftless, cruel, tyrannical, drinking to excess, and filling the house with drunken, carousing friends. As soon as the law would permit, Miss A. had been taken from school and told to find a job. Her meager wages were confiscated by her stepfather who even begrudged her car fare and lunch money. She begged her mother to get a divorce; but when she refused, Miss A. continued to live at home, since she could not leave her mother "at the mercy of that brute." Her job was dreary and physically exhausting; she had no friends or outside interests; though she pitied her mother, she was disgusted by her abject acceptance of abuse. Too "beaten down" by life to feel either bitterness or hope for escape, she lived days of loneliness and hard work, nights of terror over her stepfather's drunken brutality.

After the accident in which she sustained a skull fracture, she felt "shaky" for several months, and had many aches and pains; though the hospital records showed that she had made a complete recovery and no doctor consulted could find an organic basis for her complaints. She returned to work and accepted physical troubles with the same resignation with which she had permitted the muddy waters of her entire life to engulf her.

She was sitting alone with her mother one night when the stepfather came home with three friends, the four of them "roaring drunk." The women retreated to the kitchen and listened in mingled disgust and fright to the carousing in the next room. Suddenly one of the men lunged into the kitchen and grabbed Miss A. by the right wrist and breast. Her terrified screams aroused the neighbors who summoned the police. The police arrested everyone in the house and bundled them all off to jail. Miss A. was hysterical with fright and humiliation over having been "locked up like a common criminal." The next morning she was dismissed; but she discovered that she had no sensation in her right wrist or breast where she had been seized. Soon the anesthesia involved her entire right side.

Treatment of Miss A. was not directed toward her tension or symbolic symptoms but toward persuading her that she had a right to lead her own life and to make it as happy as possible. The advice given her was very specific: to move out, taking her mother with her if possible; to pay more attention to her personal appearance; to take a secretarial course in one of the free night school classes; to develop, forcing herself if necessary, new interests and to cultivate friends; and finally to adopt a new attitude toward her past experiences. They had been harsh, cruel, ugly—yes, but they were past; nothing could undo them; but they were like a hideous nightmare from which she had awakened. Her attention was to be given to her *new* life, and having both determination and courage, she turned all her ability toward achieving it. Within a week the anesthesia disappeared as did also the pain on opening her eyes (symbolic of her wish to shut from her vision her whole unlovely life and particularly the sight of that worst night which had culminated in her arrest) as did also her headache (a tension symptom). Her life did not become a glamorous and romantic one; but when last seen, six months after she had started her new program of living and thinking, she spontaneously stated that she felt better than she had for years and that she was happier than she had ever thought she could be.

It is relatively easy to determine that there is a disturbance in function when tickling the back of the throat, sticking pins in the skin, etc., bring about no reflex response; but when a patient complains of inability to use his muscles or, as in the following case, inability to *hear*, it is extremely difficult to establish proof, even though there is no question in the patient's mind as to the actuality of his disturbance. Such patients will go to great lengths, spend much money, and undergo major operations to be relieved of their distressing symptoms, the effort required for such procedures being far less than that required for facing squarely the emotional disturbance at the basis of their symptoms.

Mrs. P. R., aged 40, complained of "nervousness" and "deafness." She had been well until two years ago when she awakened from a restless sleep and realized that she had not heard her alarm clock. She discovered that she could not hear her children or her sister unless they shouted. Repeated tests and examinations revealed no pathology. Mrs. R. learned a little about lip reading and she could still hear shouted words; so it was possible to converse with her. She was persuaded to tell her story; and as she became increasingly engrossed, the examiner gradually lowered his voice and spoke several times with his handkerchief before his lips. By the end of the interview, the patient was responding to questions asked in an ordinary tone and when it was impossible for her to read the examiner's lips. When her story was finished and direct questions were asked about her hearing, the difficulty returned in full force.

Mrs. R. had been happily married ten years when her husband died, and she was left without money or property and with two children, aged six and eight. She had had a little training in millinery work and was able to secure a job, which however paid little. She lived with her sister-in-law, who was on the border line of poverty and unhappily married. As a result of the whole unhappy situation, Mrs. R.'s children were poorly dressed, poorly nourished, and constantly scolded, while Mrs. R. herself was made constantly to feel that she was in the way, and was inescapably the audience for the interminable bickering and quarreling between her sister-in-law and her husband. Mrs. R.'s one solace was her mother, who was always sympathetic and understanding. When she died (four years after Mr. R.'s death), Mrs. R. was plunged into even deeper despair. She began to hear noises in her ears, and even though no ear specialist was able to find either cause or cure, the symptom greatly increased her "nervousness." The last straw had fallen two years ago, when her older daughter came home in tears because she had been told not to come to a school party. When the child repeated the cruel words, "You always dress like a beggar," Mrs. R. felt that she just couldn't bear to hear any more of her sister-in-law's nagging, her brother's abusive tirades, her childrens' disappointments, the ringing of the alarm clock, the whirring of the machines in the shop, and the noises in her ears. When she awoke the following morning, she found that she could hear nothing.

Mrs. R. had found her escape, symbolically, in her deafness; and this conversion symptom was the poor woman's inadequate manner of trying to overcome the stress under which she labored.

The *eye* also may be the site of symbolic symptoms. There are patients who have the conversion symptom of being unable to see; and others who can see only that which is immediately before them. Even more common is continuous blinking of the eyelids (blepharospasm).

Mrs. C. E., aged 34, complained of quivering eyelids. Two years earlier she had returned home to find her son sprawled on the front porch and bleeding from a gunshot wound. She screamed and fainted. When she regained consciousness—even after being reassured that it was a neighbor's child and that his wound was superficial—she found she could not open her eyes, even when she tried to push them open with her fingers. After many months, she was able to open her eyes for short periods of time; but she blinked constantly and her eyelids quivered incessantly. The shock had been great—so great that the symbolic symptom of shutting from view the tragic scene persisted for months after she knew that what she feared had not happened.

Closely allied to the tension symptom of stammering or stuttering is a symbolic symptom involving the *voice*. This conversion symptom of aphonia (inability to speak above a whisper), like all others discussed in this section, indicates repressed and eventually dissociated ego-wounding experiences or memories, and is a symbolic expression.

Miss F. D., aged 18, was unable to speak save in a whisper. Sometimes she could sing; and, occasionally, she could for a moment or two speak in a normal tone; but for the most part she could only whisper.

When she was five, her father had deserted his family. Her mother developed tuberculosis, and for twelve years spent most of her time in sanitariums. The child was reared by her maternal grandparents who lavished upon her every luxury but who never ceased to criticize and berate her father for having disgraced his wife and daughter by running away. Florence adopted her grandparent's attitude and felt both shamed and resentful of her father. When her grandparents moved, Florence told her new friends that her father was dead. Shortly after the death of the mother, when Florence was seventeen, the father reappeared, and expressed his eagerness to assume his responsibilities as parent, apparently being motivated largely by a willingness to assume also responsibility for the fortune he was confident his child would inherit from her grandparents.

Used to having her slightest whim gratified, Florence was for the first time confronted with a situation which she could not mange to her liking. All her smoldering resentment against her father burst into flame, and even worse was her embarrassment over how she could explain to her friends the premature resurrection of her father.

Miss D.'s inability to speak in a normal tone was clearly her symbolic method of expressing her repressed dissociated hatred of her father and her shame both over having to speak to him and over being caught in her deception which would require endless talking to explain away.

An interesting symbolic symptom, obviously involving both the body and the mind, is *amnesia,* or the complete forgetting of one's past. Daily one reads of persons found wandering aimlessly, unable to tell their names, unable to recall their address, and unable to explain how they reached the spot where they are found. In senile patients or persons with actual brain disease, this loss of memory is understandable and it is always accompanied by other signs of mental derangement. Patients suffering from amnesia, however, manifest only the one symptom: complete inability to recall anything concerning their past life. In practically all cases, what has happened is that the person, confronted with some intolerable situation which he can't handle, or overwhelmed by the weight of memories which he has "dynamically forgotten," *must* escape, and quite unconsciously so completely dissociates himself from his disturbing past or his distressing present that he converts himself into a new person who has no connection with his unresolved problems.

Miss L. H., aged 17, was found wandering aimlessly. Questioned, she was unable to tell anything about herself. She did not know her name or where she lived, whether she had brothers, sisters, or parents, how or when she had reached the park; in fact, her entire past was wiped out.

Under hypnosis, Miss H. revealed enough to make it a simple matter to get in touch with her relatives in a distant city.

The patient told of an unhappy home ruled by a tyrannical father who prided himself on being a stern disciplinarian. Louise, who shared her father's determination, was always "in hot water." She quarreled with her parents and defied her father's dictates whenever she dared. Two days before she was found, she had stayed out all night. Dread of going home to face certain and drastic punishment was more than she could bear; and psychologic processes working to save her from pain enabled her to dissociate to such an extent that she literally did not know who she was. It remained an unsolved mystery how she had traveled 125 miles; for she had no money when she left or when she was found.

Only a few of the more frequently encountered symbolic or dissociated conversion symptoms have been enumerated, but a sufficient number perhaps to make clear their common denominator, namely, that they all spring from unresolved, inadequately dealt-with, emotional disturbances. The complexity of life has multiplied almost *ad infinitum* the number of disturbances we may encounter; and the complexity of the human organism offers countless foci through which the disturbances may manifest themselves.

Not all, but many persons who develop symbolic symptoms are so accustomed to evade unpleasant issues, and refuse to deal frankly with reality that they fall easy prey to quacks, charlatans, and faith cults. Nowhere else is there more shifting in the population than in the realm of faith cults. Faith A holds out roseate promises of health, prosperity, happiness, and power; its jargon is impressive; its members are called on for nothing more strenuous than "faith" (and financial support). The only trouble is that the promises are not redeemed. However, Faith B "guarantees" to teach (at ten dollars a lesson) the secrets of inner strength, how to triumph over adversity, how to capitalize on hitherto unrealized hidden power, etc.: secrets revealed to the "leader" in far away Tibet in return for his saving the life of the dying lama. (Apparently the more fantastic the yarn and the higher the admission price, the more eager are the gullible to belong!) A few lessons—or many—and you have the same problems, the same limitations, the same aches and pains; so you abandon Faith B. But the cousin of a friend of yours has for years been a member of Faith C and she—so off you go, certain this time that you have the real thing. The same lack of self-discipline which makes a person shy away from meeting and overcoming difficulties, the same tendency to evade and avoid rather than face and deal with problems makes for the easy credulity on which quacks and charlatans thrive.

By the same token and for the same reason, it is often easy by suggestion to give a patient temporary relief from his symbolic symptoms. The presence of his symptom indicates his proneness to do emotional rather than cortical thinking, and it is easy to suggest other ideas which for a while and superficially he will follow. Granted even that there is a permanent disappearance of a particular symbolic symptom, there is still the more than even chance that other dissociated conversion symptoms will come to the fore; for the basic cause has been left untouched, uncured. Symbolic symptoms are the outgrowth of a general attitude, an habitual reaction pattern; and unless it is changed to a more mature, a more objective, a more courageous, and a more healthful one, new symptoms are bound to arise. Making such a change is an arduous and sometimes very discouraging task; but it is possible; and whether you think primarily in terms of your personal happiness or of your value to society, it is a task the rewards of which more than compensate for the effort expended. Future chapters will be given over to telling you how you can do it.

CHAPTER XII

SEX AND MARRIAGE

The universality and the urgency of the sex drive should certainly have entitled it to better consideration than it has received. We have overemphasized and underemphasized it; we have debased it, sentimentalized it, and even tried to hush it out of existence. Sex is a natural and tremendously important aspect of life, to be understood and managed as such. Sex problems—whether of masturbation, marital adjustment, continence, or what not—like all other meaningful problems must be both understood and solved.

It would be interesting to analyze why the subject of sex has gathered about it such a mass of misinformation and why the vast majority of persons still find it quite impossible to discuss the matter without a sense of impropriety or of treading on forbidden ground. The reasons are multitudinous and complicated; though for most the apparent reason is no more than that they were taught that way by their parents' attitude of reticence and their companions' attitude of secrecy. Persons usually forget the important adverb "where" in the quotation, "Where ignorance is bliss, 'tis folly to be wise." Since both race preservation and personal happiness depend upon proper utilization and direction of the sexual drive, it is time to stop glorifying ignorance by calling it "innocence" to realize that ignorance about the nature of our own fundamental desires is not "bliss"; and to turn to the subject of sex with frank objectivity and the desire to understand.

There are two fundamental urges: (1) self-preservation (securing food and protection from environmental dangers) and (2) race preservation (reproduction). Our food-getting techniques have improved so that it is possible for civilized man to concern himself with secondary values, with the result that we wish in addition to life-sustaining food to have also gleaming silver, beautiful china, spotless damask, flowers, and candlelight. We wish pictures on our walls, rugs on our floors; we seek to make our dwelling places spiritual as well as physical havens of refuge. Those who are fortunate, take food and shelter for granted and seek in addition variety, color, beauty. In the same way, sex for civilized man means infinitely more than ability to reproduce; it means companionship, sharing interests and responsibilities, establishment of a home, rearing of a family, self-realization and fulfillment, love. Not only have we enlarged the meaning and signficance of food and sex to include secondary values; but with reference to the former, at least, we are constantly increasing our knowledge. Food chemistry is attracting an ever greater number of research scientists; and all of us talk glibly about proteins, calories, and vitamins. There is no reason, no more *logical reason,* why persons should be diffident or shocked about trying to understand the basis for a rich and satisfying sex life than that they should be timid about knowing how to plan a well-balanced meal. Incidentally, we hope that many of you are smiling about this long introduction and realizing that it is tribute to the fact that, logical reason or no logical reason, most persons still feel that sex is a subject which "nice persons don't talk about."

There are three major misconceptions of the nature and rightful rôle of sex. The first and by far the most pervasive one is that sex represents man's "baser nature" (presumably nonexistent in the case of women, at least prior to the twentieth century!), that it is "low," "lewd," "carnal," "dirty," "sinful," something to inhibit, and to hide. Parents if not shocked are embarrassed by children's sex questions, and either berate them for being "dirty-minded," or evade with the familiar formula, "You're too young to know." Dire punishments are threatened, "if I ever catch you talking this way again"; and the child's sexual curiosity, which was no more intense than his wonder about the thousand and one other things that

make him ask, "how, why, when, and where" becomes focused.
He gets his answers in the worst possible way, from misinformed
persons who by their own attitude communicate the feeling that
the whole subject is one about which to be shamed and secretive,
to leer and make dirty jokes. Rare and fortunate is the person who
gets his sexual information from a person who neither magnifies
nor belittles the importance of this ultimately mysterious ability of
mankind to find joy in the merging of hopes and dreams as well
as physical satisfaction in the union of bodies.

Because the subject has been a forbidden one, its fascination has
increased. The minute anything seems unobtainable, its possession
becomes more desirable. Tell a child, or for that matter an adult,
not to open a box, unlock a door, or look out a window and he is
immediately possessed to do so. Refuse to answer questions, and he
will seek and find information elsewhere. In the case of sexual
curiosity more is involved than just the "natural" tendency to do
whatever is forbidden or consider desirable whatever seems inac-
cessible. The sexual drive is a real and insistent part of each one of
us. Caught between their own desires and the teachings, or rather
lack of teaching, they have had, adolescents often devlop either
morbid preoccupation with the problem or intense guilt feelings,
being sure they are wicked or sinful. If you were fortunate enough
to learn objectively and sanely the facts of sexual life, perhaps it
will appear that we are overemphasizing the importance of this
distortion of the basically normal and potentially beautiful nature
of sex. Any physician, minister, or social worker, however, can tell
endless and often tragic stories to confirm the statement that distorted sex information or unself-disciplined sex indulgence is at the
basis of many unhappy lives. It is difficult to erase early impressions,
particularly those charged with emotional tone; consequently many
adults who *know* that sex is right and normal and that it may be
both a releasing and a fulfilling experience still have a "hold over"
of feeling tone that makes them unwilling or unable to live that
which they know. Men and women alike, for example, perpetuate

the fiction that sex pleasure is a male prerogative; and countless women married for years never permit themselves to enjoy sex.

We have recently swung to the opposite extreme; and in many quarters, shamed silence has been replaced by a glib volubility which while not so harmful as furtiveness, repression, and guilt is nevertheless a reflection of a warped sense of proportion. The world is deeply indebted to the psychologists, psychiatrists, psychoanalysts, and sociologists for lifting the taboo, for recognizing and emphasizing sex as a meaningful and thoroughly respectable part of human life; but here as elsewhere the general rule has held true; the greater the repression, the more violent the reaction when restraint is removed. Many authors write as though sex—usually interpreted in a very limited sense—is all of life. The stork myth is no more fantastic than the speech an "emancipated" mother made about the education of her seven-year-old son: "Of course I have always answered Tim's questions. He knows all about how babies are born; but I don't know how to explain the pleasure of intercourse to him." Of course she didn't know, and for the best of all reasons: no seven-year-old could possibly be interested enough in feelings he had never experienced to ask questions, let alone understand explanations. The ascetic, glorifying starvation and chastity, is no more lopsided than the glutton or the one who exalts promiscuity: both are attaching disproportionate importance to single elements of life. The medievalist (there are many living in the twentieth century) who by branding sex as "lustful" and "sinful" would attempt to stamp out its evil is no more absurd than the "modern" who insists on reading sexual implications in everything from the distorted elements of a fantastic dream to the innocent play of children. The one refuses to face facts realistically; the other rivets his attention to a single fact, and excludes all others.

A third misrepresentation of sex is epitomized by the mawkish sentimentality of the movies, wherein the heroine forever fair is eventually won by the hero, forever fine and noble. Anyone who has tried marriage and establishing a home knows that life is not a perpetual courtship, accompanied by starlight and with violin obbligato; it is rather a matter of stretching the budget; coping with Nick's measles and Sally's temper tantrums; sharing troubles, disappointments, triumphs, and successes, offering encouragement, making adjustments, learning to compromise; forgetting self and immediate desires. The Cinderella story is rarely enacted save in reel life; however beautiful the legs or soul of the ten-cent-store clerk, the odds are all against her meeting, let alone marrying, the millionaire owner's son and living happily ever after.

If we grant that the sex drive is "natural" and fundamental, ridding ourselves of the traditional notion that it is basically vile and to be suppressed; if we avoid overemphasis on its importance; and if we refuse to sentimentalize about it, the fact remains that it is a tremendous force, one which must be understood and controlled. Any great power—electricity, steam, patriotism, or sex—is capable of acting as a creative force or as a destructive element, depending largely on how well we understand its potentialities and how skillfully we manage it. Self-motivated control is always more effective than that resulting from external compulsion. External force, if strong enough, can compel subservience; but in the last analysis it is bound to be self-defeating, as well as dwarfing and distorting in its effect on the person it temporarily controls. Only by having some true understanding of his own nature, desires, and potentialities can man arrive at a wise tolerance of himself and of others; only by developing and exercising an understanding self-discipline can he achieve a liberating freedom for himself and contribute most meaningfully to the society of which he is a member. It is toward such understanding that the next few pages are written.

NORMAL SEX ATTITUDE AND PRACTICE

Children are highly sensitive to atmosphere and simian in their imitativeness of attitudes. Fortunate is the child of parents whose sex attitudes are sane and normal and whose adjustment to each other and to life is at least fairly happy. Children are curious about sex; they are curious about everything under the shining sun. Their capacity for asking questions is limited only by the number of hours they are awake. Childish curiosity is extensive rather than intensive; and unless something happens to rivet the child's attention on a particular subject, he will hardly wait for an answer before he has moved on to the next "why" or "how." If his questions meet rebuff, if he is silenced or punished, if he is aware that the person questioned is embarrassed or angry, then his attention will immediately be focused, and what was a casual question will take on a special interest and he will be possessed to know.

If a child asks questions, and he will, answer him honestly and directly in simple language and without complicating details which he has not asked for and will not comprehend. Usually, the small child who asks, "Where do babies come from?" is satisfied when told, "From inside Mother's body." If he asks how the baby got there, tell him, "Daddy planted the seed inside Mother's body." Don't try to make up pretty little stories about the flowers and butterflies; give him an honest simple answer; and two minutes later he will be asking you, "What keeps stars up in the sky?" or "Why can't cats swim?" or any one of the countless other questions which may interest him. If a child takes his questions or problems to someone besides his parents, parents have only themselves to blame. If you won't answer him, someone else will.

As the child approaches adolescence, there is a recrudescence and intensification of his interest in sex, because of physiological changes in his own body and because of his awakening sex impulses. At this time he needs to be given specific and scientific sexual information. If parents, because of their own training or experiences, find it impossible to give such information frankly, objectively, accurately, and without embarrassment, they should call upon the services of some capable friend or the family physician. If the person who gives sexual information acts as though he were examining as briefly as possible an unsavory but inescapable subject, or befogs his meaning with vague statements about "right and wrong," what is "nice," and what "decent" persons do, say, or think, the listener will not be helped and will assume that the subject is one to be avoided and about which to be furtive; and at the same time will be possessed to find out more.

In our civilized world the economic and cultural set-up is such that a person matures sexually years before he can establish a home and legitimately give expression to his sexual impulses and desires. He must, for the good of society as well as for his own, conform to its demands. In other words, he must learn just what his problem is, what is expected of him and why; and finally, how to exercise self-control. Anyone with a problem has a right to know just as fully as possible all the known elements of the situation; and the adolescent has a right to know and understand himself in relation to society; for it is only on such understanding that true self-discipline can be built.

First, he needs to know the anatomy and mechanism of reproduction, and he needs to learn it in direct and scientific terminology, not in vague euphemisms. The seed which the father plants in the mother is called the sperm cell; this sperm comes from the male penis, an organ which all males have; when one is married, the penis is introduced in the female opening, called the vagina; and the sperm, or male cell, travels into the uterus and its tubes where it joins the female cell, called the ovum. When the cells unite, an embryo child is conceived and gradually, during a nine-month period, develops into a full-term infant that is born of the mother. One advantage in having a physician give or supplement such sex instruction is that he can more clearly explain the physiology of sex, the function of menstruation, the manner in which the child is developed, etc. Many parents have difficulty in answering questions simply because they do not have the necessary information and terminology. Explain to the child that though he may have sexual desires, maturation of the sex organs does not occur until much later, and that since the sex act may result in the production of children, he must postpone the gratification of his desires until he is older—old enough indeed to have a family of his own. He has already learned that in many instances he has to postpone or even give up his own wishes, not because they are wrong but because he is only one of many and must often do what is good for all.

The adolescent should also be informed about masturbation. Usually quite accidentally children discover that pleasure may be derived from manipulation of the genitalia. In the boy, there tend to be spontaneous erections which are followed by manipulation and often by ejaculation. This phenomenon is entirely normal, usually occurring first at puberty and continuing at regular intervals for two or three years. As the boy becomes increasingly more interested in physical and social activities, the practice disappears. No physical or mental harm results from masturbation as such. Harm comes from the feelings of guilt which the child develops when, caught in the practice, he brings down an avalanche of blame, reproach, and threats from his parents. Often not knowing the facts themselves, parents haul out all the old threats and fears with which their own adolescence was made a nightmare and with them bludgeon their offspring, hoping to scare them away from a practice which will "surely end in heart trouble, tuberculosis, early death, insanity," etc.—any or all of them. The more emotional the parental outburst, the greater the harm done. The child continues his practice, because the sensation is pleasurable, but he is haunted by fears, by the feeling that he is sinful or wicked or depraved. Not understanding why he feels as he does, he is tormented by remorse and guilt. Far from making the child stop, such tirades do little save terrify the child and focus his attention on a phase of his development which ordinarily would disappear of itself. Girls masturbate less frequently than boys do but when they do the phenomenon is entirely normal.

If masturbation is excessive; that is, if it occurs frequently and too long after the period at which it normally ceases, it may be well to consult a physician. Ordinarily all that needs be done is to fill the child's life with enough social outlets so that his attention is focused away from himself and upon other interests. Explain the situation to him: tell him that his continued masturbation is neither wrong nor harmful, but merely indicates that he is not growing up as fast as he should. For an infant to cry for his bottle is perfectly normal; for a five-year-old to do the same thing would prove that he was still a baby. For a five-year-old to spend hours on the beach playing in the sand is to be expected; but a big boy of ten would rather swim. Make it clear to the child that masturbation belongs to a phase of development and should be outgrown just as are other stages in the progress toward becoming a man or woman. The purpose of such explanation is not to make the child feel ashamed of "being a baby," but to make him understand the situation as it actually exists. The emphasis should be not upon stopping masturbaiton, but upon becoming more integrated, more mature, more "grown up." Such an honest and clear explanation has a far greater and more beneficial effect than could any punishment or threat even though sufficiently potent to have a restraining influence. Threats and punishments usually do more harm than good; for one of two things must eventuate. Either the one threatened submits only until he is a match in strength for the compelling force and then rebels, usually with violence, or else he remains a slave to the domination of another, a weakling incapable of self-reliance or self-control.

L. E., a young man of 27, in conversation one day made the following statement: "If my dad had never done another thing for me, I'd always admire him for one conversation we had when I was about fifteen. From other boys I had learned to masturbate and they had all told me how 'mad' my father would be, if he ever found out. I didn't do it often; but when I did I felt ashamed and wicked. I was uncomfortable about not telling my father; for I usually told him everything. When I was in my first year of high school, some man gave the boys a lecture on sex hygiene, which scared me half out of my wits. All I heard were his dire prophecies of what befalls boys who 'abuse themselves.' I went out of that auditorium feeling like a leper and a social outcast. For two or three days I was the most miserable kid you could imagine; but finally I broke down and 'confessed' to my father. I thought that he would turn me out of the house and I braced myself to meet his wrath. He looked at me quite calmly and said quietly, 'You think right well of your dad, don't you? Well, I did the same thing when I was your age, and every other boy I knew did too. It's something you outgrow, Son, just the way you've outgrown that squeaky voice you had a year ago. It doesn't mean a thing in the world except that you are growing up.' Then after a pause, while he continued dressing 'Say, I'm getting pretty stout. Think I'll try to manage one night a week swimming in the Y pool. How'd you like a junior membership. You can swim every afternoon. I'll have to hump myself; or the first thing I know, you'll be beating your old dad; and that'd never do.' That was all; the subject was never mentioned again until years later when I tried to thank him. Then he said 'Well, I've never forgotten the hell of fear I went through. I'm mighty glad to have saved you from it.' "

Contrast that experience with the following case.

Mr. S. P., aged 23, came for medical advice, giving as his symptoms: muscular fatigue, headaches, dizziness, and excessive weakness. He was overwrought about his condition, sure that he was going to die. Thorough physical examination revealed no organic pathology. During the examination, Mr. P. made several vague references to his "hopeless condition" and when persuaded to explain admitted that for many years he had been practicing masturbation, and he was sure that was what was the matter with him.

When Mr. P. was 13, his father had caught him masturbating and had not only beaten him cruelly but had told him terrifying stories. He even went so far as to take the child to a mental institution "to let him see with his own eyes what happened to such persons." He was never allowed to forget his "sin." It was referred to constantly, and every mistake or failure was attributed to that one source. Torn between fears and desires (the more urgent because kept constantly before him) he did not cease his practice, but accepted himself as being a hopeless and lost case. He developed many hypochondriacal complaints, his symptoms the outgrowth of the tension caused by his guilt feelings. The very intensity of his desire to avoid masturbation so focused his thoughts that he found himself almost unconsciously practicing the act.

In the male, nocturnal emissions may occur. These emissions result from normal activity of the male sex glands and are in no way indicative of disease. Occurring quite frequently in adolescence, they tend to cease later in life. This phenomenon should be explained to the maturing male just as the function and mechanism of menstruation should be explained to the girl.

Such explanations, given in a direct and straight forward fashion, do much to help the adolescent weather this rather stormy period. We may have made it sound too simple, as though merely understanding the anatomy of sex and being reassured as to the normalcy of his feeling were all the adolescent needs in order to manage his sexual impulses and desires. The emphasis which the child will place upon sex will be determined by many additional factors, chief among which are: constitutional predisposition; attitude toward the opposite sex; psychological predisposition (introvert or extrovert); standards of morals in his home and community; nature and amount of physical work and social activities in which he engages; amount of general tension under which he already lives; etc. The problem of adjustment is, therefore, always a highly individual one; and the whole point of this discussion is not to say what is *the* one right way, but simply to emphasize that a tremendous help toward adjustment and control is given when the person *knows* all the available facts.

A tremendous amount of nonsense has been uttered on the subject of continence; those who laud its value being no more extravagant in their over statements than are those who anathematize it. So far as we know, continence is in no way harmful, *provided* the person's attitude is one of complete understanding and his abstinence a matter of deliberate, conscious choice. Persons who speak as though sex relations were the sole end and aim of human experience and who assume that whoever does not experience them must surely be thwarted, distorted, and abnormal indicate by such expressions that their concept of sex is limited to include only physical contact, which is only one, though a major, element of a much more complex aspect of human experience. When one recognizes his own drives and decides, for whatever reason, not to give expression to them, he can healthfully and happily live without sex experiences and be in every way entirely normal. Harm occurs when the sex drive is not understood, not permitted recognition, no matter how insistent its demands may be, and is not consciously and adequately sublimated.

SEX AND MARRIAGE

So many wise and so many foolish words have been written about sex and marriage that it seems futile to attempt to give additional information; yet there are several *practical* suggestions which are rarely emphasized and which are helpful in "making a go" of this business of establishing a home—a business in which there are a distressing, and quite unnecessary, number of failures and bankruptcies.

Though most of us grin sympathetically over the lines

> . . . and nature has contrived
> To struggle on without a break thus far,—
> Whether or not we find what we are seeking
> Is idle, biologically speaking.[1]

we still believe personal happiness and "Whether or not we find what we are seeking" are tremendously important.

Marriage is a social institution and its perpetuation depends on many factors other than "Nature's" purpose that the species be continued. For marriage to be successful there must be much more than the initial "love" which attracts two persons, makes them find each other desirable, arouses their sexual impulses. There must be shared interests and enthusiasms, there must be compatability of temperament, mutual appreciation for the wishes and whims as well as the "rights" of each other. There must be the

[1] From *A Few Figs From Thistles,* published by Harper & Brothers. Copyright, 1922, by Edna St. Vincent Millay.

kind of emotional maturity which excludes self-seeking, self-pity, or self-indulgence, and makes possible intelligent planning. There must be a sense of humor (a sense of proportion, if you prefer) which will enable both to see little things as little and big things as big; or, in other words, a sense of fundamental values which will preclude the tendency to "make mountains out of mole hills" and reduce to unimportance the minor irritations which inevitably occur when two persons live under the same roof.

Now what actually happens? Most persons wish to be married, whether it be for financial security, status, "love," "having a home of one's own," companionship, having children, or merely because "it is expected." This last-mentioned reason probably motivates more women than it does men. For so long woman was financially dependent on some male that it behooved her to make an alliance which (she hoped) would guarantee support after her father's death. Moreover, since society recognizes only those alliances legitimatized by state and church—sometimes one, sometimes both—the only way a woman can prove publicly that her charms and desirability are comparable to those of other women (such proof is a sacred obligation with many women) is by marrying: preferably a "good catch." How many men does the average woman meet? That man is always the pursuer and woman the coy quarry is a fallacy perpetuated by male wish thinking. (Incidentally, the "professional secrets" involved represent the one field in which women are universally loyal to each other!) However, even granting that woman plays at least a coöperative rôle, you must still admit that her field of activity is limited. The Helens of Troy who can launch a thousand ships are few and far between; most women have relatively few proposals of marriage, and from those few must choose. (One woman married in March, she said, because it was the only month in which she had not promised to marry some other man; but she was a rarely charming exception to the general rule.) When you think of the dozens of hats a woman will try on before she buys one, never intending to wear it more than a few dozen times, or if you have ever witnessed the agony of decision a man experiences in selecting a car, even when limited by price to not more than three or four possibilities, it does seem absurd that persons should have such limited opportunity when it comes to choosing a mate with whom presumably they intend to spend the next twenty to fifty years. (Have you ever noticed in the newspapers the pictures of persons "celebrating" their golden anniversary? Almost always one looks grimly triumphant; the other, chastened and subdued!) Since so many marriages occur on the basis of limited selection, many are bound to be between incompatible persons. When the incompatability is not only physical but spiritual (i.e., a matter of personality and temperament) marriage tends to be a rather complete failure, and not only are the husband and wife unhappy but the children reared in such a home are subjected to a constant bombardment of tension, whether overt or unexpressed.

Not only is the choice limited, but, poets to the contrary notwithstanding, marriage does not overnight change fundamental character and personality. During the period of courtship, no one is quite normal. The excitement, the thrill, the ecstasy, the divine inflatus—choose your own terminology—of the chase often makes the participants appear to be quite other than what they actually are. Many the wife, who worried during her engagement over her lover's profligacy has wakened to find herself married to a "tight wad"; many the husband who in his prehymenal days traitorously wondered whether such unadulterated sweetness would eventually cloy discovers himself married "for life" to a veritable Xantippe. Have you noticed that all the great love stories of the world tell of love frustrated by circumstance (preferably death since it is final)? Anthony and Cleopatra, Launcelot and Guinevere, Tristan and Isolde, Romeo and Juliet, etc. In each instance, something happened to prevent *marriage* of the lovers, so one was left with the dream undimmed, all the illusions intact. Such a reflection is not designed to make you conclude that all marriages are doomed to failure but simply to draw your attention to the fact that more than the ecstasy of love is needed to make a marriage happy.

In marriage, as in every other relationship, the nature of the general reaction patterns of behavior will play an important rôle. If a man, or a woman, has all his life been selfish, domineering, demanding, expecting to be waited on hand and foot, and assuming that his every word expresses final truth—if such a man marries, he will carry into the new relationship his habitual attitudes and one of two things will happen. If his wife is a "worm," their marriage will be a negative failure, in that she submerges her potentialities for self-fulfillment and he continues his immature and unhealthy way of life. If she is equally "set" in her own emotional and immature attitudes or is sufficiently mature to be unwilling to live with a spoiled child of a husband, then the marital state will soon become martial. The same will happen if the woman, or man, has the attitude that her charms justify her existence, that it should be her mate's pleasure to assume all responsibility, cater to her slightest whim, and devote all his free time to making his "little darling" happy. Of course there is still another possibility: one can change his attitudes, one can "grow up"; and very often the "love" which first attracted is sufficiently strong to make both not only willing but eager to be different, to make necessary changes. No matter how satisfying the sex relation may be, it cannot long withstand the atmosphere of constant bickering, quarreling, faultfinding, and tension which grows like a miasma out of incompatibility. Frustrated sex experience then becomes part of a vicious cycle, wherein dissatisfaction leads to more personality clashes and they in turn to decreased sex satisfaction. The darkness of this all too common picture is relieved by realization that what appears irreconcilable incompatibility is often avoidable maladjustment.

A major mistake, made by husband and wife alike, is taking the mate for granted. Many persons apparently conduct their marriages on the theory that one need not run for the street car once it has been caught. Well, you'd better, if you wish to stay on the car and if you wish the trip to be pleasant. This taking for granted, which is no more characteristic of one sex than the other, is rooted in egocentricity, a polite synonym for selfishness.

If you are the home-maker you are keenly aware of the deadly monotony of preparing breakfast, washing dishes, making up or doing the laundry, making grocery lists, getting the big children off to school, feeding the baby, making the beds, dusting the furniture, sweeping the floors, deciding whether the curtains "can go for one more week," preparing the lunch, washing the dishes, feeding the baby, changing the baby, answering the back door bell, answering the front door bell, answering the telephone, sewing on buttons, darning socks, wondering how you can convert the remains of Sunday's roast into something or other that will not elicit, "Do we have to have hash every night? Surely I make enough . . . ," changing the baby, welcoming the children home from school, watching your spotless kitchen reduced to chaos by the ravenous vandals who bear your name and who, having eaten the last cookie, betake themselves to the yard to play hard and work up a good hearty appetite for the supper which you must start preparing in a few minutes. But first you must change the baby and take out a few minutes to admire the pinkness of his toes. The baby starts his five o'clock vocal protest against the world just as seven-year-old Tom comes in with a cut finger, and as you wash his grubby paws and bandage his finger, you make a mental note that he's about to "go through" the elbows of his sweater. A glance at the clock tells you that you will have to "step on it," because "Big Tom" is always hungry as a bear when he gets home, and grumpy if dinner is not ready. So you step on it. You do not feel like a martyr; you "love" your husband, home, and children. You do wonder how your mother managed with less money, more children and no "Mamie" to come in on Tuesday and Friday to do the heavy work. And it would be nice if the telephone did not invariably ring three minutes after the baby had gone to sleep. And it would be fun to have dinner together—just the two of you—and not have to persuade Sally to eat her vegetables or mop up the milk after little Tom's dramatic account of how he threw the ball. It must be pretty nice to meet interesting persons every day, have regular hours (your work is never done) and have everything done for you. Men are funny, anyhow. They never think of saying "thank you" so long as the supply of clean shirts, darned socks, and mended linen is ready for them to grab; but how they do "take on" if one button is missing! Does Tom think he's "too good" just once in his life to offer to help wash the dishes? He sits in a comfortable chair all day with nothing to do but push a buzzer when he wishes someone to wait on him. Men have a pretty easy time of it. By the time the potatoes have burned, you *do* feel sorry for yourself; but being a "good sport," you "snap out of it" with, "I guess I'm just fed up with kitchen and kids. I'll tuck the children in early and we'll have Art and Frieda in for a rubber or two of bridge. There's enough chocolate cake (Tom's favorite) for refreshments." So you corral the children, override their protests that their hands are already clean, change the baby once more, and have dinner ready to serve as soon as your lord and master comes home. You wait until the first pangs of hunger have been assuaged before, "How about a little bridge tonight? I'll hurry with the dishes (if only he'd *offer* to help) and get the children—"; but you are interrupted with, "Oh, good Lord, not tonight Mary; I've got a heavy day tomorrow and I'm going to turn in early." Now what happens? Well it depends. Maybe you say what you think, or maybe you "bottle it up" inside you; but you spend the evening playing, audibly or silently, variations on the theme: "It's all very well for him. I stay home all day taking care of his house and his children, and what thanks do I get? A paid housekeeper would fare better; at least she'd get one afternoon and an occasional Sunday off." And so to bed.

If you are the breadwinner you are keenly aware of the constant pressure and the anxiety under which you struggle. Every morning the same rush to get the train; you have an appointment at nine; there are always a dozen and one calls to make before the day starts. If you could afford a decent secretary instead of that gum-chewing stenographer who hasn't a thought beyond the color of her finger-nail polish. Maybe next year. You lost that big order yesterday. Are you slipping? That's the second time in three months that you've "muffed" a big order. First thing you know the "Big Boss" will be telling you, "If you can't do the work, there are plenty that can." The letters that *must* go out first thing are not on your desk ready to be signed, but instead a note telling you that the stenographer went home early with a headache the evening before. A "friend" drops in to "borrow ten, just till Friday, Old Man." You knew when he came in what he had come for, and he knew that you knew; but he had to waste twenty minutes talking about yesterday's ball game (*you* never have time to go to ball games) before casually suggesting that you act as his banker. The telephone begins ringing. You discover that your half-witted stenographer has made two appointments for the same hour, and it's too late to telephone either one. So it goes all day. Gulping your lunch you permit a few envious thoughts to turn homeward: "Women have it pretty soft. Nothing to worry about; just tell you what they want and you do all the rest. Act as though money grows on trees. Pretty swell wife though, and the best kids in the world. Really ought to be carrying more insurance. Maybe . . ." You think up a way in which you may be able to get another chance at that order you thought you had lost. If you "swing it," it's pretty certain you'll get a promotion and then you'll see about that insurance policy. Too late to do it today. You'll just relax this evening after you've played with the children a little while—wish you had more time with them the way Mary does—and think out a sure-fire scheme for landing that order. It's been an irritating day and you're dog tired; but you go home feeling pretty well satisfied with yourself and the world. Before you've had five bites your wife is after you to have a whole houseful of guests who never know when to go home. Now what happens? Well it depends. After you have said, "No," maybe you go on to tell her all that you think, or maybe you pretend to read the paper while you think to yourself: "No wonder there are so many divorces. A man works like a slave all day while his wife lolls around the house. What thanks does he get? So long as there is plenty in the bank, *she* doesn't care. Not even enough to ask one thing about my work. What would she know or care, if I tried to tell her what I have to put up with every day? "Help-mate" indeed; some bachelor coined that word! Etc." And so to bed.

The marriage just portrayed is nearly ideal; for both persons really care about each other. It illustrates, however, what happens when each of two persons living together is so engrossed in his own problems that he has no imagination about those of his mate. Both must appreciate that marriage is a coöperative endeavor and that there must be mutual adjustments, mutual consideration. It won't hurt you, even if you are dead tired, to take Mary to the show or to play bridge; after all housekeeping isn't particularly exciting or diverting. Nor will it hurt you, even if you have been cooped up in the house all day, to see how tired Tom is and suggest that you go out tomorrow instead of tonight; after all the business of making a living is pretty exhausting. This matter of mutual appreciation and adjustment is not a book-keeping affair of equating: I did this for him; therefore he should do this for me; I changed my desire to suit hers last Tuesday; therefore she ought to be willing to do so and so to please me. It's not a matter of "ought" and "should," but rather the kind of creative imagination that enables one to identify his or her feelings with those of the other, plus the kind of affection that finds happiness in the happiness of the other.

Accustomed as we are to more sentimental terminology, we may feel that "respect" is a rather cold word with which to express the basic essential for a happy marriage. "Respect" means much more than mere politeness; though so far as that is concerned most marriages would be happier if man and wife extended to each other the same courtesies they accord strangers and acquaintances. By respect we mean attaching to another personality the same importance we give our own, making allowances for shortcomings, granting the validity of the other person's thoughts, feelings, wishes. Don't marry a person persumably because you like him or her "as is" and then start your missionary work to make him over. Don't be merely a reflector for your mate's glory; do a little shining of your own. Don't place a wife or husband on a pedestal and then feel resentful when you discover, as you most surely will, that he or she is "of the earth, earthy." Don't get illusions of grandeur about yourself and expect your mate to be your faithful echo. Don't get the notion that because you spend your days doing the world's work that your wife may not have an idea or two worth listening to. Don't, because your husband can't tell a symphony from a concerto, fancy that you are a delicate and spiritual soul married to a clod incapable of any sensitivity. The more points of view, the more interests and enthusiasms, the more ideals and goals you hold in common the more harmonious your life together will be; but on the other hand, the more different abilities you possess, the more particularized and individual gifts each has to contribute, the more enlarging and stimulating your companionship can be. The word "companionship" is perhaps the key word. Certain countries today would have women serve only in the capacity of housekeeper and childbearer; and, unfortunately, many men living outside the confines of those countries apparently have the same idea. Such a relationship may serve nature's purpose of race preservation, but it fails utterly to satisfy mankind's quest for response, self-fulfillment, happiness.

Sex contact may be merely the satisfaction of biological needs or it may be that plus joyous self-fulfillment and a kind of ecstatic peace. Which of the two it is depends very largely on the attitudes we have just discussed. The greater the sense of spiritual at-oneness two persons have, the more probability there is that their shared sexual experiences will be mutually satisfying. It is true that sexual compatibility does much toward making for marital happiness; but it is equally true that the sexual excitement characteristic of the first few months of married life decreases in intensity and that unless marriage is established on much more enduring values there is little chance for a permanently harmonious adjustment. Moreover, sex contact itself is much more likely to be completely satisfying if it occurs when there is psychological harmony. The biological purpose has been served when the male spermatic cell is discharged into the female vagina; the human purpose is fulfilled when both persons experience both the mounting excitement which precedes orgasm and the peaceful relaxation which follows it. Orgasm is really a sudden release of tension built up during the sexual act; and the pleasure experienced is not only that of stimulating the sensory endings in the penis and vagina, but also relief of the built-up tension. Too often only the male reaches orgasm, and the wife having been aroused (having had tension built up) is left with a feeling of unreleased energy, frustration. Much tension other than that created during the sexual act is released through orgasm.

If intercourse is to be mutually satisfying and if it is to fulfill all of its ecstasy and peace-producing potentialities, then there are several things which it is well to understand. First of all physical togetherness is most meaningful when it is the expression and culmination of psychological harmony. Sex contact may be physically satisfying but it cannot be psychologically pleasurable if there is strain, disagreement, or bitterness between the two persons. It should occur only when both persons wish it and when each really desires the other. The experience is more nearly perfect if husband and wife can reach orgasm simultaneously; and it is entirely possible for this condition to be realized if the husband, remembering that most men are more quickly aroused to sex ardor than are women, will indulge in much love-making, much petting, until his wife has reached his own state of excitement. Almost all women attach as much importance to preliminary love-making as they do to the sex act itself, and the tenderness expressed both in word and gesture, the feeling of belonging to, and being cared about by, the mate are essential if the woman's joy is to be complete. It is entirely possible and eminently desirable that husband and wife remain lover and sweetheart, each seeking and wishing the happiness of the other, each rejoicing to give a maximum of understanding, inspiration, comfort, and pleasure to the other: only by thus losing does one find himself.

If the foregoing pages have emphasized both the normalcy of the sex impulse and the desirability of using it to derive the maximum of pleasure and self-fulfillment, then only one more word need be said. And that word is *self-control*. Implicit in all that we have said is the idea that the powerful driving force of sex is one capable of either destructive or constructive significance. The results of power unrestrained and directed toward selfish goals are obvious—whether it be economic, political ruthlessness symbolized by persecution, concentration camps, suppression of freedom, and terrorism or whether it be illegitimate pregnancies, venereal diseases, and perversions expressive of rampant sexual drives. There are, in addition, countless concomitant evils which though less patent are nonetheless harmful, disintegrating, and degrading. Space does not permit enumeration, much less elaboration, of all these deleterious results but a single statement must suffice: any power which is uncontrolled and undirected becomes the enemy and not the useful ally of its owner whose status is soon changed from that of master to that of slave.

It is important that you remember that we are talking not about laws or external force or even conformity to the accepted code. Obeying the law, when the law is backed up by a force stronger than the individual will or desires is at best but negative in results. Self-control, on the other hand, is a positive force both in the development of personality and in terms of social good. Self-control implies these elements: (1) understanding one's impulses, both as to their function and normalcy and also as to their potentiality for good or harm; (2) conscious setting up of values or goals which one wishes to attain both as a person with particular desires and drives and as a member of society with definite obligations and responsibilities; (3) the willingness and the requisite will power to postpone, and if need be renunciate, immediate gratification for future satisfaction. Not fear, not force, but intelligent self-direction is essential if we are to have a society in which there is a chance for creative self-expression and if we are to have a mankind capable of creative social endeavor.

CHAPTER XIII

A REALISTIC PHILOSOPHY OF LIFE

Abstract theories about life as a whole or any particular aspect of life are useless; yet it is essential that we have some general philosophical orientation to give both meaning and direction to our efforts. Such a philosophy of life will be most valuable if it takes into realistic account both our individual desires and our social needs and if, at the same time, it furnishes a dynamic method of establishing and attaining goals.

Throughout this book, one of the major emphases has been that the human organism is a totality and functions as such. Acting, feeling, and thinking are not distinct and independent abilities: Man's actions are motivated by his feelings (desires); the success or failure of his actions is reflected in accompanying and subsequent feelings; and his thinking *can* be used to direct his actions. The plea of this book is that we avail ourselves more fully of this directing capacity of the cortex. We have seen how attitudes can bring about painful and distressing physical symptoms and we are familiar with the disturbing emotions concomitant with ill-advised actions. Since action and feeling (body and emotion) are so interrelated, it stands to reason that if we utilize our cortical ability to direct our actions and to discipline our emotions the result will be a better integrated and more efficient organism, and consequently, a greater degree of happiness. The problem for each one of us becomes that of exercising cortical control and wherever necessary of retraining our attitudes so that instead of lashing our bodies with the whip of our emotions we can rather direct our energies toward the achievement of chosen objectives.

Your symptoms may be many or few; they may be predominantly physical or primarily psychological; no two persons present identical pictures. Somewhere in the world there may be a Mr. A. who is irritable, short-tempered, given to temper outbursts, etc., but who is "strong and healthy as an ox"; and there may also be a Mrs. B. who has gastrointestinal upsets, a palpitating heart, severe headaches, etc.—all without organic basis—but who is always even-tempered, tolerant, and emotionally stable. If such exist, they are rare, for ordinarily a person with physical symptoms of tension will manifest his general state of tautness psychologically as well; and vice versa.

At last we come to the heart of the whole matter—*What can you do about it?* To understand why you are as you are, to have an intellectual appreciation of the problem—these are not enough. There must be a solution; but a merely theoretical solution will not enable you to live more effectively, more happily unless, understanding the principles involved, you are willing to put the suggestions into practice. If you are willing and if you make the requisite effort you will get results.

We are about to say that there are three requisites for a life of maximum effectiveness and happiness; but first a word of warning. Effectiveness is a relative term; happiness is a relative term; and an attempt to codify and categorize the elements essential for the achievement of these relative states cannot hope to be more than suggestive. When anyone says, "There are three (or thirty, or three hundred) elements in a happy life," his words give the false impression that the problem is simple; and whatever else life is or may be, it is never simple. If you will remember that the terms used are generic, inclusive, and suggestive rather than absolute and final, we may say that in order to live with a minimum of physical or psychologic disturbance and with a maximum of happiness (the least pain and the most pleasure) everyone needs to have: (1) a philosophical orientation toward life; (2) healthy and mature attitudes; and (3) adequate energy outlets. These three elements of the good life are not separate and unrelated: one's philosophy is meaningful only when achieved, and the achievement is conditioned on the other two elements; one's attitudes are the person himself, his closest approximation of his philosophy; and the energy outlets are an essential element in his technique of self-realization and fulfillment.

PHILOSOPHICAL ORIENTATION

When we say that everyone has a philosophy of life we do not mean a set of abstruse metaphysical concepts but a code of values, an ideal pattern by which he measures his own performances and that of others. We have reference not to what the person "says" his philosophy is but to the principles by which he actually directs his life. Many persons, for example, would include the ideal of democracy in their verbal philosophy; but unless their actions show that they respect other persons as being on a par with themselves, the words mean little. No one can superimpose his code of values on another; everyone must evolve his own; and yet we should like to suggest some elements which we consider essential, if one is to feel at home in the universe.

A philosophy of life furnishes a general plan, a design, which gives meaning to our individual and corporate efforts. What are your values? What do you most desire? What are your goals? What are you willing to work for? We are not talking about vague daydreams, imaginary Utopias, but those values which seem worth the best effort of which you are capable, those ideal ends whose challenge continues, no matter how many setbacks you experience, no matter how difficult is their achievement. Is life worth living? What makes it worth living? More important than your answer to the question, "What are you willing to die for?" is your reply to "What are you willing to live for?" Your answer to such questions constitutes the substance of your philosophy of life. Many persons, unfortunately, have no such guiding principles —drifters, bound for no particular destination, living in haphazard fashion from moment to moment, comfortable when life goes well, but "lost" in the inevitable frustrating experiences of life. If life were easy, there would be no necessity for a pattern; but conflict is forever present in human experience, and there is no life wholly free from pain, disappointment, and at least some degree of defeat. An adequate philosophy of life enables one to meet such experiences with some degree of equanimity, to see individual incidents with perspective and in proportion. If you wish to see far horizons from some mountain top, you do not howl and moan over every little scratch incidental to the climb.

Though the term, "philosophy of life" is high sounding, it does not necessarily follow that one's values are fine or one's goals worthy. There are selfish, petty, ignoble philosophies. Do you know persons whose values are apparently little more than "creature comforts," who ask no more of life than does a well-fed and pampered cat? Do you know others so "possessed by a dream" as to be utterly indifferent to the presence or absence of immediate comfort? Most of us represent neither extreme; so it becomes pertinent to ask, "Just what constitutes a mature philosophy? What values are worth seeking? What 'pattern' will best provide for my needs and at the same time give opportunity for the highest self-realization of which I am capable?" What we are all seeking is happiness, but happiness is a relative term, its specific meaning varying from person to person. Only you can answer specifically what constitutes your "happiness"; but there are a few general principles which may aid you in formulating an adequate philosophy. For a few minutes be deliberately and coldly selfish. Say, "I don't care about values or goals or ideals; and the other person's misery is his own affair, not mine." All right; but you still must answer, "How are you going to be happy?"

Be realistic. Life is neither a rose garden, nor a garbage dump; it's neither and it's both. There are many arid places which can be turned into gardens, and many dumps which can be removed. This is not a perfect world, nor is it a hopelessly evil one. It is a pluralistic universe: one of many goods, many evils, many possibilities. Above all it is a growing world, an elastic one, one which can be reshaped and changed. How can such a realistic view aid you in your pursuit of happiness? Remember that for better or for worse it's the only world we have; it's the only stage on which we can play out our little tragi-comedies. If you close your eyes to the actuality of evil in the world you are thereby not only refusing your opportunity and your responsibility for doing something to change it but you are also living in a fool's paradise which sooner or later is bound to come crashing down on your head. Ignoring poverty, hunger, injustice, stupidity, disease, pain, cruelty, war, ugliness, and death does not rob them of their vitality; indeed, the reverse is true. Whether we like it or not, we're all in this mess together; and so long as there is disease in the world, *your* health is in danger; so long as there is poverty, *your* financial security (if you are fortunate enough to have such) is menaced. Prattle all you like to the effect that "all's right with the world," that "everything is for the best," that "right is always stronger than might," that "good must always prevail over evil," or any other of the empty platitudes with which lazy men are wont to rationalize their unwillingness to make this the kind of world they say it is. While you are mouthing your precious little phrases, the shadows are growing darker and drawing closer to engulf you; and they will.

Blatant optimism which refuses to face the ills and pressing problems of life is no more unrealistic than is defeatist pessimism which is so conscious of wrong, sordidness, and crime, the indifference of nature and the ruthlessness of mankind that it fails to recognize the actual and potential goodness, beauty, and truth which are as inherently a part of nature as are their opposites. Being realistic means recognizing that nothing in life is static—nothing is eternally good; nothing is irredeemably bad. Nature, including man, is in the process of becoming; and what it becomes is in large measure dependent upon our efforts. There are no guarantees that we will fail or that we will succeed; though all evidence indicates that evil unchecked by human effort grows rampant and that good fostered by man's endeavor flourishes. Such a philosophy offers not security (there is no security except that which we ourselves create and maintain) but a challenge. It saves one, on the one hand, from the rude shock of discovering (and there is inevitably enough "pain" in each life to make such discovery a certainty) that life is not the "sweetness and light" proposition which he had fondly imagined and, on the other hand, from the stunting and paralyzing attitude that one is a helpless victim of forces which he is powerless to control or modify.

Two specific aspects of this realistic philosophy need elaboration. First: you, the complex resultant of many forces—constitution, environment, previous experiences, inculcated attitudes, etc.—too, are in the process of becoming; you, too, *are capable of modification and change*. It is as unrealistic to say, "Well, I've always been this way; I can't be any different," as it would have been for the Wright brothers to proclaim, "It's ridiculous to talk about flying through the air; it's never been done and never can be," or for Koch to have despaired with, "Tuberculosis is a mysterious malady which we will just have to accept. Others have tried to find its cause and have failed; there is nothing more to be done." Don't accept anything you don't wish until you have done everything in your power to change it. You will be surprised at your own capacity for directing your universe and for re-forming yourself. Part of your success in viewing yourself realistically lies in understanding your own basic drives (see page 243) and in evaluating properly your specific assets and liabilities (see page 240).

The second aspect of this realistic philosophy which you need to recognize is that *you are not only an individual person but a social unit*. That we live in groups, and are part of our so-called "civilization" gives us tremendous advantages, but also imposes countless restrictions and responsibilities. A few minutes ago we suggested that you be calculatingly selfish in your pursuit of happiness; and now we add a paradox to the effect that your best chance for achieving personal happiness is by subjecting your wants, wishes, whims, and caprices to the best interests of the social whole. It is not that you renounce your needs and desires, but that you have a better chance of adequately fulfilling and realizing them if you are realistic in appreciating that you are at once father and child, creator and creation of the civilization of which you are a part. Much of the world needs changing and you can help bring about the change; but you can no more bring about desired modifications and improvements by retreat from, or defiance of, the existing order than you can adequately solve your own problems by jumping out the window. In other words, a mature philosophy might well be characterized as a "chastened optimism," "chastened" because it recognizes how stupendous is the problem, how multiple are the difficulties, how little civilized as yet is our civilization, "optimistic" because it recognizes that the problems can be at least partially solved, the difficulties overcome, and the civilization both broadened and deepened. Such a philosophy recognizes the universality and urgency of our basic need for personal self-realization and satisfaction but at the same time is aware that it is in a social setting that these satisfactions must be secured. A philosophy, therefore, which seeks only individualistic goals is doomed to be at best an inferior code; for the very nature of the set-up implies that personal happiness is conditioned by social well-being, and that "no man liveth unto himself, and no man dieth unto himself." The only way to secure even a partial guarantee of self-centered happiness is by unselfishly working to make this the kind of world in which all men have the chance to achieve the same values which we prize most highly for ourselves.

We have spoken of a philosophy of life as being a pattern. It is important that you appreciate the fact that patterns are flexible, subject to modification; that they are an outgrowth of our experience and of our best reflection; and that they are of value only when they are *used*. A road map locked up in the glove compartment of your car will not aid you in arriving at your destination; blue prints filed in the architect's desk are of no value to the contractor; a philosophy of life which is merely verbalized means nothing either to the speaker or to the hearer. Only to the degree that you "practice what you preach" is your sermon valuable.

Working out a healthy and happy life is in many ways analogous to weaving a tapestry. In the latter there are three essential elements: the weaver, the pattern, and the materials with which to execute the pattern; in the former, man, his philosophy, and the world in which he lives. It is futile to argue which of the three elements is most important; each is meaningless without the other two. Whether the tapestry is a crude snarl of threads or a finished work of art depends not only on the design which the weaver attempts to follow, not only on the quality and color of the thread furnished, but also on the *skill* of the weaver. The pattern gives only the general outline; the detail must be worked out by the weaver. The blending of colors, the evenness of stitches, the tying of knots, the requisite imagination to change the design to achieve a more beautiful effect: all these and countless other skills differentiate the artist from the factory worker. The analogy holds good for human life. Why is it that two persons living in about the same cultural and economic world, having comparable constitutional weakness or strength, and holding much the same theoretical philosophy of life turn out to be such different persons? One is well adjusted, getting from, and giving to others pleasures and happiness, doing his work with zest and efficiency, enjoying his family, friends, and play, largely untroubled by physical aches or pains: "getting a kick" out of life; whereas the other person is forever dissatisfied, converts his work into dreaded drudgery, finds his family unappreciative and his acquaintances selfish, dull, or critical, does not know how to plan and "thinks it's silly anyway," has many minor physical disturbances, and looks upon life with a jaundiced eye? The answer is to be found in the skill with which he manages that which he has to manage; and the matter of skills, in this instance, is largely a matter of *attitudes* and of *energy expression*. In the next chapter, we shall discuss two fundamental attitudes which we believe are the basic groundwork out of which spring the countless specific attitudes which are both the materials and the skills with which the human organism can approximate the creation and realization of its philosophy of life.

CHAPTER XIV

INTELLECTUAL OBJECTIVITY AND EMOTIONAL STABILITY

A definitely formulated philosophy of life gives a measure by which to evaluate your achievements and failures and a compass by which to locate yourself when in the confusion of life you temporarily lose your sense of direction. There are great advantages in "traveling light." Don't take a two-month supply of clothes for a two-week vacation! The seasoned traveler carries no excess baggage; knowing from experience what he will need, he makes certain that he has it with him. What are your *basic* values, your *definite* goals? Don't clutter your philosophy with a lot of vaguely conceived ideals, with mutually contradictory goals, with Utopian dreams, and visionary schemes. Travel light; but be sure that you have the essentials.

Your attitudes about life and your philosophy determine and are determined by each other; so if we speak of attitudes as being a means toward achieving one's philosophy, you will remember that we must, for the sake of clarity, talk about philosophy, then about attitudes, and next about energy outlets as though the three were sequential; whereas, in reality, it is the synchronized interplay of the three which creates each personality. What, then, are the basic attitudes for living a mature, happy, and efficient life? What are the attitudes we must cultivate if we are to avoid both the physiological symptoms of tension and the psychologic symptoms of irritability, hypersensitivity, worry, the sense of inferiority, guilt, futility, etc.? When we say that the two attitudes most conducive to mental and physical health and happiness are *objectivity* and *emotional stability* you will, of course, realize that we are using generic terms which cover many specific attitudes. Nor are these two attitudes separate; for objectivity is a means toward emotional stability. The relationship between specific and general attitudes is a controversial subject. Do countless immature, emotional, and unstable attitudes add up to form a general attitude of unhealthful immaturity, or are specific symptoms and characteristics a reflection of, an outgrowth of, the general pattern? Such a question is in the same class with, "Which came first, the hen or the egg?" The practical situation is that: whether your personality is one of integration, happiness, and adjustment or the reverse is determined by the number, pervasiveness, and intensity of your emotionally mature attitudes. So let us consider these two basic elements in emotional maturity: *objectivity* and *emotional stability*.

OBJECTIVITY

Of the many dictionary definitions of "objectivity" the one most clarifying and illuminating for our purpose is that which reads, "Treating events or phenomena as external rather than as affected by one's reflections or feelings." You must understand the word "object" in a very broad sense, as including all else besides yourself. You—the subject—are not separate from the rest of the world; you are molded by it, you respond to it; your very nature is determined by it. Nor does the world have significance except in terms of you and all its other inhabitants. Every person is the center of his own universe; and this being true, it behooves each one of us to understand as adequately as possible his own nature and that of his world. Our basic egocentricity makes it easy to interpret everything in terms of our wishes and our fears, and therein lies a grave danger. Our wishes and fears do not change facts; living is a continuous process of adjusting; so it follows that we will have a better chance of realizing our wishes and escaping danger if we face directly and unemotionally all the factors (both subjective and objective; i.e., our own nature and whatever constitutes our environment) with which we must cope. When we say that to be emotionally mature and therefore happy you must cultivate and practice the attitude of objectivity, we are really urging the necessity and desirability of facing facts, regardless of how they conflict with your wishes, fears, preconceived ideas, or prejudices. There are at least three phases of this problem of facing facts: (1) intellectual understanding of the relative nature of truth; (2) emotional willingness and desire to discover and abide by whatever truths we find; and (3) active training of our responses to become cortical (conscious) rather than emotional, to base our decisions on known facts rather than on wishes and fears, to let our thinking ability control our feelings and direct our actions.

The nature of Truth.—There is danger in capitalizing abstract words. The moment we say that man must seek Truth we sound as though Truth were a thing-in-itself, divorced from, and independent of, man; and it is not. Whether the truths we live by are reflections of an immutable absolute or whether there is no ontological reality to correspond to the term is a question for philosophical gymnasts. Whatever may be the ultimate nature of reality, the world as we experience it is a pluralistic one, forever characterized by change. It is a world of many values, many goods, many evils, many goals, many choices, many pleasures, and many pains. Moreover, each one of these terms is a generic one to describe states which are themselves constantly changing in content. If you are an adult you are quite different from your seven-year-old self. Perhaps you were a good little boy and perhaps you are now a good man; but the elements which constitute the "goodness" are quite different. You have changed; think how your ideals have changed; your wishes and your fears have changed. Everything that is alive is constantly changing—life means growth and growth implies change. We change, the physical world changes; the social, economic, and cultural worlds change; everything is relative—even Truth.

To understand the relative nature of truth is the first step toward objectivity. Yesterday's heresies are today's truths; today's radicalism will be tomorrow's conservatism. In every realm new truth is discovered, violently resisted, and finally accepted, only to be superceded by a newer truth. The way of the discoverer is hard; rarely is a man a hero within his own generation. We burn him at the stake, literally or figuratively, and generations later enhalo him. Think of Socrates, Galileo, Pasteur, Darwin or any other of the persons whose "truths" we now regard as almost axiomatic, and then recall the reception these same ideas initially received.

Many things which were "true" yesterday are not so today. The world was flat and now it is spherical; the sun once stood still and now it moves; the physical world was once an inert mass and now its basic nature is movement; kings had "divine rights" and now have few if any; the insane were regarded as "possessed by devils" and now are treated as are the physically ill; illness and plagues were considered an expression of God's wrath over the actions of his recalcitrant children and now they are human problems which can and must be solved by human intelligence. We smile indulgently over the ignorance, the superstitions of bygone days, but rarely wonder whether succeeding generations will find equally amusing our cherished beliefs which we "know" are "true."

Are you perhaps saying, "Well, if truth is relative, why seek it? How can I face facts if the facts are constantly changing their faces? How can I know when a fact is factual and a truth is true?" Before answering these questions, let us ask you one. Are you willing to face whatever facts may be ascertained, irrespective of how they conflict with your preconceived ideas or wishes? Knowledge unapplied is worthless. To admit the relative nature of truth is only the first step in being objective; and intellectual assent is always easier than practical application of the implications of any admission.

Perhaps it is our desire for security that makes us resent change, that makes us cling so blindly and so stupidly to whatever is ours, whether material possessions or preconceived ideas. (See rationalization, p. 144.) The more emotional tone is associated with an idea, the harder is it for us to subject it to analysis. The fact that we should like a stable world of eternal verities does not alter the situation: the world and everything in it from the very appearance of its surface to our ideas about it are constantly changing; and if we are to adjust ourselves to the world in which we live, we must seek to know as much as we can about every situation.

At the opposite extreme from the "die-hard" who "knows the truth" and will "listen to no nonsense to the contrary" is the vacillating person whose mind is so open that nothing stays in it. Momentarily fascinated with each new idea, he never holds any one long enough to test its value. Midway between these equally immature and self-defeating extremes lies the midcourse of reasonable agnosticism, of tentative belief. *To admit that no truth is final and to be willing to abide by new discoveries does not mean that the partial truths that we do have are valueless.* We have said that this is a world of multiple choices; and the best choice is always that which takes into consideration all available pertinent facts. Do you know persons who always go to the same summer resort, because that is what they have always done? Do you know still others who never get beyond the travel-folder reading stage, because each day a new notion of the perfect place to go strikes them?

Fortunately, one need not be impaled on the horn of rigidity nor insecurely moored to indecision. One can plan and plan intelligently, taking into account (if it is a vacation he is planning) the time and money he has to spend, the recreation he most enjoys, whether he wishes solitude or company, etc. Even when he has made his plan carefully, he must be prepared to make minor changes or even alter it altogether. If he hears that there is a typhoid epidemic in his chosen vacation spot, he probably will not say, "Well I've made my plan, and I'll just go right on with it" or, "If I can't do what I planned, I'll just stay home." He still has the same amount of time and money at his disposal; he is still the same kind of person; and there are countless other places in which he can have an equally good time. *He alters his plan to in-*

clude the new fact. We have constantly to do the same kind of modifying and altering in matters ranging in importance all the way from ordering today's groceries to planning our careers. We need to cultivate the same kind of flexibility in our thinking that we show in the daily conduct of our lives. If we have unseasonable weather, we dress accordingly; if the main highway is blocked, we take a detour; if we need the services of a physician and our own doctor is out of town, we call another; if the restaurant is all out of roast beef, we order lamb chops, etc. In these situations and countless others like them, we recognize the *practical necessity* of flexibility, and we act accordingly. Though we often fail to recognize it, there is the same practical necessity for modifying our ideas, for flexibility in our thinking.

Usually the person whose *general attitude* is one of objectivity finds it easier to be objective about specific situations; and the reverse is also true: one who meets particular irritations in a calm, objective manner is almost always a person whose consistent attitude is one of facing facts and of delaying his reactions so that they may be guided by the actualities of a given situation instead of being the spontaneous expression of his "feeling."

Why, having admitted the difficulty of ascertaining the truth about any situation and having emphasized how hard it is for us to respond cortically instead of emotionally, do we urge not only the desirability but the necessity of seeking to approximate as closely as possible the truth of every situation, and having found those partial truths to face them resolutely? The answer is, "self-protection." You must carry on your quest for happiness in the world as it is; and your chance of success is much greater if you seek obtainable goals and evade actual dangers than if you live in a world of groundless hopes, impossible dreams, baseless fears, senseless efforts, imagined dangers. Dancing after the mirages invented by your wishes and seeking to escape the miasmas of your fears lead to defeat, whether that defeat be expressed by physiologic symptoms of tension or psychological symptoms of unhappiness, or both. You can be your own best ally or your worst enemy, depending on how intelligently and how honestly you are willing to face facts; the world can help or hinder you in your pursuit of happiness, depending on how intelligently and honestly you are willing to face facts. Now we are ready to answer your questions as to how you can be sure of facts, how you can recognize truth as such.

Determining the validity of facts.—You never can be *absolutely* certain of the whole truth of any fact or situation; but you can be *practically* certain, and you can approximate the truth. The big Hitlers and the little Hitlers talk as though they were omniscient (mental institutions have a large population of patients with comparable illusions of grandeur); but any sane person realizes that he can never know all there is to be known about even the simplest fact, even the least involved situation; for the facts themselves and the situations are constantly changing. Moreover, being emotional as well as thinking creatures we cannot hope to attain an entirely detached attitude. So what is the best we can do?

Koch, a German scientist, discovered the germ which causes tuberculosis. Being a true scientist, he made no pronouncement until he had studied and experimented extensively; and then he formulated rules which he considered basic for establishing the causal relation between any germ and any disease process. These rules (Koch's Postulates) are applicable in many fields other than medicine. Briefly stated they are: that one must be able to (1) discover the organism or germ in the person suffering from the disease; (2) grow that organism in pure culture; (3) reproduce the disease by injecting the cultivated germ into some susceptible animal.

Before Koch's discovery, explanations of the cause of tuberculosis had been as numerous as they were bizarre. Koch's discovery was met with derision (as new ideas generally are), and many set out to prove his contention false. Wherever and whenever his experiments were repeated, however, the same results were obtained; and the scoffing and derision gave place to conviction that one part (the cause) of the truth about tuberculosis had been established.

Very properly you object "That's all very well for laboratory experimentation with germs; how can I apply these postulates to finding out the truth about political situations, religion, international relations, my neighbors, my family, myself?" You can't— not with the same degree of accuracy; but you can go a long, long way in that direction. Though we cannot use the laboratory technique of controlled experimentation where human values and human relationships are concerned, we *can* use the scientific attitude of approach. What was Koch's attitude? He wished to know the truth; he had no preconceived conclusion into which he tried to fit facts; he was willing to examine all available evidence; and finally, he drew his conclusion only after all other possibilities had been eliminated and after repeated trials effected identical results.

For the sake of example let us assume that you are opposed to, hate, or fear Communism (any other "ism" would do just as well). How much do you know about it? Where did you get your information? Have you read *Das Kapital*? It's amazing how few "dyed in the wool" Communists have! Is it Marxian ideology that you object to? (Perhaps the Communist party is as far removed from Marxian theory as organized Christianity is from the teachings of Jesus.) Is it the Russian or the American brand of Communism that you oppose? Is it the Marx, Lenin, Stalin, or Trotsky variety that arouses your ire? How do they differ? What good, if any, has Communism accomplished? What evil, if any? Where did you get your facts? Are they facts or propaganda? Is there any actuality in Russia to correspond to the phrase "dictatorship of the proletariat," or is there only a giant bureaucracy? How do you know? Where did you get your facts? The point is not whether you do or do not believe in Communism, but on what truths, on what facts is your belief based? Listen to the other side, look at the other cartoons, give heed to counter-arguments. Don't go to the other extreme, and "swallow whole" whatever you hear; demand proof, present your own facts and truths in rebuttal; if they have validity, they will not only stand but be strengthened by searching examination. Or take the matter of your race prejudices. Begin to ask yourself questions. How much anthropology do you know? What scientifically established proofs substantiate theories of race superiority? Or even of basic racial differences? What do you know of the history and culture of the "offending" race? Of the whole group, how many representatives do you know? Whatever experiences you may have had or however intensely disagreeable those experiences may have been—with what percentage of the group have you come in contact? What are the characteristics, attributes, and attitudes you most dislike? Are they the exclusive possession of a particular race? In short, what are your facts? What is the truth? How valid is your proof?

It is not enough to read only with your eyes or listen only with your ears; you must weigh and evaluate; you must definitely and consciously wish to know the truth. To be truly objective one must be able honestly to say with Max Eastman:

> Truth, be more precious to me than the eyes
> Of happy love; burn hotter in my throat
> Than passion, and possess me like my pride;
> More sweet than freedom, more desired than joy,
> More sacred than the pleasing of a friend.[1]

One thing that will help enormously in our quest for truth, in our attempt to be objective, is for us to admit and recognize the inescapable fact that we are all prone to "wish thinking." To say "The subject determines the object" is another way of saying, "You'll find what you're looking for"; and they both mean that we must constantly guard against "interpreting" facts in terms of what we wish to believe. Recognizing this factor will help not only in "checking up" on your interpretation of facts but in evaluating the truth of the facts as given by others. You are not

[1] Max Eastman, *Colors of Life* (1918), Alfred A. Knopf, Inc.

the only person who colors facts so that they will more nearly harmonize with your general scheme of wishing; we all do—and for the most part unconsciously. Have you noticed how many newspapers give in parallel columns "both" reports of war activities. A city is bombed. How much damage was done? How many casualties were there? What counter-attack was there? How effective was it? Read both accounts and you will be amazed at the discrepancies; you will begin to wonder how much you can ever really know of what is going on. Have you also noticed how much more eagerly you read the papers when the headlines indicate that "your side" is winning? It is so much easier, so much more pleasant to believe what we wish! Many once-free nations would not perhaps today be "occupied" had there not been so prevalent this tendency to wish thinking, this inability to believe possible of occurrence to themselves the same dire fate that had befallen others.

Whenever you hear an impassioned plea for anything and whenever you are so sure about anything that you resent criticism, start checking to see how much of your "thinking" is merely verbalized wishing. Not only in major issues but in minor ones as well this universal tendency toward wish thinking (fearing may act in the same distorting fashion) is operative. We minimize the faults of, and make excuses for, our friends, and, conversely, find it difficult to believe in the authenticity of some generous/deed or gesture made by our enemy. We judge disliked groups by the "lunatic fringe," but resent having our own group "misjudged" by inferior representatives. We discredit information not in line with our preconceived ideas; and jump to believe whatever substantiates what we wish to be true. Wish thinking is natural, just as countless other manifestations of our desire to avoid pain are natural; but the point is that such thinking is self-defeating, for our wishes do not change realities, and we cannot, by refusing to take cognizance of facts, bring about their destruction. Cultivating the attitude of objectivity is a practical matter of finding out all we can, evaluating situations in their entirety instead of responding emotionally to single elements which so often color our interpretation of "facts": doing all of these things not as an end in themselves but as a means toward an end; namely, that we reduce to a minimum the sources of tension, thereby increasing our health and our happiness.

How to be objective.—The only way to be objective is by being objective—a thoroughly exasperating and at first sight a meaningless recommendation. But think a minute: how did you learn to swim, type, sell insurance, bake a cake, or plead a lawsuit? Not by vaguely wishing that you could; not by intellectual assent that such a skill would be an asset; not by envying other persons possessing the ability. Every skill from making beds to making friendships, from running an elevator to running a factory is the result of practice. Obviously not all persons have the same aptitudes; some things come easier to you than do others; and as a general rule any skill which involves the training of thinking and feeling is more difficult of achievement than is one of purely physical dexterity.

Those characteristics which we label "human" are a relatively late development in the evolutionary process. Long before the beginning of mankind's experiment of social living, long before the elaboration of the wishes and fears to which civilized man is subject, the human organism was engaged in the process of physical adaptation to the world in which it lived. In other words, man has had an infinitely longer time in which to perfect his muscular and physical coördination, to manage his body, and to make it serve his purposes than he has to learn how to get along with his fellow man. As a consequence, man is much more ingenious in the invention of things, in the manipulation of his body, in the control of the external world than he is in his psycho-social adjustments. Another complicating element in the matter of perfecting our social and psychological skills is that human values are not static, and the standards by which to measure achievement are not mathematically exact. An analogy will make this point clear. An expert typist has two standards by which to measure his performance: accuracy and speed. The first is an absolute standard which can be met; the second though a relative standard is quite definite in that past performances by champions have been taken as the norm which one may attempt to equal or better. Compare the typist to the musician. What is the difference between a player piano's rendition of *The Moonlight Sonata* and Paderewski's? As far as accuracy is concerned, the former probably is more mechanically perfect; but the fire, the feeling, the interpretation are lacking. All the qualities essential for great music are to a degree intangible and do not lend themselves to exact measurement. The typist can say, "This is a perfect job"; the musician, however great, is forever unsatisfied. In much the same way, we can only approach our goals so far as the cultivation of mentally mature attitudes is concerned.

But now to return more specifically to the problem of how to be objective. By practice, by repeated effort, by persistent trial. Our great aid is our cortical capacity for *delaying* response. Thanks to our cortex we do not have to respond in reflex fashion; we can hesitate long enough either to forego response or to choose that response which our judgment, not our feelings, deems best.

Take a simple example. A "friend" because she "thinks it only fair" repeats some unkind comment that a mutual acquaintance has made about you. What do you do—make an equally derogatory speech (a childish attempt to "get even") or are you hurt so that thereafter you are uncomfortable in the presence of both the original speech-maker and the reporter? Before you permit— and it *is* a matter under your control—your autonomic nervous system or your psychological peace of mind to be disturbed, ask yourself a few questions. Is the criticism just; that is, do your actions, speech, or attitudes warrant such a statement? If so, there is no more occasion for being hurt or angry than there would be to feel the same emotions if your physician told you that you had a sore throat. In both instances, your problem is a practical one of effecting a cure. Don't rationalize when you ask yourself this question; don't make excuses and don't grudgingly admit that even if it is true, "certainly she is a pretty one to be criticizing others, when this, that, and the other thing are wrong with her." All that you say may be true; but those facts are neither your affair nor your excuse. On the other hand, don't be a "worm"; don't be a martyr and accept unjustified criticism with a supinely weak, "Well, I guess I must be like that, if that is the way I appear."

EMOTIONAL STABILITY

Repeatedly we have stressed the point that convictions are of value only when they result in action: a philosophy of life is of value only when its owner attempts to actualize it in his own experience; intellectual awareness of the desirability of finding and facing the truth is of value only when the person attempts to practice that which he believes. Why do some persons apparently find it relatively easy to meet major and minor crises with a minimum of emotional turmoil and others naturally "go to pieces" on the slightest provocation? The answer lies largely in the degree that the person has related what he knows to what he feels, in the degree of his *emotional stability*. Emotional stability, like objectivity, *is an achievement, not an endowment;* it is a skill perfected by practice; and essential for maturity, effectiveness, and happiness.

The meaning of emotional stability.—If the statement just made is true: that emotional stability is an (perhaps, *the*) essential element for developing an integrated and satisfying life, then it becomes important that we know quite clearly just what this expression both denotes and connotes. The dictionary definition of stability (from the Latin, *stare:* to stand) is, "strength to stand or endure without alteration of position or material change"; and among other synonyms given are: firmness, constancy, steadfastness. Once more we are confronted with a *relative* term which must be defined in terms of its present application and use. Complete stability would imply utter rigidity and would preclude the possibility of change, growth, or progress; and there is no such fixity anywhere in the universe. The Rock of Gibraltar looks like a pretty solid proposition; but, according to the physicists, it is in reality a whirling mass of atoms and electrons. Rocks, the earth, and minerals are *passively* subject to the influence of forces outside themselves. When we speak of them as inanimate objects, we have just this characteristic in mind: the inability to change, to adapt. Plants represent a step away from inflexible rigidity, a step toward adjustability. They are subject to, indeed wholly dependent upon, external forces: soil, moisture, sunshine, etc.; but the seed germinates, the plant grows, blossoms, seeds, withers, and dies: all of these processes being *active* ones which are manifestations of change, growth, being alive. Even less stable or fixed are animals, thanks to their power of movement. Their freedom from external forces is greater; likewise, their responsibility for maintaining life. They can and must seek shelter; they can and must find food. It is a strange but true paradox that the more freedom any organism has the greater and more demanding are its obligations. Man less than any other form of life needs to subject himself passively to external forces; and, by the same token, man more than any other organism must do something about adjusting himself and manipulating his world. His greater degree of flexibility (or relative instability) makes it possible for him to do so.

When we speak of the desirability of stability we mean, therefore, not fixity nor rigidity but rather a controlled and directed flexibility. When we use the word "instability" we mean a flexibility which is self-defeating because it is excessive. We have constantly emphasized that extremes are dangerous, that excess is always eventually self-defeating. Enjoy eating, but don't become a glutton; be generous, but don't become a profligate; find pleasure in reading, but don't retreat from the world to become a bookworm; take care of your health, but don't pamper yourself; sensitize yourself to the sufferings of the world, but don't agonize about situations which you are powerless to change; be thrifty, but don't be a miser; be flexible, but don't be unmoored; be stable, but don't be immovable.

Emotional stability is something infinitely more important than external manner. In the first place, there are wide racial and individual differences of temperament; so that to judge a particular person's degree of emotional stability demands far more knowledge than that which can be gleaned from observing his behavior or his speech. Of two persons equally frightened, one may scream and the other be "paralyzed" into silence; a grief-stricken person may lament and beat his breast or he may be dry-eyed and tight-lipped; anger may express itself in stormy speech and violent gesticulation or in acidly and icily quiet words. So far as the effect of emotion on the generation and perpetuation of symptoms is concerned, external manner is of little significance and the internal state of feeling is all important.

So thoroughly does civilization inhibit spontaneous expression of emotion that we tend to discount all excessive manifestations as being "show"; and, conversely often mistake repression for absence or control of feeling. Little children learn not to cry when they are hurt, not to scream and kick when they do not get what they wish, even not to shout too loudly or play too hard—for fear of disturbing the neighbors upstairs, to say nothing of papa's newspaper reading or mama's telephone conversation. Prize fighters whose sole intention is to beat each other into a senseless lump shake hands before they start their mutual assault; the defeated candidate congratulates his successful opponent; a "rooting" section which hisses or boos the enemy team must bear the stigma of "poor sports"; etc. In civilized, "polite" society, we rarely have the privilege of acting or speaking in accordance with our emotion of the moment. We mask our irritation, indifference, or boredom; we assume interest we do not feel; we urge tiresome guests to stay just a little longer, when with all our hearts we wish they had sense enough to go home; we muster a hearty laugh for an oft-repeated and rather inane joke; in other words, we try to make our manners conform with what we think is expected. That these social amenities are essential for the smooth functioning of communal existence seems incontrovertible; and if your manner reflects how you really feel, there is no cause for concern. For example, if you enjoy tennis, enjoy it so much that the playing and not the winning is the element of greatest satisfaction, then when you congratulate your successful opponent your action and your emotion are so integrated as to make your manner appropriate and right. If, however, you make smilingly correct conversation with Mr. A. while internally you seethe with repressed rage over the "dirty deal" he "put over" on you; if you "steam up" enough synthetic gaiety to be the life of the party and all the time feel inadequate and sure that persons don't like you; if, in other words, your manner belies your true feelings, then so far as your body is concerned, your socially acceptable manners are worse than useless.

When we speak of emotional stability, then, we mean neither absence of feeling nor cultivated ability to conceal it but rather direction and control of our emotional responses. Before elaborating this point, it might be well to show just how and why excessive instability is detrimental to the efficient functioning of the organism.

In the last analysis, excessive instability and excessive rigidity come down to the same things: they make it impossible for the organism to choose and follow the most appropriate response. One can artificially create circumstances which will so frustrate an animal as to make him neurotic. If a dog is given food every time a bell is rung, he will soon learn to look for food whenever he hears the sound; and at the first note of the bell, the salivary process will begin, preparatory to the ingestion of food. If a bell with a slightly different tone is rung and no food given, the dog becomes confused. He does not distinguish tones sufficiently well to know which means food; one time his body gets ready for eating and there is no food, another time he is right, and still another the food is there when he "thought" it would not be, etc. As a result, the dog becomes irritable, sometimes refusing to eat at all. He has lost control, lost the ability to fluctuate appropriately and advantageously. At this point of marked instability, the animal is abnormally irritable, as far as both his physical and his psychological reactions to external stimuli are concerned. This abnormal irritability is the basis of neuroticism.

In man who has so much greater flexibility, there is far more opportunity for this exaggerated instability; and consequently man, more than any other animal, is subject to marked neurotic traits. *Exaggerated instability tends to be the result of prolonged and excessively intense responses to inadequate stimuli.* Simultaneously normal flexibility is gone, and vacillations between extremes are so great that the person is no longer capable of making adjustments.

Unfortunately, instability in man not only prevents proper adjustment; but the existence of such instability means *per se* that the organism is not functioning smoothly. Overreaction, even though initially psychologic, inevitably reverberates physically; and there is a coincidental overactivity of the normal physiologic functions, a disturbance in what Professor Cannon calls "homeostasis." By homeostasis, Dr. Cannon expressed the concept that everything in our body tends to fluctuate between two opposing tendencies. The heart has one set of nerves (sympathetic system) which make it beat faster, and another set of nerves (parasympathetic) which make is beat slower. These two sets of nerves are continuously active; and when one set exerts too great an influence, the other set immediately goes into operation to bring about a normal balance. In the same way practically every other function in the body tends to vary between two extremes, in such a way that a fluctuating normal level is maintained. The inherent irritability of the human body requires this constant control which tends to bring about not an absolute but a relative stability which is easily modifiable to meet changing conditions.

There are conditions in which one of the controlling systems is impaired and as a result the organ involved "goes haywire." In paroxysmal tachycardia, the sympathetic system is so excitable that the heart, instead of beating the normal 72 per minute, may beat as fast as 240 times per minute. There has been a loss of parasympathetic control, and the natural irritability of the heart causes it "to run away."

In the same way, in emotional instability, there is loss of adequate control and a swinging of emotional reactions to extremes. A person with emotional instability is one who is out of control, whether that loss of control results from internal lack of training, or external pressure.

Emotional stability, then, means both preventing the arousal of undue emotion and controlling that which we have so that it is creative rather than destructive. Emotion is the driving force which urges us toward greater achievements; but like every other powerful force it is destructive or constructive depending on how it is utilized. The volume and force of water furnished by a fire hydrant is valuable when used to put out a fire; it is worse than useless when used to water a bed of seedling plants. Mosquitoes are annoying, but you do not need a machine gun with which to destroy them; and moreover, if you use such a weapon, you will do more harm than good, even provided you manage to slaughter the offending insect. Kill the mosquito—yes; but don't wreck the house and break the windows in the process. You have certain inadequacies and limitations; everyone does. What are you going to do about them? You can refuse to admit them, even to yourself; or, you can wallow in your misery, rivet your attention upon your shortcomings, and develop a sense of inferiority which will nicely paralyze your will and guarantee to keep you forever unhappy. In the third place you can with objectivity and emotional stability meet the situation. Don't shrink away from the fact (even if you push it out of conscious awareness, it will lurk in the background waiting to pounce); face it for what it is worth, neither magnifying nor minimizing its importance; do what you can to correct it, expending your energy on doing and not feeling; and in those rare instances wherein nothing can be done to ameliorate the situation, deliberately and consciously cultivate an attitude of acceptance without emotional disturbance.

In the next chapter we shall discuss various immature reaction patterns stemming from lack of objectivity and from emotional instability, and we shall attempt to give you a technique both for overcoming them and for substituting attitudes which are mature and efficient. But first, look a little more closely at the elements inherent in emotional stability. Two things seem to be of particular importance: a *sense of proportion* and the *habit factor*.

Sense of proportion.—To emphasize the value of having a sense of proportion is just another way of pointing out the worth of having an adequate and definite sense of values or of having and practicing a mature philosophy of life. As we pointed out earlier, having a code of values, knowing what we can reasonably expect of ourselves—the world being as it is, and we as we are—gives direction to our efforts, enables us to disregard minor irritations, furnishes us with goals. Such a philosophy offers the kind of pattern which is essential for stability; without it we are blown by every whim, every caprice, every momentary desire.

Having an ideal goal is the first step; actualizing it necessitates selection and rejection and still later organization.[1] One's philosophy gives the standard by which to select and reject; and it is this selection and rejection which forms the groundwork of proportion. What is really important? What is your major objective? On what are you expending your energy? Are you "throwing away all your money for a penny whistle?" Are you squandering your emotional force on trivial, inconsequential matters? Are you allowing your body to develop tension symptoms and your spirit a jaundiced outlook on life because you permit yourself to overemphasize minor and incidental irritations? Look back over the events of this day. How many times have you felt irritated or hurt? List every grievance, and then look lovingly at each one. How important is it?

[1] *Vide* Ch. XV.

Are you irritated by the way your husband always sloshes his coffee into the saucer and mumbles indistinguishable replies from behind the barricade of his morning newspaper? You'd wash the saucer anyway, wouldn't you? You are pretty insistent about not being interrupted when you are listening to a favorite radio program, aren't you? The children are ten minutes late getting home from school at noon. There is a mad scramble to get them fed, washed, and back on time for the afternoon session. Were you so irritated by their tardiness that you indulged in a lunch-long monologue to the effect, "If I can spend the morning (you really spent about half an hour) preparing your lunch, it does seem the least you could do would be to get here on time to eat it?" Which is more important—a fallen soufflé or the crestfallen spirit of a child who had come home bursting with enthusiasm about the school movie which ran ten minutes over time? Was the irritation you expressed in banging up the telephone when a wrong number was given you proportionate to the gravity of the moment's delay? *Why* did the presence of Mrs. J. ruin the afternoon's party for you? "Because," as you say, "I can't endure the way she neglects her children and picks on her husband," or is the real reason envy of what appears to be her greater popularity? In either event, how does she impinge on your territory? What is she to you? Is she hurt or affected by your disapproval, dislike, or envy? *You are.* Grant that she is thoroughly disagreeable and irritating, the question remains, What is she to you that you should permit your feelings about her to give you a headache either literally or figuratively? Perhaps you are not irritated by unimportant things; you have "real" troubles. You have dreamed of your son's becoming a famous doctor, and he's never happy except when he's covered with grease and is tinkering with the insides of some old machine. After all the money you've spent, and all the fine plans you had. . . . Well, what about it? Would you rather *make* him be a second-rate and dissatisfied doctor or permit him to be an expert and happy mechanic? If one must be sacrificed, which should it be—his happiness or your pride? You are worried about business: raw materials are increasingly difficult to obtain; wages are going up; orders are coming in faster than you can fill them; etc. Are your stewing and fretting, your blaming the political party in power, your carrying your business problems home and to bed with you going to change the situation? What do you wish most from the ten to forty years you yet have to live? Is your bank account really more important to you than your health, the harmony of your home, the happiness of your family and friends? Even if it is, you still are defeating your own purpose if you worry instead of plan, if you allow anxiety and overconcern to strangle your cortical ability to choose the most effective solution to your problem.

Emotional instability occurs when one expends emotion out of all proportion to the irritating stimulus; and developing a sense of proportion which enables one to see big things as big and little things as little is a real help toward reducing the number of tension-producing emotional responses. Keeping rather constantly before you your sense of relative importance will not make you immune to disturbing or distressing events; but it will give you a kind of mooring, which will help you "weather" the storm of life.

Don't confuse emotional stability with apathy or placidity. *There are occasions which demand emotional outbursts.* There are great wrongs to be righted, great deeds to be accomplished, great values to be achieved. The zeal, enthusiasm, and fervor characteristic of those who accomplish significantly is essential; for it both furnishes the energy necessary for continued activity and releases the feeling tone engendered by what the person is doing. It is when emotion is divorced from directed activity, when it ceases to be a con-comitant of "doing" that it becomes harmful. Let us be more specific. A fireman called on to risk his life to save persons trapped in a burning tenement is excited. He faces actual danger, and his body gets ready to help him meet it. More sugar pours into his blood stream, his heart beats faster, etc. His activity and his emotion work together toward accomplishment. Compare his situation with that of a person who reads all the distressing details of an accident, avidly reads descriptions of the shrieks of the dying, the smell of burning flesh, and all the other stomach-turning details which journalistic skill is able to present—reads it, wallows in the misery of it, is haunted by the memory of it, is afraid to leave home for fear of what might happen to the children, breaks into a cold sweat every time she hears the fire siren, etc. Emotion thus evoked is "dead end" in that it accomplishes nothing; worse than useless in that it reverberates by giving rise to symptoms of a tension nature and to the creation of psychological uneasiness or unhappiness. We are not inveighing against emotion as such but against misplaced or misdirected emotion. It comes back to having a sense of proportion: spend all you have and never count the cost when what you are working for justifies such an attitude; but don't "waste your substance in riotous" emotional explosions, when all you accomplish is assorted aches and pains in your body and a ruffled disposition which makes you a misery to yourself and a blight to everyone else.

Intellectually comprehending that values are relative and that few call for any great expenditure of emotional force is a useless bit of information unless implemented and put into practice. The emotions are slow to learn what our "minds" readily apprehend. All our explanation of the relative nature of truth and values and all our discussion of the intellectual basis for a sense of proportion can be compared with grammatical explanations given to an adult. The ideal situation would be for a child never to hear anything but correct speech, for then his imitative speech would automatically be perfect. What actually happens is that he is exposed to good, bad, and indifferent diction; he learns some things right and some things wrong; his good speech and his poor speech become habitual and for the most part unconscious. If the time comes when *realizing* that he has speech difficulties he *wishes* to correct and improve his diction, the first thing he must do is *understand* the rules

involved. But memorizing the rules means nothing; even understanding the rules means nothing unless the person is willing to
undertake the long and often discouraging process of breaking
down old habits, substituting new ones, practicing until he *automatically* and almost unconsciously says the right thing. Identically the same statement can be made about all other skills: it is
the application of the rules which is important, whether one is
learning to play bridge, swim, drive an automobile, orchestrate a
musical composition, or be emotionally stable.

We have said that there are great occasions which call for great
outbursts of emotional force; but for most persons the day's work
and not the world's work is the problem. Most of us are not called
on to deal with major crises, to undertake Herculean tasks (though
there are days when bringing back the Gorgon's head would seem
child's play in comparison with facing an irate "boss"; or cleaning
the Augean stables, mere recreation as over against a six-room
house on Monday morning, with its litter of Sunday newspapers,
night before dishes, laundry to be collected, and toys to be fallen
over). For most of us life is more or less a routine matter of doing
more or less monotonous tasks; but despite the routine and monotony, there is amazing variety in the number of irritating situations which can "crop up." What are you going to do about them?
Be reasonable; don't expect the impossible of yourself. You have
washed and waxed the kitchen floor until it gleams. In rush your
three children (one is enough) with their muddy rubbers (you've
told them a million times to leave their rubbers on the back porch!),
and what few square feet of floor surface they fail to cover before
your agonized protests register the lumbering pup takes care of.
Now what? Will you smile sweetly and in dulcet tones enunciate,
"Viewed under the aspect of eternity what is a kitchen floor as
compared with the tender feelings of a little child?" Not if you
belong to the tribe we are pleased in our more optimistic moments
to call "human." Nor is it highly probable that you will kill the
dog and toss the children back into the rain. Do you clamp your

lips, and martyr-like set about restoring order from chaos? Don't; it's bad for your blood pressure! Do you scold and berate, feel sorry for yourself, and put on a "Queen of Tragedy" act? Don't; it's too hard on your own body and peace of mind and on those of your children. Do you sadistically "get even" by refusing to let the children go to a long anticipated and promised movie? (You are naturally and perhaps even righteously annoyed; but do something to release your tension quickly. Remember Gilbert and Sullivan and "let the punishment fit the crime." Get the kids to help clean up the mess (washing mud from a floor is an amazingly effective technique for aiding memory about taking off rubbers!); and by the time the mud has disappeared, your irritation will have spent its force. Losing your temper, being irritable, feeling sorry for yourself, feeling anxious, worrying, making "snap judgments," criticizing, being intolerant of your own shortcomings and those of others: all these and countless other immature reaction patterns lift their ugly heads in everyone's life; and their occasional appearance does not damn one as being emotionally unstable. It is wise to let emotion come to the surface—but let it come in a directed, constructive fashion; and, having relieved it, forget the incident as quickly as possible.

The habit factor in emotional instability.—Whether or not a person can rightfully be called emotionally unstable depends not upon such *externals* as facial expression or tone of voice; not upon the *appropriate*—however mild or strong—emotion evoked by a particular situation, but upon the *chronicity and intensity with which the person overreacts.*

The trouble with emotionally unstable persons is that they have often unconsciously fallen into the habit of overreacting to every stimulus. Their irritation, worry, intolerance, or criticism has become reflex, automatic. They worry with impartiality about the war, rising prices, what the neighbors will think, whether "Junior" isn't too young to go away, what may have happened when their husbands are ten minutes late in getting home, whether they should get slipcovers or have the furniture reupholstered, what Mrs. D. meant when she said, "Your best friends are always your worst enemies," how to keep the children from reading those terrible comics, etc. To be concerned over a problem which must be solved is natural, and the mature person sets about solving it; to make major problems out of minor decisions is both immature and indicative of emotional instability. "Everything gets on his nerves." It's that word, "everything," that is the "give away" of emotional instability.

It takes repetition to establish any habit—good or bad. It is harder to uproot an old habit and supplant it than it is to acquire a totally new one. The more related "bad" habits, that is, the more specific manifestations of a general attitude which is immature and unhealthful one has, the more difficult will the change be.

You will recall that we have stated elsewhere that it is rare for a person to have a single tension symptom; usually such symptoms come in hosts, hordes, and multitudes. The man with tension headaches usually has other physical evidences of his general state of tension; the woman with tension gastrointestinal disturbances usually has additional complaints and symptoms, etc. The same is true of the psychological manifestations of tension: rarely does one present a single immature reaction pattern, a solitary evidence of emotional instability and immaturity. Usually the specific attitude is a reflection of a general attitude; and the problem becomes one of changing the general attitude. The ultimate goal of changing the basic general attitude of immaturity to one of objectivity and emotional stability must be gone about piecemeal fashion. The weeds have to be uprooted one at a time; the new seeds planted; the tender young plants cultivated and protected; careful outlook for outcroppings of the old weeds kept; etc. And its a hard job.

How to achieve emotional stability.—Briefly stated (it's not so simple as it may sound) this is the technique you must follow: (1) *make an inventory;* i.e., face yourself, take stock of your habitual responses, decide which attitudes are your allies, which your enemies; (2) *will to change;* and (3) most important of all—seize every opportunity that presents itself to *put your new attitude into practice.* You know what you want, the kind of person you wish to be, the difficulties you must overcome, and that it is possible for you at least to approximate what you desire. This resolute facing of the situation, this clarifying of your position is at once the beginning of, and the means toward, further emotional stability. It gives you something on which to rely and it furnishes the goal toward which you are to direct your efforts. You wish to be well and you wish to be happy; toward the achievement of those goals you are willing to do whatever is necessary, no matter how drastic, no matter how long it takes. For some of you—depending on the pervasiveness, the chronicity, and the intensity of your unhygienic attitudes—the process will be a simple matter of homeopathic doses of relatively easy-to-swallow medicine; for others it will be a matter of major and very painful surgery; but for both extremes and for all the "in betweeners," the reward—a sane and happy mind in a healthy body—is worth the effort.

CHAPTER XV

ACHIEVING MATURITY

Lack of objectivity and emotional instability manifest themselves in countless immature attitudes, which in direct proportion to their number, pervasiveness, and intensity give rise to physical symptoms and create a state of general unhappiness and ineffectuality. They are alike not only in origin but in cure. Only when we find and eliminate their causes and only when we retrain the total organism to respond automatically in an emotionally stable and objective fashion can we approximate living on our highest potential level of health and happiness.

Human beings are basically nonconformists; even in our diseases of body and spirit we maintain our individuality, no two persons ever presenting identical pictures. Nor are we even wholly self-consistent in actions, thoughts, and feelings. Miss M. T. rather prided herself on her excessive "nervousness": she was afraid of thunder and lightning; of mice and June bugs; of being "held-up" and of having her apartment robbed; she would not let the window-washer come, unless there was someone to "protect" her (from *what* she never got around to telling); "nothing could induce" her to go out alone after dark; she would not learn to swim for fear of drowning, and when the sidewalks were icy, she was sure she would fall and break her bones. Yet she drove a car with ease, calmness, and great pleasure. Traffic jams, rough roads, even dangerous mountain driving were "nothing" to her.

Mr. R. B. was hypercritical of everyone and everything. The national government was "going to the dogs," his local government was run by "crooks and thugs"; all women and children, his own in particular, were spendthrifts and ingrates; all church members were hypocrites or ignoramuses—sometimes both; bathing beaches were "indecent" and movies "immoral"; the friendly neighbors were "snoops" and all others "snobs"; the poor were "shiftless no-accounts, deserving no better than they got" and the rich were a "pack of thieves"; nothing escaped the lash of his tongue except, strangely enough, the company for which he worked. It could do no wrong. Mr. B. had made a small invention from which his company made thousands of dollars and for which he was given a testimonial dinner. When acquaintances suggested that some more material expression of the company's gratitude might have been appropriate, Mr. B. was as heated in his employers' defense as though his own personal integrity had been questioned. He worked overtime without complaint; and when he suffered a reduction in wages, said "it was necessary." These examples may seem extreme, but we are all more or less extremists; and it is just in this tendency to be excessive that most of our troubles originate. We respond emotionally in situations where little or no emotion is appropriate or necessary; and we overrespond to situations which are inherently capable of stimulating only a very mild irritation. We are so in the habit of responding emotionally instead of thinking, so in the habit of overreacting that our emotional instability is second nature.

As you read the following discussion of some of the more typical and common immature and unhealthful reaction patterns, keep in mind what you know about objectivity and emotional stability and notice how many specific reactions reflect a lack of either or both of these attitudes. Above all, keep constantly before you the realization that this difficult business of growing up, of *becoming a mature adult* capable of coping with your life and solving its problems *is not a matter of intellectual comprehension but of putting into practice that which you understand.*

Do you *worry?* Are you *intolerant* of yourself and of others? Do you *magnify or minimize* (one extreme is as immature and unrealistic as the other) *your liabilities and your assets?* Are you *self-important,* valuing too highly your own opinions and wishes? Are you *self-deprecatory*, giving too much weight to the opinions of others? Do you feel *self-pity*, or *self-blame*, out of all proportion to the gravity of your troubles or mistakes? Do you have *guilt feelings* about past performances or present inclinations? Are you *critical?* Do you bear *grudges?* Do you try to *get even?* Are you easily susceptible to *flattery?* Are you *emotionally dependent?* Are you *indecisive*, finding it difficult to "make up your mind" or to stick to a course of action? Are you *rigid*, unwilling to alter your ideas and plans? Do you *shirk responsibilities?* Are you too easily *depressed or discouraged*, too easily *elated*, too *credulous?* Are you *irresponsive* to, or mawkishly *sentimental* about the needs and troubles of others? Do you *hate, fear, complain, pout, sulk*, have *temper tantrums?* Are you a *martyr?* Are you *hypersensitive?* The list of questions could be prolonged, but you can supply the variations and elaborations.

Your first problem is to *face the facts* and take an inventory of yourself. Which attitudes are characteristic of you? How pervasive and automatic are they? You can "take stock" alone, or you can get someone to help you. In either instance, be sure before you start that you really *wish to know the truth*. Too often when we ask for criticism what we really wish is either approbation or confirmation. How do you feel about a friend's truthful though uncomplimentary reply to so simple a question as, "How do you like my new hat?" If you can be entirely honest, you may not need someone else to help you face the facts; but the chances are that you cannot. Wishing to know the truth about your personality problems no more guarantees that you can discover them than is wishing to know the true condition of your physical health any sign that you can make an accurate diagnosis. Even doctors when they are ill rarely rely wholly on their own medical knowledge but call on other physicians for assistance. Right at the start, then, you have an excellent opportunity to test your "objectivity"; for certainly there are few harder tasks than listening calmly to a candid enumeration of our faults. Several elements in the situation make it difficult. Your feelings are not hurt, if your physician tells you that you have tonsillitis; you do not feel insulted, if an X-ray reveals that you have a broken bone; for in neither case is your ego, your self-esteem, your pride involved. In one instance we feel ourselves victims of circumstance, and in the other are at least dimly conscious of being more or less responsible. Then too it is humiliating to a chronologically adult person to be reminded or told that his conduct is childish, even when it is, particularly when it is. Most persons would far rather be considered "wicked" than "silly" or "foolish." Many a man who would smile complacently over being called "a shrewd business man" or "a clever politician" would be "fighting mad" if anyone suggested that he cheated at cards. Many a woman who smiles mysteriously when her friends marvel at her husband's giving her everything she wishes would be outraged if labeled a "nag." Most of the reaction patterns discussed in this chapter *are* immature (a kind word for childish), petty, and foolish; and we should so like to appear to ourselves and others as being built on a grander scale than we are; we should prefer our sins to be scarlet rather than a drab, dishwater gray! Most of us are so clever at "putting on our make-up" of self-deception, and are so habituated to our "false front" that it is a rude awakening to meet ourselves eye to eye and with no protective camouflage. Don't go to your best friend and say, "I'm not intolerant, am I?" Don't, with a glint in your eye that warns him he'd better not be honest, ask your husband, "Do you think I'm a nag?" Your friends and your husband (we hope) are prejudiced in your favor and would rather not hurt you; they will gloss over your mistakes and give you a whole new set of excuses. You are in trouble: you are neither so healthy nor so happy as you wish to be. You need help; go to the person who can furnish it. Go to some objective friend, your doctor, a psychiatrist, your minister—go to someone who understands human beings in general and you in particular; get the "low-down" on yourself, and face it. Listening won't be a happy experience; neither is having an oculist tell you that you must wear glasses an exactly joyous occasion. Your subsequent freedom from headaches and your increased ease in reading, however, more than compensate for your momentary discomfort. *Knowing what you have to fight is half the battle.*

How important are you—more or less than you habitually assume? Probably, more; and that answer is just as true for the pompous, overbearing, domineering man as for the obsequious, shrinking, afraid-of-his-own-shadow man. You are more important, because not only are you the center of your universe but you are capable to a large degree of shaping both yourself and that universe. So the first facts to be faced are your *liabilities and assets.*

There are two or three truths to bear in mind, as you inventory your liabilities and assets. No one ability is the *sine qua non* of success and happiness. You know persons with Herculean *physical strength* who are maladjusted and unhappy, others of unusual *mental ability* and attainments who are lonely and discontented, still others of entrenched *financial security* who get from and give to life little joy. Similarly, no one liability precludes the possibility of achieving a full and meaningful life. Physical handicaps can be overcome; "brains in one's hands" are as valuable and happiness-producing as is intellectual ability to solve abstruse problems; the ultimate values of life—love, friendship, loyalty, faith in life and its possibilities—are not dependent upon the possession of material goods. Finally, what you do with what you have is more important than the wealth of your assets or the stringency of your liabilities.

This matter of personal liabilities and assets, like everything else in life, is a relative matter. You are never so miserable but there are others worse off; you are never so lucky but there are others who seem more fortunate. Health and happiness are relative terms; and your goal is to approximate as closely as possible the attainable degree of perfection in each. In attaining this goal no other thing will help you more than a clear and unemotional realization of just what are your capacities and your limitations. Much of our unhappiness comes from our vague, undefined, amorphous, and often mutually contradictory wishes. A person would starve if he sat around thinking: "It would be nice to eat. I'm sure there is some rare delicacy that would exactly suit me if I just had it." If you are hungry, bestir yourself to get food. You may have to content yourself with hamburgers instead of porterhouse steak; but hamburgers are sustaining, and they can be mighty good. The whole point of evaluating your assets and liabilities is to enable you to marshal your abilities, compensate your handicaps, and then work toward realizing your wishes.

There are two dangers against which you should be warned. *Don't overemphasize either your assets or your liabilities.* Self-importance and self-pity are both immature, self-defeating attitudes. If you are inclined to attach undue significance to your achievements or abilities view yourself "under the aspect of eternity," see yourself as one of the countless millions dead, living, and yet to be born. How important are you—really? What have you accomplished? What credit do you deserve? Have you fully utilized your superior advantages? Have you assumed responsibility in proportion to your abilities? The self-important man is rarely happy; for the bubbles of his self-esteem are forever being pricked by the failure of others to be properly impressed. Remember the countless thousands who in their day and generation thought equally well of themselves—and are now forgotten dust. Measure your achievements by those of your peers and superiors. Remember that the man who is insulated in self-esteem and self-importance, who has lost the "divine discontent" which makes him strive toward even greater heights is to all intents and purposes dead, even though the funeral service has not been held. On the other hand, riveting attention on your handicaps and liabilities, is equally unrealistic. A curious quirk leads many persons to feel that they are being more realistic if they focus their attention on the ugly, the hopeless, the painful. Perhaps this reaction expresses revulsion from sentimental and Pollyannaish interpretations of life; perhaps, an unconscious device to enable the person to shirk the responsibility of doing what he can to remedy the situation. Sometimes it is convenient to consider a situation as hopeless; for then we are absolved from all obligation to try to change it. If you are inclined to self-pity force yourself to enumerate and contemplate every advantage and asset you have; and if your sources of self-commiseration insist on saying, "Yes, but—", then list your liabilities too and analyze them relatively; that is, compared with your assets and with the troubles of others. Make what advantageous changes you can but don't make your situation worse by wallowing in self-pity which at best is sterile and at worst paralyzing.

The second warning is this: *evaluating your assets and your liabilities is a preliminary to strenuous action.* "In whatever condition you find yourself" *do not* "content yourself." The advice given by St. Paul may have been valid in a world convinced that the end of all things temporal was at hand; but it is not applicable to us. If you are fortunate enough to have many assets, then you are called upon to take full advantage of them, to bear the responsibilities which they entail; if you have many liabilities then you are called on to do everything in your power to correct or compensate for them. *The call is for action not for contemplation.*

That it is the *attitude* which one assumes toward his liabilities rather than the inherent nature of the handicap that is determining and all important is illustrated in the following cases:

F. H., aged 40, has a variegated assortment of tension symptoms: she has headaches, stomach upsets, and pains in her arms and legs. She can't sleep at night or stay awake during the day. She is "too tired" to clean her house, shop, visit or have visitors: too tired for everything but to talk endlessly about her "sufferings" and how happy she could have been except for her father.

As a young girl she was interested in dancing as a career; but her father had "notions" about the dangers of the stage. He "put his foot down" on F.'s desire to become a dancer; and for the past twenty-six years she has lain under that foot, squirming a little and complaining a lot, but never *doing* anything to circumvent her father's objections. She is right when she says that her life is a failure; wrong, that it was all her father's fault.

All her life, T. D., aged 30, wished to be a dancer. She studied dancing, made scrapbooks about dancers, went to concerts and dreamed and worked toward the day when she would be a star. At seventeen, she was the pride of her teachers and was training with the ballet for the forthcoming opera season. Rheumatic fever kept her in bed for fifteen months and left her with a permanently damaged heart. Her plans had to be abandoned and her dreams renounced. After a long convalescence she opened a dancing school for little children; still later she organized a Dance Council which does remarkable work in popularizing the dance and in bringing artists to her city. That she is sometimes wistful over the vanishing of her own dreams goes without saying; but she did the next best thing, and is happy, enthusiastic, integrated, of value to her community, a joy to her friends; and a shining example of the possibility of wresting success and happiness out of apparent defeat.

INTOLERANCE

Honest and fearless facing of one's liabilities and assets is easier of achievement and more significant if done on a background of some adequate understanding of human nature as such. To the christening of Civilized Man came many "good" and many "wicked" fairies: many of our assets represent no particular personal worth, and many limitations are simply part of our human heritage for which we are not individually responsible. You may not think very highly of the human race; but you are part of it, and you cannot hope to understand yourself or anyone else unless you take into account the common denominator of those assets and liabilities held in common.

We have attempted to present a realistic picture of man—forever fleeing pain and pursuing pleasure, forever dominated by drives which demand fulfillment but which must conform to the almost equally insistent demands of an inhibiting and often frustrating environment. What was once man's greatest ally—an automatically functioning body geared to assist in direct achievement of pleasure and escape of pain—can easily become civilized man's greatest liability unless he learns to exercise his cortical ability to delay responses, thereby controlling the production of emotion. If we understand that we are imperfectly equipped to achieve in any absolute sense that which we seek, then we are prepared for the inevitable failures which will attend our efforts, and such understanding is the basis of tolerance.

True understanding, of which tolerance is one manifestation, is of the heart as well as of the head. It is not enough grimly to admit human limitations—yours or those of mankind, nor does it suffice blithely to dismiss them with an "Oh well, it's human nature to make mistakes"; for it is within human power to learn from previous mistakes and to avoid repetition. Recognizing the present reality of an undesired condition rarely means that we need accept it as unchangeable and inescapable. We shall have more to say on this subject; but right now we are concerned with those persons who despite their intellectual awareness of the universality of mistakes, failures, and limitations are still emotionally intolerant.

Civilization and all its members are lopsided in development. We are more skillful with our hands than with our thinking; we can learn faster with our heads than with our viscera. As a consequence, most of us present a bewildering array of inconsistencies. *Only when you can face facts unemotionally will you be on the road toward the achievement of tolerance.* Tolerance is a matter not of what you *think* but how you *feel* about any particular person, institution, or idea. You may study anthropology and become intellectually convinced that "racial superiority" is a myth; but if you continue feeling superior (or inferior) purely on the basis of the accident of birth into a particular race you are not tolerant. Are you theoretically willing that every person live his own life as he sees fit and yet irritated that your husband doesn't see fit your way? How tolerant is the person who assents that "one religion is as good as another," but automatically distrusts the integrity of anyone of differing faith? Do you intellectually realize that truth is relative, yet find yourself emotionally disturbed when you hear the expression of ideas radically opposed to your own? Does it distress you to see your children working out a quite different code of behavior from yours, even though your head tells you they have the right to solve their own problems in their own way? All along, the question is not of your external manner, or of what you say, or even of what you think but of how you *feel*. All your intellectual insight will avail little to save your body from the development of tension symptoms and your "spirit" from being sandpapered if you continue *feeling* tense and irritated by whatever does not conform to your particular desires, notions, or prejudices. And *you can train yourself to feel that which you think.*

We have talked at length about the value of having a sense of proportion, of realizing that in the scale of relative values there are relatively few things which are ultimately important and certainly very few which call for any great emotional outburst. Your infrequently used cortex can enable you both to evaluate the significance of particular incidents and to delay your responses until you have deliberately chosen the most appropriate one. The great hindrance is the habit factor: we are in the habit of being intolerant, of being upset by the limitations and errors of others and ourselves, of "getting wrought up," even when we know we are making mountains out of mole-hills. Intolerance (inability to understand intellectually and to accept unemotionally facts as they are) of others leads to criticism; [1] intolerance of ourselves leads often to self-blame and to guilt feelings.

Self-blame and guilt feelings.—You have made mistakes; you probably will make more within the next twenty-four hours. Some of your actions have been ill-advised; no doubt others will be. You have tried your best and the results, it seem to you, could not have been much worse if you had made no effort. You have done those things which you ought not to have done, and you lave left undone

[1] *Vide* p. 250.

those things which you ought to have done. Well, what about it? How do you *feel* about your limitations, failures, mistakes? Do you excuse yourself by pleading the frailty of human nature or by blaming someone else? Or do you go to the other extreme and excoriate yourself for every major and minor error? Both attitudes are unrealistic, immature, and detrimental, the one encouraging you in lazy acceptance and the other consuming so much energy and creating so much tension as to make it impossible for you to do anything constructive toward rectifying your mistakes and profiting by them.

For what mistakes are you blaming yourself? How important are they, measured by an absolute standard or relatively as they affect your or anyone else's well-being? The person given to self-blame rarely concentrates on a single mistake; he crucifies himself for all his actions. He should have spoken when he kept silent; he should have held his tongue when he spoke. He should have foreseen (no one else did) the slump in the market. If only ten years ago he had bought that piece of property which has doubled in value. He could have written to his mother oftener while she was still alive. If only he had had her come live with him (he knows that she much preferred to live in her own home), maybe she would still be alive. He ought never to have gotten into that argument last night. He should have used a different approach when he interviewed Mr. M.: that's probably one more good customer lost. Whatever the self-blamer does is wrong; he blames himself when he is at fault and when he is not; and what does all such self-inflicted unhappiness profit him or anyone else? Nothing.

There are two mature—objective and emotionally stable—attitudes which we may cultivate toward our own mistakes, attitudes which are constructive and conducive to growth and happiness. *We can profit by our mistakes*. Much of our knowledge is acquired by trial and error. One plan doesn't work; we try another and another, until we find one that does. We seem to be more clever in the realm of things than where human values are involved. One or two experiences of pouring boiling water into glasses which have contained iced drinks suffice to teach Mrs. A. a less expensive technique of washing dishes; but it takes many more and much more painful experiences to teach her that the "frankness" on which she prides herself is considered "rudeness" by others. When once or twice Mr. B. has to have the blades resharpened or the rust removed, he learns to put his lawn mower away in a dry place; but it takes much longer for him to learn that his children respond better to suggestions than to commands. One of the most discouraging things about the human race is the slowness with which as persons or as nations we learn to profit by our mistakes. Apparently we have to learn everything the hardest way, by repetition of our own stupidities and their painful consequences. We know that nothing has ever finally been settled by war and that war is unjustifiably expensive both in material and spiritual values; yet we have not worked out any other way of settling difficulties. We know that children must live their own lives; yet parents feel abused and neglected when their own children insist on their freedom; and the children, in their turn, feel more or less guilty over breaking away.

Perhaps most of our personal mistakes are not sufficiently painful in their consequences to force us to avoid repetition; and so we repeat the mistakes until they become habitual. When we begin to reap the cumulative effect, the problem is no longer simple of solution and we are overwhelmed. A single example will illustrate. You learn that your child has gone to someone else for help. You are hurt because you really love him and would do anything for him; also your pride is hurt that anyone should know that he felt he had to go to an outsider. Why? Have you made some major mistake in your relationship with your child? The chances are that you have made dozens; and that even when you saw that you were not eliciting the desired response you made no attempt to correct your own mistake; you were too busy trying to make him correct his. How did you act, what did you say, how did you make him feel when he broke the cellar window? When he brought home poor report cards? When he stole apples from the neighbor's yard? When he played hooky? When he "forgot" to do his chores? When he made all the thousand and one mistakes that every normal child does make? Had you been even partially as aware of the mistakes you were making in your guidance of the child as you were of all his misdemeanors and had you been willing to profit by your mistakes, modify and change your own behavior, had you exercised your sense of proportion to see his childish pranks as being just that, and had you expressed an attitude of true understanding, the present deplorable situation would never have developed. In other words, we may say that *whereas blaming oneself for one's mistakes is profitless and a waste of emotional energy, being aware of, sensitive to, one's mistakes can lead to improvement.* Analyze your mistakes; don't brood about them. Because you are an imperfect human being living in an imperfect world it is inevitable that you will make mistakes; but whether those mistakes serve as guideposts to lead you to a better road or whipping posts to which you tie yourself for the sake of senseless suffering depends on your understanding and your willingness to conduct your life in accordance with what you know.

We said that there are two mature attitudes to be assumed toward our mistakes, the first being wherever and whenever possible to learn what we can from them, and avoid their repetition. The second sounds deceptively easy. When nothing can be done to rectify a mistake, when the harm done—great or small—is irretrievable, just forget it. Sometimes our mistakes are not our own fault; forget them. By "forgetting" we do not mean "repressing." Face the mistake squarely for exactly what it is worth and then throw it away. Yes, it's too bad that you disregarded your father's urging you to go to college. Maybe if you had listened to him then, you'd have a better job now. But what of it? You are forty and have two children to support. You can't possibly go back twenty years and redecide. To blame yourself for your shortsightedness, your folly, your willfulness, or whatever else you may wish to call it, cannot change the situation, but it can and does make you perpetually discontented and unhappy. Forget it; utilize your energy to avail yourself of present opportunities. A friend asks your advice. You give him your best judgment; he accepts and follows it with disastrous results. Your best judgment was evidently in this particular instance poor judgment; but blaming yourself will not help. Forget it. If remembering your mistakes of yesterday enables you to avoid making the same mistakes today, remember them; if remembering them does nothing but make you unhappy and regretful, forget them.

Guilt feelings are self-blame intensified and usually localized to some particular fault, sin, or mistake. There is a wide discrepancy between our natural desires and the conduct which Society demands. The experience of the average child is to have certain words, acts, or ideas shrouded with fear because they are labeled "wicked," "sinful," "dirty," "terrible," etc. Ordinarily he is not taught, but punished or terrified into conformity. This is not a black and white world wherein some things are eternally good and others unmitigatedly bad; but we stupidly try to act as though it were. Conflict between the urgency of one's desires and the potency of inculcated codes of right and wrong gives rise to guilt feelings. A person has hammered into him the idea that a certain act is "wrong" or "sinful." Usually the more insistent the condemnation, the more the person's attention is riveted to the "forbidden fruit." [2] Despite his fear and his belief that what he does is wrong, he commits the act and then suffers agonies of remorse, feeling that he is "hopeless," "lost," "damned," or whatever other state has been represented to him as the inevitable consequence of his evil-doing.

That more guilt feelings center about sex than any other aspect of human experience is not hard to explain. There are more taboos and more reticences on this subject than on any other; and at the same time the urgency of sexual desires is such as to demand expression. Throughout this book we have been pleading that you

[2] *Vide* p. 185.

really understand yourself, understand yourself as both a physical organism dominated by needs and desires and as part of a social whole whose welfare is in part your responsibility. The relationship between the Self and Society is complicated and interrelated. You make it and it makes you; the more stable it is the greater chance you have for integrated happiness; and its stability, in turn, is determined by its constituent members. Most ethical and moral codes are for the good of Society, and ordinarily the individual member is happier when he conforms than when he rebels.

Don't excuse your wrongdoing—whether it be breaking the moral code, underpaying your employees, careless driving, drinking to excess, or anything else. If you are convinced that you are militating against the good of Society and hence at least indirectly against your own happiness, understand the situation and *unemotionally set about changing it*. On the other hand, don't expect the impossible of yourself—don't berate yourself because you like one of your parents or one of your children more than the other; don't feel that it is all your fault when things go wrong; don't, for Heaven's sake, be eternally dragging out some old "sin" or mistake that you have made and try to use it as an explanation for your present troubles. You forgive and forget the wrongs others do to you; you understand that the unkind speech was an expression not of a desire to hurt you but a release of tension; you appreciate that your doctor did all he could to save the life of your loved one, even though his efforts failed; you judge the specific act of your friend not as an isolated entity but against the background of your whole relationship with him. In short you are tolerant of the shortcomings of others; exercise the same tolerance toward yourself.

CRITICISM VERSUS TOLERANCE

Perhaps you are not so vividly and vocally aware of your shortcomings as you are of those of your fellow man. It may be the "hypocrisy," "dishonesty," "stupidity," "selfishness," "dullness," "shallow-mindedness," "stinginess," "profligacy," etc. of your associates and acquaintances that evoke from you a running commentary of adverse criticism. Perhaps you spend little time reproaching yourself for mismanaging your own life but instead utter diatribes against the corruption of your government—national and local; against the abominable manners and worse morals of the younger generation; against the way your company is run by a gang of "slave drivers." You may not spend bitter hours shadowed by the guilty sense of your own mistakes but instead constitute yourself judge and jury to hand down verdicts on the guilt of others. Often, however, intolerance is so pervasive that the tendency to faultfinding is manifested in both directions—toward ourselves and toward others.

The word "criticism" comes from a Greek word, meaning "able to evaluate or discuss." "Evaluate" means to "establish the true worth"; and had we retained the original meaning of the word, we would now be urging the desirability of bigger and better criticism instead of warning you against the tension and unhappiness producing potentialities of excessive criticism. Seeing faults is undoubtedly part of evaluating, but we have so emphasized that aspect that we consider "criticism" as synonymous with "faultfinding." Even worse, we are so accustomed to harping on whatever is wrong with ourselves and the universe, that we have forgotten the purpose of evaluation; namely, to correct and improve. One blithely proclaiming in the face of all that is wrong and painful, "whatever is, is right" is no more unrealistic, no more untruthful than the misanthrope ranting or wailing "whatever is, is wrong." Undoubtedly there is much that needs change and correction but it is worse than futile to seek out faults and failures and then do nothing about them.

Most *faultfinding, nagging, hypercritical persons* do precious little thinking about what they say; they *have practiced the art so long that they automatically release their own tension and unhappiness by a constant stream of invective* about this, that, and the other person, thing, or situation and, unfortunately, are unaware that they are thereby increasing their irritability, tightening their initial tension. Our bodies are "keyed" to overcome dangers; and if we keep lashing ourselves into a genuine or synthetic state of being ready to escape and then do nothing for release, it is inevitable that our bodies, as well as our dispositions, will be tightened to the breaking point.

We have commented elsewhere on the universal tendency to be much more articulate about our pains or irritations than about our satisfactions. You are entirely unaware of the smooth functioning of your car; but a sudden and unexplained knock in the engine rivets your entire attention. How often do you comment on the efficiency with which the giant machinery of the postal system operates? How articulate are you when an "important" letter is delayed? The newspapers write volubly about the meat axe murders and the gangsters, but say nothing about the tens of thousands who live in at least some semblance of harmony. All down the line the same thing holds true: we are much more aware of, much more attentive (at least verbally) to the wrongs, maladjustments, and ills of life than to those aspects of our experience which are good.

Have you ever tried to analyze *why* we are so faultfinding, so inclined to adverse criticism? Intellectual understanding may help; though the task of substituting tolerant for hypercritical attitudes is primarily a matter of practicing to react without undue emotion, of *feeling* (as well as knowing) that most things which disturb us are really unimportant, and of making conscious efforts to find in persons and situations qualities and aspects which do please us.

Insecurity is probably the basic reason for our intolerance, as it is for many other immature and unhealthful attitudes. Nothing is fixed, nothing is assured; there are countless sources of danger from without and almost as many from within; we dream Utopias, but we never realize them; we need absolute security, and at best our securities are partial and easily undermined. We wish psychological as well as physical security; and every other little security-seeking ego is at least a potential danger to our own. It is almost as though we were "sea animals living on land and wanting to fly in the air." Jealousy and envy sometimes are the source of our criticism; but what are they ultimately but expressions of insecurity—fear that the other person has something which we have not? Sometimes criticism is an oblique kind of rationalization—a turning away from the disconcerting contemplation of our own inadequacies to find comfort in dilating upon the so much worse faults of another. We would bolster our own shaky little egos by pointing out the even less secure status of others. Criticism may stem from a sadistic impulse to retaliate: we have been hurt alike by "the slings and arrows of outrageous fortune" and by our failures to do, be, and achieve that which we wish; and being hurt, we wish to inflict pain on others. Of all self-defeating attitudes probably no other is more patently so than hypercriticism: consciously or unconsciously wishing and needing security, the faultfinder, by harping on the shortcomings of others, further alienates himself and further intensifies his sense of lonely inadequacy.

N. S., aged 23, was fairly "dragged" to a psychiatrist. Her mother stated that though Nora had had everything money could buy, she had always been "impossible," quarreling with her family, teachers, and schoolmates. She refused to go to college and for four years had done nothing but "loll around the house finding fault with everyone and everything."

The vehemence and volubility of the mother's criticisms of her daughter gave clews to the source of some of the difficulty. First attempts to talk with Nora were met by a barrage of: "If anyone is crazy it's certainly Mother with her everlasting interference and trying to run other persons' lives." "Why shouldn't I criticize others? Do you expect me to pretend I think nit-wits are wonderful?" "Whose business is it but my own that I'm not popular?" The violence with which she proclaimed that she neither needed nor wished friends was indicative of the loneliness which she was attempting so valiantly and so futilely to conceal from herself.

Her father had taken it for granted that his first-born would be a son, and was bitterly disappointed when Nora was born. Nora could not remember when she had not realized her father's disappointment, and as a child she had longed to "make up" to her father. She tried to "be his son"—wore boyish clothes, played boys' games, maintained a fine disdain for girls and their "sissy" ways. Her efforts were unavailing; her father, for the most part was indifferent though occasionally he was harsh. When Nora was six, her sister was born, and from then on things were even worse. The whole family relationship was a complex mess, with everyone feeling inadequate and everyone evidently resolved to "take it out" on the next person. The father became increasingly engrossed in making money and more and more disinterested in his family. The mother felt guilty because she had not borne her husband the son he wished; she was herself unstable and unhappy, having been reared by a domineering mother who had overprotected her. She felt vaguely resentful of her children, holding them somehow responsible for her husband's lack of interest in her; she felt acutely resentful of his lack of attention, and was loud in accusation. He refused to speak for weeks at a time; she demanded affection of her children; and Nora's stony refusal to make "loving" gestures brought down further avalanches of self-pity and criticism. It was in such an atmosphere that Nora had lived—feeling unwanted, unloved, constantly criticized and berated, her attempts at getting response all abortive and repulsed—it was small wonder that she had grown to be a bitter, critical, unloved, and unloving person.

Her only hope was to train herself to disregard the misery of her home, desensitize herself to it, steel herself against it. She needed to admit that the one thing she had always wished most was affection, response, and tenderness. Her efforts to gain such response from her father had failed; but that fact need not mean she must wall herself off from all companionship, all friendship. To break down the habits of years would be hard, but it could be done. She had everything to gain and nothing to lose by such a procedure: to accept the fact (with as little emotional tone as possible) that the love and affection which she in common with all other normal persons desired was not to be found in her home and then to seek it elsewhere.

The key to curing hypercriticism, faultfinding, and nagging lies in that last phrase: "seek it." It is not enough to understand why you are hypercritical, and to realize intellectually that faultfinding is an ineffective technique; you must consciously seek to supplant your hypercritical response by one of tolerance. It may sound Sunday-schoolish, but try it out: try to discover something to praise in the person you most dislike, try being agreeable, try not only to refrain from making the unkind comments that automatically come to your mind and tongue, but find something pleasant to say in their place. (It is surprising how many of the Sunday-school admonitions have actual validity.) Approach and tackle this problem from the most thoroughly selfish point of view, if you like. Assume that you care nothing about the other person who is hurt by your criticism. All right, what do *you* gain from it? It does not take superior insight or wisdom to see the faults of others; they are as obvious as our own. Has your constant faultfinding made your children into little angels? How much has your husband changed along the "nagged-out" lines you have tried to make him follow? He has changed all right; he is more irritable, more short-tempered, more unreasonable (all reason save our own seems patently unreasonable!); but have you gained anything save the reputation for being a "nag"?

It is not giving away professional secrets to admit that all persons are susceptible to flattery or, stated more subtly, that all persons respond better to praise than to censure. Every man wishes to be a hero; and he will come nearer being one, if you keep him constantly aware of his heroic qualities than if you eternally harp on his defects. Every child wishes the admiration and approval of his parents, and praise rather than nagging will elicit his best efforts. This tolerance of mistakes and this deliberate finding of praiseworthy attributes must, to be meaningful, be a matter not only of words but of feeling. Saying to your wife, "How pretty you look tonight" and meanwhile feeling, "It's the first time in many a long day, and it wouldn't have happened today, if that bunch of cackling hens hadn't had their bridge party" will be no indication that you are learning the fine art of substituting praise for blame. Don't use praise as an entering wedge for censure. Don't say to the young vest pocket edition of yourself: "Junior, that grade in arithmetic is wonderful; but what about those leaves you promised to rake and burn yesterday?" Don't in one breath thank your secretary for having worked overtime, and in the next with imperfectly concealed irritation wonder whether it would be possible for her to stamp the envelopes a little more carefully (you're a neat soul with a passion for orderliness—why does the girl *have* to be so sloppy!).

We are concerned not with your *manners* nor with your ability to *say* the tactful or flattering word at the right moment. What is important is your *feeling;* for if your hypercriticism expresses basic irritability and maladjustment, curing a single symptom will do no good; there are dozens of other equally disturbing ways in which the underlying trouble will manifest itself. Curing yourself of the tendency to nag, find fault, and criticize is a twofold problem (as is the cure of every other tension- and unhappiness-producing habit of reaction) of: (1) finding the cause and (2) retraining your attitude. Your intelligence will aid you in discovering the facts that must be dealt with; but the important thing is that you put your knowledge into practice, and that can be done only by retraining your emotional responses. Nora, for example, had to realize that the cause of her vituperative faultfinding was not the faults, foibles, or limitations of others but was instead a defensive mechanism, developed as the result of feeling inadequate and rejected. She had to desensitize herself to the old pain and face the fact that she must *do* something to gain the love which she had so sorely missed. That she would not find such response at home was obvious; then she must seek elsewhere. She had spent her life "licking her wounds," in all her reactions keeping perpetually operative her unhappy childhood experience; hurt herself, she had indiscriminately attacked all others. To have new feelings she must have new experiences; therefore she must develop interests, cultivate acquaintances, do things which she enjoyed, etc. She must avail herself of every chance to practice her new attitude; and that attitude was not the negative one of repressing the bitter words

that rose to her lips, but the positive one of finding satisfaction—
great or small—from whatever source she could. She had to stop
blaming or resenting her parents and understand them. They
were as they had always been—an unlovely way certainly; but one
to be disregarded since it could not be altered. To expect her to
cultivate an attitude of happiness about her childhood would have
been patently absurd; but to learn simply to dismiss it, to feel
nothing about it, was possible and was achieved by the methods
outlined above.

Remembering that the habitual response of which you are trying
to rid yourself was a long time in the making will help you in the
often discouraging process of establishing your new pattern. And
another encouraging thing for you to remember is that in this
drastic cure of eradicating causes and establishing new attitudes
you are doing much more than correct one particular symptom:
you are automatically ridding yourself of the other symptoms—
whether physical or psychological—which had their origin in lack
of objectivity and emotional stability.

Grudge-bearing.—Sometimes intolerance manifests itself as inability to forgive and forget some particular wrong. The grudge-
bearer cherishes his ill will, fans the flame of memory, never permits himself to forget. Of course you have been treated unfairly.
Who hasn't? Look carefully at the little fountain of bitternesss
which you are allowing to poison your life. Did someone "out-
smart" you in a business deal? Did someone take credit for, and
profit from, your bright idea? Did a trusted friend betray your
confidence? Did someone slight you socially? Did someone humili-
ate you in public? Unpleasant experiences, surely; and far be it
from us to recommend that you be a worm and cherish the foot
that steps on you. But there are two or three things that we should
like you to consider. In the first place, have *you* ever been misunderstood? Unaware of some particular sensitivity or of some painful
experience one of your hearers may have had, you carelessly made
a comment or told a joke that was taken to be "personal" in appli-

cation. You undoubtedly have learned to take a racial, religious, and political census before you venture a story; but those three "sensitive" spots are only a minimal portion of the tender, "no trespassing" areas most persons possess. When you discover that with no evil intent whatsoever you have managed to hurt or insult another, if you have any imagination you begin wondering how many other times you have been the innocent offender. Isn't it possible that you are harboring some slight or hurt that was just as unpremeditated, just as unmalicious as some of your own gauche or careless errors? But you *know* that the injury was intentional and deliberate. Find out. It is amazing how many such "certainties" are dissipated into thin air when brought into the open and discussed. Any experience important enough to cause you emotional disturbance is worthy a few minutes conversation—unless you prefer pinching your bruises to be sure they are still painful! If you discover that the wrong was indeed deliberate, motivated by ill will—what then? If a wrong can be righted and it is worth the necessary energy, then *do* whatever the situation calls for; if not, forget it—forget it not because you love your enemy, but because you love yourself too much to permit whatever armor of integration and security you have managed to fashion for yourself to be dented, much less broken, by the darts of ill will. One final word: if instead of one or two cherished resentments you have many, then you'd better stop worrying altogether about the other person and find out what's the matter with you. It may be that your basic trouble is hypersensitivity grounded in a sense of inferiority.

FEELINGS OF INFERIORITY

One of the most frequently encountered and one of the most harmful attitudes is that designated as an "inferiority complex." The person suffering from this attitude perpetually feels inadequate; and no matter how others may evaluate his worth, and indeed no matter how he himself may intellectually appraise himself, continues to *feel inferior*. He may, and often does, admit, "I can compare my work with that of others and see that what I accomplish is just as good; but I always *feel* that it is inferior."

That such an attitude will have a crippling effect on one's efforts and keep him perpetually unhappy is so obvious as to need no elaboration. The problem is how to rid oneself of such a burden; and it is a real problem. Just how difficult a task it is becomes apparent when you consider some of the characteristics of the true inferiority complex.

Inferiority feelings are not based on facts. It is not a task poorly done nor a relationship inadequately fulfilled that evokes the inferiority complex; the feeling is already there waiting to shroud any and every activity. The feeling is not dissipated nor even mitigated by objective scrutiny. Whether the objective verdict is "superior," "average," or "inferior" simply does not enter the picture so far as the feelings of the subject are concerned. Consequently, *inferiority feelings are not subject to modification by reason;* that is to say, a person cannot be argued (even by himself) out of his emotional response. He will agree with you on a dozen and one different instances that he is not in fact inferior; but his feeling will remain unchanged. Moreover, the inferiority complex is a Hydra-headed monster, and no sooner is one head chopped off (one specific proof of adequacy established) than two more sources of the "feeling" spring forward. For the *inferiority feelings are pervasive;* they are not concerned with specific inadequacies, real or imagined, but constitute rather the person's whole feeling tone. A person so afflicted may focus his attention on some particular aspect of his life where his "inferiority" makes him especially unhappy; but questioned more closely, will admit that he doesn't do anything as well as others, that he always feels unequal to what he must do, etc. In addition, he will usually state, "I've always felt this way"; for in all cases, the *inferiority feeling is a habitual pattern of reacting,* in many instances of lifelong duration. The inferiority complex is a fungus growth in the rapidity with which it spreads and in its resistance; but it does not sprout over-night. The above-mentioned characteristics combine to give a cumulative effect of primary certitude; that is to say, the person who possesses or, to speak more accurately, who is possessed by an inferiority complex takes it for granted that he is as he is because no other state of being would be possible. "That's the way things are; that's the way they always have been; that's the way they always will be."

Over and over again, we have insisted that dealing with symptoms is only a temporary device; that permanent cure always demands that causes be found and dealt with; and in connection with no other symptom does this insistence come nearer being absolute truth than as concerns the inferiority complex. Your headaches, existing on an emotional basis, will not be cured until you lessen the tension which produces them, but you can secure temporary relief through medication; and the same statement can be made about practically every other physical ache or pain you may have. There is no partial relief for a sense of inadequacy; the whole pattern of reaction must be changed. Dozens of times you have convinced yourself intellectually that facts do not justify your feelings, and yet your feelings have persisted; so obviously your solution is not further argument but to probe in your memory, to unearth if possible the source of your general feeling. You say, in effect, "With my head I know that I am not inferior; yet I always feel so. How did I get this way? I've always felt this way. Always is a long time. Did I feel this way before I went to school? *Why* did I feel so? By whom or by what was I measured and found wanting?"

In this self-questioning, this search for cause or causes of your general attitude of feeling inferior, it is tremendously important that you realize just what you are doing. You are not trying to make a comprehensive catalogue of all your actual inadequacies; you are not attempting to make an exhaustive list of all your major and minor failures; what you are trying to do is to come as close as possible to the explanation of why, irrespective of your or anyone else's judgment, you *feel* inferior. Actual failure, genuine inferiority, is another story about which we will talk later on; right now we are concerned with this irrational, unjustifiable feeling which swamps persons, regardless of what they may or may not do or be.

Curing an inferiority complex involves reorientation of one's whole feeling tone about his worth and value; so it is important to come as close as possible to the cause. Understanding *why* you "have always felt this way" is the first step toward emancipation; for curing today's specific manifestations of your sense of inferiority lies in your ability to say, "I feel inferior about this particular situation, because I am in the *habit* of reacting to *every* situation by feeling inadequate. It all goes back to—whatever the source may be—when my feelings of inferiority were so poignant, so strong, that I accepted them as being the only possible feelings for me to have. I felt inferior then; I felt it so keenly that the sense of inadequacy irradiated [3] to other situations, until I developed the habit of feeling inferior all the time and about everything. My feeling then was "wrong." Even if, in the specific situation I was inadequate, my feelings were out of all proportion to the importance of what was involved, or I was not really inferior but felt so because of the stress of the situation. In either event, this habitual feeling has no basis in fact and has no connection with my present situation."

It does not matter greatly whether you find the exact beginning of your general feeling of inferiority, provided you get close enough so that you fully appreciate that you have been interpreting *all* your experiences in terms of a preëstablished emotional response instead of letting each experience evoke its own inherent and appropriate emotion. If all your life you had worn glasses the lenses of which distorted the shape and size of all objects, no amount of eloquence about the incorrectness of your concepts would

[3] *Vide p.* 143.

do you much good; you would have to get the lenses away from your eyes before you could see things straight. What was your distorting lens?

Were you the "ugly duckling"? Were you contrasted invidiously with other children? Were you the less favored one? Did you vainly seek a kind of response from one or both parents? Were you ashamed to bring other children to your home, because of your poverty, the sordidness of your family's way of living, or for any other reason? Were other children not allowed to play with you? Were you an "outsider"; i.e., did you belong to a different race, religion, social or economic status from that of the majority? Were you considered stupid in school? Were you unable to excel or even take part in athletics? Were you ridiculed or taunted because of your size, your clothes, or some unfortunate member of your family? Any single experience or any combination of experiences can be the source of what becomes an inferiority complex if the associated feeling tone of inadequacy persists and irradiates in such a way as to become the general attitude with which all other and later situations are met. Though feelings of inferiority are often an outgrowth of childhood experiences, the rule is by no means invariable. Failure in *any* undertaking—to marry the person one loves, to win sought-for recognition, to make a fortune, to be elected to a coveted office—may become the starting point of a general attitude of inferiority which spreads so rapidly and so insidiously that by the time it has permeated the life of the person involved the initial cause seems no different from all the other events of his life; for he interprets them all in the same jaundiced light of self-inferiority.

The important factor in this situation is not how you appear to others, but *how you feel within yourself*. Not your words, your tone of voice, the attitudes you strike, the manners you assume but your own internal harmony and integration are what is important. Often persons who appear both aggressive and cockily confident are in reality oppressed by feelings of inferiority. Granted that you "fool the world" (you rarely do), your accomplishment is at best negative and not to be compared with the satisfaction that comes from feeling equal to the situation—a satisfaction to which you are entitled and which you may achieve despite your habitual attitude of feeling inferior *if*, and only if, you are willing to retrain your general orientation.

You may need help in exterminating your inferiority feelings. Finding the cause is often difficult; it may not be in your conscious awareness, since we tend to repress [4] painful memories, or it may be obscured by the welter of later experiences of which you are more poignantly aware. Granted that unaided you can trace the origin, you may still need help—moral support—in the long process of desensitizing yourself to the initial cause and in the even longer effort to substitute objective and emotionally stable reaction patterns.

Mr. M. T., aged 22, had a fine position which he had held for more than a year. In addition to words of praise he had received three salary increases.

Nevertheless Mr. T. went to a psychiatrist because he was worried about his job. He was afraid his work was below standard, that he was making irreparable mistakes which would eventually be discovered, that he ought to be able to get more done in a day, etc. He was sure he caused every irritation his employer expressed. Everyone considered him unusually industrious, conscientious, and intelligent; he felt himself to be phenomenally lazy, careless, and stupid.

Questioning revealed that his entire life, exclusive of his work, was unhealthy and unhappy. He was irritable, impatient, easily hurt and violently argumentative. On the rare occasions when he went out socially it was always with men. His usual evening was a matter of eating dinner, listening to the radio, and then working until midnight redoing work which was already entirely satisfactory.

When asked how long her son had shown this tendency to seclusiveness and over conscientiousness, the mother promptly replied,

[4] *Vide* p. 126.

"Five years. Mark always was a hard worker; but he played hard too. He was just an ordinary boy with lots of friends until we moved into this neighborhood five years ago." In essence Mark's story was, "We never have 'belonged' in this neighborhood. We've always had plenty to eat and wear; but since my dad died when I was twelve, there has never been enough for many extras. Until I went to work Mother had a job clerking. I was a junior in high school when we moved here, and I never did fit in. Most of the kids had their own cars and more spending money in a week than I had in three months. I wouldn't be a hanger-on. I couldn't date any of the girls because the best I could do was take 'em to a movie. I didn't go to many of the school parties, because I wouldn't go where I wasn't as good as the next fellow. I guess I just didn't have what it takes any more than I do now for my job"—and he was back discussing his inadequacy in his present position. To Mark his job was his whole problem; to the psychiatrist it was obvious that his feeling of inferiority about his work was significant only as a symptom of a much more fundamental difficulty; namely, a general and pervasive feeling of inadequacy and of being a "misfit."

To have argued with him about the excellence of his work would have been breath wasted. What he had to do was realize that he had gotten off on the wrong road five years earlier; he had to understand that though the reaction of his seventeen-year-old self was a perfectly natural mistake for a sensitive adolescent to make it was nevertheless a mistake. Confused in his sense of values and unable to cope with the situation, he had felt that the fault lay in him; and so keen had been his sense of inadequacy that it had irradiated to affect every aspect of his life. Finding the cause was only the first step. He had to go out socially, "make dates," cultivate acquaintances, and talk even though he felt timid; he had, in short, to build up a whole new pattern of acting and feeling. After a few weeks he reported "I guess I never learned the right line of talk; now that I have, the girls seem to like me as well as anyone else."

Cure of his overconcern about his job was a side result of the basic cure of his general sense of inferiority. When he no longer felt concern about his social difficulty he no longer even thought about his inferiority at work.

The longer the inferiority sense has existed the more difficult it is to find the cause and the more arduous is the task of removing it; but just as it is only when the roots of poison ivy have been destroyed that one can be free from that source of irritation so it is only when the basic causes of an inferiority complex have been removed that one can be free of the paralyzing and multitudinous manifestations of that self-defeating attitude.

The therapeutic value of frank, concrete, and detailed discussion can hardly be overestimated. It is not so much that new and illuminating facts are brought to light but rather that one discusses his emotions factually instead of emotionally reacting to facts; and *it is always the attitude toward the fact that is significant rather than the fact itself.*

The principle of treating such unwarranted feelings of inferiority depends, then, upon determining the causative factors and eradicating them by the process of understanding and desensitization and by active participation in social relations. Practicing attitudes of objectivity and emotional stability toward the whole evolution of one's life and the whole social scheme removes inferiority feelings, substitutes a healthy and happy outlook on life, and makes possible a higher level of self-realization.

We have dwelt at such length upon this subject because the problem is so widespread and is the source of so much unnecessary unhappiness; but perhaps we should not leave it without one final word. If you are a typist and, realizing that your work is inferior, quake every time your employer speaks to you, don't spend your evenings wondering whether your "quakes" are the result of the fact that your older sister was prettier and your younger sister smarter: spend them working to improve your speed and accuracy. If your sales record is falling off, don't waste energy trying to figure out why you feel inadequate. There is nothing to figure; the reason is obvious: you *are* inadequate in that particular situation, and your concern should be to rid yourself of the inadequacy itself. There are real inadequacies which must be met and dealt with. In the vast majority of instances, we can do much by way of improving ourselves physically, cosmetically, financially, professionally, socially, etc. The feeling of inadequacy accompanying a task poorly done should serve as a spur to improvement. We are inadequate in countless ways; but whether our specific inabilities are worth our attention can be determined only by whether or not they interfere with the attainment of our chosen goals. Take a very simple example: do you both know and feel that you are a poor bridge player? Mr. A., a traveling salesman, is frequently asked to "make a fourth." If he refuses, he feels that it was not politic, that maybe he would have made a valuable "contact," etc.; if he consents, he is embarrassed by his poor playing. Mr. A. would do well to cure himself of his specific feeling of inferiority by the simple expedient of taking a few lessons and improving his skill. Mr. B. and his wife "go with" a group who are bridge enthusiasts; Mr. B. will enjoy his social life more if he learns to play a good enough game so that his partners will not be forced to like him in spite of his abominable playing. Mr. C., however, does not know one card from another, has no desire nor reason to learn; and consequently, his inadequacy at cards in no way constitutes a problem. Do you feel inferior when you attempt to speak in public? If your vocation or your avocations necessitate your talking before groups, then your inadequacy is a practical problem which must be met and overcome.

In summary, then, we might say that there are *three kinds of feeling of inadequacy*. The first is almost wholly intellectual and is little more than the temporary and completely undisturbing realization that there are countless things which we don't know or can't do; e.g., pearl diving, tapestry weaving, glass blowing, ballet dancing, weight-lifting, conducting an orchestra, building bridges, etc. The second is the concomitant of actual inferiority in particular situations. The "feeling" is appropriate and proportionate to one's actual failure, and it serves as a stimulus to improvement. Removal of the inadequacy automatically dissipates the feeling. The third kind, to which we have devoted most of this section, is the true inferiority complex: a general feeling tone of inferiority which accompanies all activities, irrespective of their objective worth and unmodified by one's intellectual evaluation of the merits of particular instances. It is cured not by improvement in specific skills or abilities and not by intellectual conviction that one is not inferior, but by finding the source of the complex, changing one's emotional reaction to that cause, and retraining one's entire orientation so that each situation is allowed to evoke its own and its appropriate emotional response.

MARTYR COMPLEX

One of the strangest attitudes is exhibited by the person "who enjoys his misery," "wishes to remain ill," or "glories in his martyrdom." Usually such an attitude expresses desire for attention or unwillingness (often unconscious) to face disturbing problems which otherwise would demand attention.

Do you know "professional invalids" who spare their unfortunate friends no details of their "suffering," or, worse yet, "bear their cross" in silence—a silence louder than shouting from the housetop. They smile wistfully and are "not quite equal to" the theater party you suggest—"But you run right along, Dear, and have a good time. I'll be all right. If anything should happen, I have the doctor's telephone number." What can you do? You're caught either way. You're 99 per cent sure nothing will happen—it never has in the past. If you go, you feel like a brute; if you stay, you are bound in time to feel resentful. Maybe it's a sad commentary on human nature, but our capacity for sustaining deep concern over the static condition of someone else is short-lived. If you can manage this week to be in an accident, next week to have an emergency operation, the following week to develop a blood clot, and to spend the fourth week in an oxygen tent, you may be able to keep your friends agog with interest; but thereafter you'd better get well, because you can't hope indefinitely to be the center of interest. If your husband and your children are bound to you by no more secure ties than their feeling of sympathy for your suffering then you can be fairly certain that sooner or later the sympathy will be replaced by a sense of being tied to a dead weight.

Don't "sacrifice everything" for your children and then feel like a martyr. It is bad for you and for your children. If the happiness of another is really more joy-giving to you than would be gratification of your personal desire, you have had your pleasure and have no right either to feel noble or to expect the recipient of your generosity to wallow in gratitude. Very often what we are pleased to call "self-sacrifice" is at best a stupid and empty gesture from which no one benefits. Many children are crippled by their parents' sacrifices, robbed of the opportunity to develop and exercise their own initiative, and fettered by the feeling that they ought to be more grateful than they are. Once more, exercise your sense of proportion. Rarely an occasion is so important, so significant that our personal desires need be forgotten and all our resources— material and spiritual—devoted to the cause whose value transcends more immediate satisfactions. But ordinarily speaking you have the right to pursue your own happiness, and pursuing it you will make other persons much happier than you will following the road of constant self-abnegation. Your daughter will be happier to be able proudly to display you than she will be if you look like a "frump" so that she may have more clothes than she needs (unless you have already made her into a selfish pig by your false heroic self-sacrifices); and your son will be happier to have a father who takes off an occasional Saturday afternoon to go fishing with him than he will to have you grubbing away, a slave to your desk, so that he may be sent to an expensive camp.

Virginia F. was a junior in college when her mother became seriously ill. Virginia was a good student but not popular. She concealed her hurt by stoutly maintaining (rationalization) she had no time for the "foolishness" of parties and dates. Her mother's illness offered honorable escape from a pride-wounding situation; and Virginia left college resolved to devote her life to her "poor little mother." The remainder of her life was devotion—with a vengeance. She did everything for her mother, including the things which her mother would have much preferred doing for herself. Her mother recovered; but Virginia's devotion continued and spread to include her two brothers. In retrospect her popularity "suffered a sea change" which turned it into something glamorous she had gladly given up for the sake of her dear family who just couldn't get along without her. In time she was a trifle wistful— never accusatory—over having given up her own happiness for her family. Eventually her mother died; but Virginia still had her two brothers to take care of. The fact that they were full grown, able-bodied, and earning their own livings did not "register." They were so accustomed to take her at her own evaluation of self-sacrificing nobility that they never questioned what they "owed her for all she had given up," even when they were irked because they felt it would not be "right" for them both to go out on the same evening and "leave poor Virginia alone."

When the brothers were married, Virginia's martyrdom presented even more of a problem. Each brother tried having her live with him; but the sisters-in-law, not having been reared in the Virginia cult, resented her. The brothers, bored by her eternal self-abnegation, nevertheless felt guilty when they remembered all she had done for them. They established her in an apartment and tried to see her as often as possible. She became increasingly difficult, her self-pity and sense of martyrdom growing until she became openly accusatory of neglect. She leads an empty, meaningless life, a misery alike to herself and to everyone else.

RIGIDITY VERSUS ADJUSTABILITY

Throughout this book we have been urging the desirability, indeed the necessity, of avoiding extremes and of seeking the "golden mean." We have emphasized, too, the value of flexibility, of being able to adjust to and be modified by existing circumstances. Look now at some typical attitudes which all too commonly indicate failure to appreciate both the detrimental nature of extremes and the worth of adjustability.

Rigid personalities.—Most of our actions, physical, mental, and emotional, are habitual: our posture, gait, routine of dressing, tone of voice, "manners," the kind and amount of food we eat, sleep, religion, politics, attitudes toward family, friends, neighbors, acquaintances, and strangers, and the manner in which we express those attitudes. We go through many a day without once making a conscious decision; we simply follow the established pattern. There is value in routine provided—a tremendously important proviso—the routine is a means and not an end, provided we do not permit it to assume disproportionate significance. Use your routine; don't let it use you. If you are upset and irritated when you have to change your established routine you can safely assume that your habit is becoming your master instead of your servant. Yours is a "scientific baby," fed, bathed, dressed, and put to bed according to schedule. He and you undoubtedly profit from his well-organized life; but if Grandpa comes a thousand miles to see Hezekiah III and arrives ten minutes after your offspring is tucked away for the night, don't make Grandpa wait till next morning; it won't hurt the baby to have his routine off schedule once, and it will make Grandpa inordinately happy to see this latest twig of the family tree. If you always have windows washed on the first Monday of every month, don't stew and fret because it storms some particular window-Monday; you are more important than the windows; and what earthly difference does it make, anyway, if they are washed this week or next? If you are a model of neatness, such orderliness is no doubt a valuable asset; but if your day is ruined—whether you vocalize or bottle your irritation—when your secretary mislays a paper, then your habit of neatness is more hindrance than help. One person who makes a fetish of carrying out her plans irrespective of how inconvenient they may be to herself or others gave a prize example of her rigidity. On the first of August she made an appointment to have a permanent wave on the twelfth. A week's unrelieved heat wave was climaxed on the twelfth, when the thermometer rose, and having risen stayed, at 105°. Her friends and even the beauty parlor operator suggested that she change her appointment but, in her own words, she'd "rather have a heat stroke than change the plan."

Rigidity may be of two kinds; though usually they are found together. First, there is the kind concerned primarily with the minutiae of living, that insists that certain things be done according to a prescribed and immutable formula. The position of the furniture must not be changed; the breakfast eggs must be cooked exactly three minutes; meals must be served at the appointed hour, though the skies fall; and woe betide whoever leaves the newspaper "torn to pieces and scattered all over the place." Have you been in homes where you dared not pick up a magazine for fear of destroying the pattern of arrangement, a pattern which by previous experiences in having your hostess restore its perfection after your vandalism you have come to recognize is sacred? Do you know bridge addicts who insist that the cards be shuffled a particular number of times and are definitely uncomfortable if others won't "do it right"? Usually it is relatively easy for these "set in their way" persons to get others to conform, primarily because the others do not care one way or the other. If towels tossed on the rack get on your wife's nerves, you'd just as soon fold them—most of the time; if your husband is irritated when his precious tools are not put back exactly "right" you try to replace them according to his plan—most of the time.

The second kind of rigidity—that of ideas and codes—is much more far-reaching in its effects and is the source of much more trouble. If you insist on taking the 8:15 train every morning when the 8:22 would get you to your office in plenty of time, no one is going to object too strenuously; but if your notion of what constitutes "sensible and decent" recreation runs counter to what your children and their companions believe, you are in for trouble and plenty of it, if your rigidity is such that you try to superimpose your code on their behavior. If you insist that china be on the right and glasses on the left side of the cabinet, probably no one will insist otherwise; but if you have a young daughter whose mind is as set on having a career as yours is set that she shall not, what will happen? The world changes: customs, conventions, ideas, ideals, morals—all change and are constantly in the process of modification. Right and wrong, good and evil, truth and falsehood—all abstractions are relative.[5] If you are truly realistic you must be flexible and adjustable; you must be prepared to have your children's conduct and ideals depart as radically from what you are "sure is right" as yours did from your parents' code. The trouble with persons who are rigid and unyielding in their convictions is that they are never willing for others to hold opposing views with the same degree of certainty and are eternally attempting to force others into conformity. You can force those who are weaker to do as you say, but only so long as they are weaker; and you can never *make* another agree with you, even though for the sake of expediency, he may refrain from expressing disagreement. Parents can make children conform only until the children are old enough to assert themselves; and many parents would be scandalized if they knew the mutinous thoughts their children indulge, even while in the act of obeying. Maybe the world would be better off if you could persuade or force everyone in it to accept your code, share your ideas; but you can't do it. That you avoid rigidity is essential if you are to avoid being broken yourself.

At the opposite extreme from ironclad rigidity which refuses to bend or yield, is the equally immature and unhygienic attitude of vacillating indecision. Living is a practical problem, or rather a multitude of problems, demanding solution, calling for action. Action without foresight is liable to be wasteful at best and destructive at worst; but, on the other hand, speculation which does not eventuate in decision and activity is sterile. It is tremendously important that we carefully plan our course and, having decided, carry through without hesitation or faltering. The old story of the mule that starved to death because he could not make up his mind which of two stacks of straw to eat first is symbolical of many persons who never accomplish anything because they cannot make up their minds. You know persons who can never decide what

[5] *Cf.* Ch. XIV.

they wish to eat—to the point that they wear out your patience and that of the waiter. You know others who do so much discussing about whether they shall or shall not go to a movie that by the time an ultimate decision is made everyone is too tired to care whether they go or stay. Have you known still others who put on and take off five dresses—or ties—before making the momentous decision as to which garment to wear? Such a way of living is ineffectual and energy wasting—and it can be "maddening" to the other person whose movements are curtailed by the indecision of the vacillating one.

Such indecision is a major or minor handicap, depending on the importance of the issues involved. For example, a child's stability is seriously affected by the indecision of parents who alternate between excessive laxity and undue severity. To be laughed at as "cute" today and punished as "naughty" tomorrow for identically the same action is bewildering. If you "think you'd like to be a doctor" but "there are many things about law that appeal" to you, you'd better decide which you wish to do; since the training and apprentice time for each is long, and in either case you'll be middle-aged before you're earning a living. What usually happens with this type of person is that the exigencies of the situation "push" him into a decision; then he spends the remainder of his life thinking how successful he might have been if he had "decided" differently. Sometimes having no controlling purpose results in attempting so many things that nothing significant or satisfying is accomplished.

E. A. was blessed, or cursed, with a natural aptitude for many types of creative work. Her family were financially able to support a dilettante daughter, and that is just what Elaine became. Her "medium" changed with the seasons: dancing, next painting, then writing, followed by singing, interior decorating, and editing an "arts magazine." She accomplished nothing of worth. She was forever discontent, changing from one teacher to another, always sure that the latest "work" was her "true medium." That she had unusual natural talent was obvious; but she lacked both the singleness of purpose and the self-discipline which are essential for achievement.

This vacillating indecision can be ascribed to two lacks: (1) clearly defined goals and (2) practice in carrying through to completion action which has been determined upon. Too often we are like children in a toy store: grabbing one thing, only to throw it aside as soon as we glimpse something else which we think we might like better.

There have been many fine and noble philosophies formulated and to them countless millions have given verbal allegiance and intellectual assent. But we and the remainder of the world are in our present sorry mess because we have had neither the ingenuity nor the persistence to put these principles into actual practice. For the moment, however, forget the world and examine your own behavior. Do you just live along from hour to hour, doing the easiest thing in the easiest fashion? Have you planned a course of action which your best judgment told you would bear rich returns in ultimate satisfactions, and then, finding the way hard, allowed yourself a temporary respite with the promise that you'd start again on some mythical tomorrow? And either tomorrow never comes, or your second attempt is even more feeble than the first and more easily abandoned. Or you never get around to even formulating just what it is you wish and so become prey to vague and undefined desires. The only reason on earth that we are urging you to decide and then to follow through your decisions is that we are convinced that only such a planned and executed life can possibly be happy. What good does it do to know that your tension symptoms express your chronic tendency to overrespond to present and past irritations unless you decide to change your habitual response to one of dispassionate objectivity; and what good does that intellectual decision do you unless you follow it by countless efforts to establish your new habit? What good does it do to decide you'd like to be a great lawyer unless you are willing to do all the arduous work preliminary to that achievement? The vast majority of our daily action is routine and calls for no decision making. It takes only a few experiments to discover the quickest and pleasantest route to work; thereafter we automatically go the same way. How long would you employ a worker who was habitually late because each morning he made several starts before deciding just which way he wished to come? Yet most of us waste much energy in equally fruitless indecision. We make and unmake our minds, and kid ourselves into believing we are making rational decisions when all we are doing is delaying action. There are situations which call for making decisions,[6] but the point we wish to stress here is that, as a rule, abiding by decision, despite discouragements, delays, and failure will result in greater accomplishments and greater happiness than will changing plans in mid-action. Don't complicate your life needlessly; don't convert the minutiae of daily existence into momentous issues; don't expect the impossible of yourself as to the number or the perfection of your accomplishments; but having chosen your goal—whether a soon-to-be-realized one or a long term one which you will spend your whole life in approximating—move toward it not with the grim determination of the rigidly righteous but with adjusting and adjustable firmness of purpose and definiteness of direction.

SYMPATHETIC UNDERSTANDING VERSUS MAUDLIN SENTIMENTALITY OR INDIFFERENCE

In Chapter X we spoke of the mechanism of "identification," by means of which one person assumes the characteristics, attributes, troubles, or triumphs of another. Perhaps no other one quality would do more to obviate unnecessary suffering than would the development of a more adequate creative imagination which would enable us in some significant fashion to enter the problems and pains of others. Our own direct experiences have a quality of

[6] *Vide* p. 315 ff.

vividness and poignancy which far exceed in intensity, if not in variety, our vicarious living. One night of walking the floor (you feel more like climbing the walls) and playing host to an abscessed tooth will teach you more about that refined torture than could all the most vividly written descriptions of that condition. Moreover, when you hear of someone else called on to endure the same pain there is a sincerity in your exclamation, "the poor devil" that indicates that in some real way you know how he feels. To a degree we are all able to enter imaginatively the experiences of others, to share their excitement, anger, joy, sorrow, etc. You, too, experience bursting pride and excitement when your son is made captain of his team; you share your five-year-old's desolation when he discovers there is no "real" Santa Claus; you are indignant when your neighbor's prize winning rosebush is wantonly destroyed by some vandal; etc.

Our creative imagination is such that we can more or less accurately put ourselves into another's position and, to a degree at least, feel what he feels. So, for example, though you have not as yet been clapped into a concentration camp, your imagination enables you to share the physical and mental pain of such an experience; though you may be so fortunate as never actually to have experienced physical want, you can sufficiently identify yourself with the hunger and cold of another to appreciate something of what he suffers. You see and hear a group of persons smiling, laughing, chattering gaily, and though they may be speaking a foreign language, you find yourself smiling sympathetically. It is this ability to enter sympathetically into the experiences of others, this capacity for sharing joys and sorrows that more than any other one thing binds us together as a human family; and it is an ability that needs to be cultivated. Sometimes a person out of his own direct, personal suffering makes a discovery that is beneficial to all mankind; but even more often such additions to human knowledge are made by outsiders who, seeing the pain of another, feel it enough to set about finding a remedy. A doctor, for example, need not be the victim of a disease before he is interested in discovering both cause and cure; one need not be on a "chain gang" or experience the brutality of "third degree" questioning before he can be interested enough to try to do what he can to destroy these survivals of savagery. Often the person doing the direct experiencing—whether it be suffering an amputation without anæsthetic, working for starvation wages, writhing under the lash of political or economic ruthlessness, etc.—is in no position to help himself; he must be helped by others. Others will bestir themselves to help to the degree that they identify themselves with the problem. Every social, every economic, every political wrong which has been improved or righted is the result of man's capacity sympathetically to share the experiences of others.

We are curiously limited in the scope of our imagination. We are inclined to remain apathetic to situations unless their implications are somehow brought close. For example, you notice an account in the newspaper of some small child who has been abandoned by his parents and are encouraged about the essential goodness of the human heart when you read in next day's paper about all the homes which have offered to open their doors for the waif. Why is it that this one mite of humanity arouses so much tenderness in persons who can read unmoved the statistics of the numbers of children who annually die of starvation? Why is it that men who are personally kind and generous in their immediate contacts permit "killing conditions" to exist in the factories which they own or control? Dozens of similar questions could be asked; and for every one the answer would probably be the same: lack of imagination.

As we said earlier, whether we like it or not we are all dependent on each other in this human quest for happiness; the good of the particular person is, in the last analysis, contingent upon the welfare of the society of which he is inescapably a part; he cannot afford to be indifferent to any of the ills of his fellow men. Try being indifferent to an epidemic of infantile paralysis, a polluted water supply, the problem of unemployment, racial and religious discrimination, war. But don't try too long, or you'll find yourself victim of the very ill toward which you assumed such complete disinterest. You may not lose your job; but you'll pay higher taxes. You may be too old to fight; but your property will be confiscated and your son killed. You may belong to the majority group; but the level of your culture will immediately be lowered if it must exist in a tangle of hatreds, fears, and prejudices. If you do not have a single kindly, generous, unselfish motive, if you stoutly maintain that the other person's troubles are his own, it is still the part of wisdom that you do everything in your power to better his condition. This philosophy of every fellow for himself, "and bid the devil take the hindmost" sounds fine; the only trouble with it is that it won't work. Hosts and hordes of persons running at cross-purposes are liable to get pretty badly snarled; and there is no guarantee who is going to be the hindmost. Moreover, most "devils" can be chased out of existence if enough men of good sense and good will will substitute pursuit for flight.

We have been talking about the value of identification, the necessity for creative imagination and sympathetic understanding; but now we must interpose one very important qualification.

There is danger that sympathetic identification may degenerate into maudlin sentimentality, unless one acts in accordance with his feeling. To weep crocodile tears over the miseries of dispossessed share croppers, to agonize about the cruelties and indignities heaped upon members of minority groups, to shudder over rat-infested tenements does the share cropper, the victim of intolerance, or the tenement dweller exactly no good, and it does you a lot of harm unless you expend the energy created by your emotion in doing something to ameliorate the disturbing conditions. Does it "break your heart" to see derelicts picking up discarded cigarette butts or rummaging through garbage cans in search of food? How much do you contribute to the Community Chest? How much time do you spend working on committees which tackle the problems which that man represents? Do you lie awake sleepless under your down comfort, haunted by visions of the homeless and cold? What do you do the following day to lessen their number? Do you harrow your soul by reading descriptions and seeing pictures depicting the horrors of dictator-scourged countries? How consistently do you live your democratic ideal?

The purpose of all these questions and of innumerable comparable ones is identical: to point out that emotion which does not accompany or lead to action is a detrimental force which serves no function other than that of breeding vicarious sadism or tension symptoms. The fact that the little each one can accomplish seems infinitesimal in comparison with the magnitude of most social problems does not absolve anyone from the responsibility of doing that little. Relatively few of us will ever be able to do anything spectacular or dramatic about solving the world's problems; and when we urge you to match your emotions with actions, we do not necessarily mean that your action has to be physically or materially expressed. You hear that an acquaintance has lost his job. What can you do? The one thing that will do neither of you any good is for you to start picturing how miserable he must be. He's always made a good salary but never saved anything. He is buying his car "on time"; how will he be able to meet the payments? What will happen if one of the children falls ill? He's past forty-five and jobs are scarce; etc. What good will all this undirected sympathy do him? None. You may be able to *do* something: help him find a new position, lend him money to "tide him over" the emergency; help him work out a new plan; maybe all you can do is listen sympathetically and intelligently and so help him clarify his own problem. But in any event, remember that you are going to have enough troubles of your own about which you will have to do something and there are going to be enough problems and miseries which you can help solve or mitigate so that you'd better not waste your energy about situations which you are powerless to affect. Such fruitless agonizing is little more than emotional debauchery.

WORRY VERSUS REASON

What are you going to do about those problems which you can and must solve? If there were no other source of conflict the very dichotomy between man's basic drives and the demands placed upon him by civilization would guarantee every man a lifetime of problems. The problems will arise, and you can do one of two things: bring to bear your best "reasoned out" solution or you can worry, thereby achieving nothing save tension symptoms in your body and perpetual unhappiness in your spirit. The universal inclination to worry arises out of the fact that simultaneously we have bodies geared for *actively* meeting danger and the cortical ability to delay our responses [7] in order to choose the best one. Worry arises when one simply delays but does not choose and follow his choice. Tension produced by the presence of the problem *must* be released. But worry, far from releasing, further augments tension by keeping the irritation constantly in operation. Reason can help because it offers a plan of activity which if followed will more or less (the degree being determined by the wisdom of the judgment) adequately solve the problem, and which gives the organism an opportunity to expend its mobilized [8] energy.

Your best reason will not be perfect, since everyone is limited in experience and in ability to foresee; but it is the best you can do.

The following tabulation will indicate the basic differences between worry and reason.

WORRY	REASON
1. The emotional tone accompanying worry is fear, disturbance, unrest.	1. The emotional tone accompanying reason is calmness.
2. The problem is vague, ill-defined, and usually confused with other sources of emotional disturbance.	2. The problem is sharply defined and, for the time being at least, excludes all other concerns.

[7] *Vide* p. 12 ff.

[8] *Vide* p. 320 ff.

WORRY—*Cont.*

REASON—*Cont.*

3. Emphasis is placed and concentrated upon the worst possibilities.

3. All possibilities, good and bad, are listed and scrutinized objectively.

4. The worst possibilities are accepted as actualities and reacted to as though they had already occurred.

4. The possible solutions are listed in the order of both their probability and their desirability.

5. No conclusions are reached; no plan of action is decided upon.

5. The best solution possible having been decided upon, a plan of action is formulated.

6. The topic of concern remains constantly in awareness, being ever elaborated and enlarged upon.

6. By a conscious effort of will the problem-solver directs his energies toward following out his plan, occupies his attention with other interests, and otherwise dismisses the subject.

7. The problem is not solved; tension symptoms arise or are aggravated; unhappiness results.

7. The problem is solved; tension is released; emotional stability is maintained.

Persons who worry about, instead of reasoning out, their difficult situations fall into two main categories: (1) occasional worriers and (2) chronic worriers.

Worry over a particular problem.—Rare is the person who has not on one or more occasions been confronted with a problem too big for him or with a crisis of so disturbing a nature that his habitual reasoning reaction has been temporarily lost. Worry under such circumstances is inevitable. For example, a loved one is critically ill. Medical science is doing all it can; you have done all you can; but so long as the outcome is dubious, there is bound to be concern, apprehension, worry. Your worry does neither you nor the patient any good; but so long as we live in this dangerous universe, so long as we have imagination and sensitivity, so long as our bodies remain imperfect mechanisms, and our technique of control over the environment is at best partial, a certain amount of worry is the inevitable fate of man.

Sometimes, the distressing situation must be accepted—"must" because at the time there is nothing else we can do. If the worry-producing situation seems liable to continue or is one of the "unsolvable" problems occasionally encountered, then the person involved must accept the fact, objectively and without undue emotion. Continued worry will create more tension and his attitude of apprehension will, by irradiation, spread to color other situations.

Mrs. E. N., aged 27, worried because she could not have a child. Despite a wide variety of treatments, Mrs. N. remained sterile and it was the consensus of her physicians that she would so continue. Mrs. N. intellectually accepted the fact of her sterility; but did not make an emotionally mature adjustment to the situation. She was "ashamed to face her husband" and interpreted any irritability on his part as reproach; she "dreaded" seeing her friends' children, and even "would rather not go to a movie, if there were children in it." She had led an active social life, but became reclusive, going out little, entertaining less, crying for hours and never forgetting her sorrow.

The cause of her worry was genuine; but her worry was not solving the problem and it was bringing into existence countless other problems. She had to change her emotional attitude; not as an intellectual exercise nor by resolving that she *would* make herself feel different but by an active and constructive alteration of her whole plan of living. She sought friends; resumed former interests and adopted a child. Instead of continuing to make one grievous disappointment the center of her life, she *changed her attitude toward the unalterable fact* and set about making the happiest life possible for herself, her husband, and the child.

Chronic worriers.—Frequently the victim of worry does not have a single focal problem which can be solved or toward which he can so change his attitude that the situation ceases to be tension-producing. The chronic worrier is in the habit of being apprehensive; his general reaction pattern is characterized by regret and foreboding. He is impartial in his choice: past, present and future, things done or left undone, immediate realities or possibilities, future probabilities—all are taken as fit subject. If a particular problem is solved or a specific situation loses its worry-evoking nature, there are countless other "worries" which claim his attention. A classic example of this type of person was the woman who worried because she did not worry so much about her older daughter as she did about her younger child, and it didn't seem right that one child should be more important than the other. The chronic worrier often states, and no doubt really believes, that if the one thing he is concerned about at the moment were cleared up, his worry would cease; but there is no more value in tackling the immediate source of disturbance than there would be in citing examples of adequacy to a person suffering from an inferiority complex. Chronic worry, like inferiority feelings, is a general and pervasive attitude which preexists and distorts the foci about which it centers. *Chronic worry is the cause and not the result of problems.*

Mrs. A. H., aged 43, was worried about their financial insecurity. She worried about the rent, the grocery bill, the milk bill, the cost of clothes. What would become of them if the banks closed? What could they do if one of them needed an expensive operation? She wore out dimes worth of shoe leather in an effort to save pennies. Her excessive concern about everything related to the spending of money was out of all proportion to the facts of the case: her husband made an adequate living; they had no debts; both carried hospital, accident, and life insurance; and their savings were invested in Government bonds.

Mrs. H. had always worried. As a child she worried when her brother came home late; when the baby was left in her care; when the dishes were not washed on time; that she would be late to school, that she would be called on in class, that she would fail in her examinations. She worried that she would not be popular and about what she should do when she was out of school. She even worried when her first boy friend kissed her, afraid that she might have contracted a disease. The financial concern was merely another focal point through which she released her life-long tendency to be emotionally upset and apprehensive.

Her lifelong habit of worrying had its roots in an unhappy and emotionally unstable home. Her father, affable and urbane when away from home, ruled his household with "an iron rod," "standing for no nonsense," and meting out drastic punishments for minor offenses. His wife and his children feared him; and Mrs. H.'s earliest memories were of being sent supperless to bed, being forced to stand in the corner, being prohibited from going out to play with the other children, etc. Fear of her father irradiated to color all her relationships; she had always been afraid that she could not adequately meet the requirements of any situation. She was never directed but always disciplined; and most of the time had no idea "what it was all about." She early developed the habit of worrying about not only what was but what might be.

Before Mrs. H. could learn to stop worrying about their finances, she had to learn to stop worrying about everything else; she had completely to reorient herself and her attitudes. She had to learn to meet life and not to shrink or run away from it; she had to learn how to meet her actual problems (by reasoning out and following the best plan) and how to change her overemotional and fearful general attitude so as not to hinder her reason, and so as not to create unnecessary problems.

This change was accomplished by: (1) detailed discussion of specific incidents in her childhood and adult life which were instrumental in producing her basic patterns or instability; (2) specific and detailed (general discussions tend to be valueless) discussion of immature and mature methods of reacting to these situations; (3) inculcation of the methods of reasoning instead of worrying about new problems, again with very specific illustrations from daily life on which to practice; and (4) continuous practice of these principles, despite numerous initial failures. Practice of these principles in the "small" things is most important; for the attitude becomes habitual and operates automatically when the "big" things come. It required almost six months to effect this change; but her friends remarked frequently how different she was, and how much more calm she seemed. The success was in large part dependent upon the desire of the patient to coöperate and her willingness to persist in her efforts.

We hope that it has become increasingly clear that stress, a generic word to cover such specific words as "problems," "irritations," "troubles," etc., is of three kinds. First, there are those actual situations which should and can be changed; they call for the best "reason" of which we are capable. We must face all the available facts, choose what seems a possible and the "best" solution, and then implement our reasoned decision with action designed to bring about the change. Secondly, there are disturbing situations which we are temporarily or permanently unable to change. Here again we must face the facts and accept their implications; but our acceptance must be both intellectually honest and emotionally objective and stable as well. Finally, there are those problems which have their origin not in conditions external to ourselves, but in our own attitudes. Only when we have trained or retrained ourselves to meet life calmly, with the appropriate degree of emotion which the specific situation calls for, without undue expectations on the one hand or unwarranted foreboding on the other, only when we have trained ourselves to "see life steadily and see it whole" can we be healthy, happy, and mature adults.

CHAPTER XVI

SELF-RELIANCE AND COURAGE

Ridding ourselves of immature, self-defeating, and symptom-producing attitudes is significant and possible only when we substitute and cultivate their opposites. The story of the man who swept out one devil, left the space bare, and to his dismay found that seven devils came to take up occupancy is applicable. Two major evidences of maturity are self-reliance and courage. Both express objectivity and emotional stability; both are practical and cultivated techniques for meeting minor problems and major crises; both eventuate in personal self-realization and the promotion of Society's well-being.

Directly and by implication we have stressed that extremes are liable to be equally harmful. To have an overweening sense of one's importance is as immature (probably not so painful) as to grovel before life in a perpetually abject sense of inferiority. There is little choice between callous indifference and mawkish sentimentality; the rigidly unyielding and the weakly vacillating alike invite disaster. The minute any quality becomes excessive it begins to lose its constructive value; for balance and proportion are essential alike to art and life. Your unselfishness ceases to be good when it makes your husband a tyrant and your children self-seeking ingrates; your broadmindedness and tolerance are no longer virtues when they rob you of your ability and willingness "to take a stand" when you should; your sensitivity to the suffering of others becomes a liability if it makes you victim of the "spectator fallacy," wherein you eternally put your self into another's place and identify yourself with all his imagined pain—most of which he did not experience. You know enough persons who are *too* good, *too* soft-hearted, *too* unselfish, *too* something or other for further elaboration to be necessary. The name of any virtue preceded by the qualifying word, "over" or "too," is well along the road to becoming a vice. There is one pair of opposites, however, where the danger lies almost wholly on one side; and these contrasting attitudes are summed up in the words "emotional dependence" and "self-reliance."

EMOTIONAL DEPENDENCE VERSUS SELF-RELIANCE

Were it possible to be entirely independent, self-sufficient, and self-contained we would thereby lose the values that make life worth living: friendship, loyalty, kindness, gentleness, love. But it is not possible; in countless ways we are dependent on others, and they on us. There is, however, grave danger that we will seek support when we should stand alone, that we will expect to be carried when we should be walking. Every living thing is dependent on forces and factors external to itself; yet each has its own particular, separate, and distinct life. An uprooted tree will die when it can no longer draw nourishment from the earth; and it will fail to reach full growth, or its potential perfect symmetry if it is too crowded. The analogy holds true for man: the strongest baby bereft of human care cannot survive (Romulus and Remus to the contrary, notwithstanding); and no one can reach full stature if the protection so essential in childhood is prolonged to the extent of stunting independent growth. A mind that knew only what it had independently arrived at would be barren indeed; but it is also true that one who takes his cultural inheritance as an end instead of a beginning is at best being lazy and at worst being dwarfed. There are various kinds of emotional dependence.

Emotional dependence on parents.—It's a funny thing, being a parent; and it's a funny thing, being a child: an intimate, complex, and often bewildering relationship, charged with great potentialities for happiness or grief. Why do you love your child? One reason is that you took care of him when he was little, defenseless, wholly dependent on you. You made his world, and that is as it should be;

but if, as so often is true, you made him your world, you did both him and yourself a great wrong. The mature life has many channels of expression, many avenues of self-realization; and trying to crowd all the meanings of life into one relationship, no matter how beautiful, means leading, at best, a partial life. Moreover, it is grossly unfair to the child, who has a right to his own life. Have you heard mothers proudly say, "I have no life outside that of my children. They are my whole world." Pity the poor children! *A child should be dependent only so long as and only to the degree that such dependence is essential or beneficial.* Of course it would be easier and take less time to feed your two-year-old and dress your three-year-old; but even the most solicitous mother eventually permits her children to do such things for themselves. Naturally you'd like to save your children pain and the price of their own folly; but every child has a right to make his mistakes and abide by the consequences; for it is only so that he develops judgment. It stands to reason that the time will come when your child must stand on his own feet, make his own decisions, solve his own problems; and if you can remember that emotional and intellectual maturity are habitual attitudes, built up slowly and as the result of experience, if you can remember that self-reliance and good judgment are not sudden acquisitions to which a person falls heir when he reaches chronological maturity or when circumstance removes the parent's sheltering protection, then perhaps you will loosen your strangle hold on your child and permit him to develop a personality and life of his own. Don't delude yourself with high-sounding phrases about "It's all for his good" or "It's only because I love him." Perhaps no other phrase is more hateful to children than the well-worn, "Mother knows best." Often she doesn't; and when she does, how did she come by her superior knowledge? The chances are ten to one that if her judgment is good she acquired it by experience. There are many things you will need to do for your child; there are countless others in which he will need your help, your advice, and guidance; but having given him birth, let him live, let him become free, self-reliant, a person in his own right. We use the word "become"; and its use is deliberate. Self-reliance is an accomplishment not an endowment; and your attitude toward your child can help or hinder him in his "becoming." May we make a few practical suggestions? They must be general; but you can make the specific application.

Avoid extremes.—If one were forced to choose between harshness or indifference and brooding, oversolicitous tenderness, the latter might be the lesser evil. But no such choice is obligatory. It is a forlorn child who comes home with a cut lip and blackened eye to be met by, "Don't bother me with your silly fights"; but perhaps even more to be pitied is the child whose mother at the first yelp of conflict sails out to "protect" her darling from the "hoodlums" who five minutes earlier were the children of her best friends. Don't expect your child unaided to cope with the conflicts he inevitably meets; but don't, on the other hand, fight his battles for him. You train your three-year-old not to cross the street alone but by the time he is seven, he has learned to watch traffic and scoot across safely. It would be absurd to expect a very small child to negotiate the traffic of a crowded thoroughfare; and, equally absurd to carry "Junior" to school for fear if he walked alone he might be hurt. Isn't there comparable absurdity in many of our expectations from, and demands upon, children, on the one hand, and in our "babying" of them and curtailing of their freedom, on the other? Harshness and oversolicitude have much the same end result so far as the child is concerned: a sense of insecurity, a feeling that everything he does is wrong, or that he need not nor cannot do anything on his own initiative. The ritual of kissing your child good-by and of waving to him from the window may, like every other symbol, be either full of meaning or an empty farce. How you treat him, not what you say, is important. And how should you treat him?

Respect your child.—It's odd how many parents assume that their children should respect them; yet are surprised when asked how much they respect their children. Respect for personality is at the very basis of our democratic ideal; and if we wish the ideal to be more than an empty phrase, there is no better place to start actualizing it than in our family relationships—women and children included! You probably respect your child's property (with the notable exception of Christmas morning fathers who insist on "seeing first how the train runs"); but how much do you respect their wishes, problems, ambitions, ideas? Are you too busy, tired, or preoccupied with "important" problems to listen? Will you "hear them out," or do you settle all differing opinions with a "You'll do as I say, and no more nonsense about it"? When your ten-year-old wishes a bicycle more than anything else in the world and is willing to work or save his allowance until he has enough money, what determines your decision: respect for his desire, or your fear that "something may happen"? Do you let him try his own way or do you force him to follow what you "know is best"? Do you listen to the sentence beginning, "I think—" or do you cut it off with, "What you think is unimportant"? Do you say, "Ten years from now, you'll know better"? It is to be hoped that ten years from now your child will have better judgment; but the best way to assure that increase in wisdom is to *let him learn,* and he can only by experimentation.

Don't make issues out of trifles.—In a few realms the good of your child is so definitely involved that you must be firm despite his reluctance or opposition; but such situations are relatively scarce. Moreover, you will get much better coöperation from your child on these few "musts" if you have not thwarted and frustrated him, superimposed your whims over his caprices, and by force of your greater strength bent his will to yours.

Wherever possible *let your child make his own decisions and abide by the consequences.* It is often so easy for a parent to play the rôle of *deus ex machina,* solving his child's problems or straightening out his difficulties that the temptation to "act like god" overwhelms judgment. Of course, you must have both imagination and tenderness in dealing with children (and with all other human beings). If, despite warnings that the toy won't work if taken apart, Junior insists on doing so, what will you do? Say with Olympian superiority "I told you so. Now you can just do without"? Rush out to get a new toy to take the place of the wrecked one? One reaction is unduly harsh; the other, renders the experience so far as the child is concerned meaningless. Help him fix it if it can be repaired; if not, help him interest himself in something else. A few experiences and he will learn—both the breakability of toys and that sometimes it is well to heed advice. If you can send your son to camp for a month or give him a year's membership in a local gymnasium, let him decide which he'd prefer; but don't try to do both. Of course you'd like to do everything possible for your child, and give him everything he wishes; but he must live in a world in which there are many disappointments, many frustrations, many times when he will have to decide and abide by his decisions; and you are doing him no kindness by overindulgence, overprotection. Help him get ready to live in the world as it is.

Above all, *don't expect to be the center of your child's universe.* There is something very appealing about a three-year-old leaning against his mother's knee and looking up into her face with an expression of complete trust and love; there is something very distressing about a thirteen-year-old who prefers to trail his mother rather than be outside playing with his "gang"; and there is something definitely abnormal about a twenty-three-year-old "mama's boy" who won't get married, or if he does feels guilty about leaving his mother alone. If your grown or half-grown child would rather be with you than with anyone else, always tells you everything, and never makes a decision without consulting you, then he is neither grown nor half-grown. If such statements are true expressions, you have robbed him of his right to independence and made him a parasite. More often what is true—so strong is the natural desire for freedom—is that despite his words he is torn between the pull of his desire to live his own life and the tentacle yankings of your octopus devotion. In either event he will be unhappy; and you have defeated your purpose of protecting him, saving him pain. Many such "devoted" parents, if they could and would be entirely honest, would admit that much of their centering of their lives in those of their children is little more than a substitute for their own unsatisfying emotional life, an outlet for their own frustrations. The child is the victim.

Cultivate interests and meaningful relationships outside your family.—This admonition is equally valid whether your interest is primarily self- or family-centered. The richer and more varied your life, the more interesting you will be to others and the happier you yourself will be. Cultivate congenial friends; pursue your own hobbies; cultivate latent abilities and potentialities; be a person, and permit your children the same privilege.

The avenues of pleasure and satisfaction are as multiple and varied as the sources of danger; and if half the amount of imagination we habitually consume worrying about possible troubles were used for seeking out pleasures our lives would be much happier, much more rewarding. We have learned the value of balanced diets for the health of our bodies; and we need to realize that the same principle holds true in other aspects of our lives. You may like steak better than any other food; but you don't, if you're sensible, eat it morning, noon, and night; you may prefer your parents or children to any other persons, but you don't, if you're sensible, devote yourself exclusively to them. Each person is like one scrap of a jig-saw puzzle: he needs many other little pieces to complement and give meaning to his own particular life. The more avenues of expression, the more meaningful relationships one has, the more nearly can he realize his own potentialities. We emphasize this point because so often persons labor under the false assumption that division of interest or affection necessarily means subtraction. You will not be less interested in your children nor will your affection be diminished because you have other interests, other emotionally rewarding associations; nor will they care less for you because they are free and independent, having many friends, many interests exclusive of you.

Our words imply that emotional dependence on parents is always rooted in parents' oversolicitude, their excessive "love"; and perhaps in most instances such is the case. Not always, however. Many chronologically adult persons are emotionally dependent as the result of unduly harsh upbringing, tyranical discipline. Our insistence is that if a person is to become self-reliant, he must be allowed to make his own decisions, accept responsibility, and develop the feeling of self-confidence that he can and must meet and solve his own problems. Whether a child is tied by the "silver cord" of possessive "love" or the iron chain of domineering crueity he will be crippled and rendered incapable of standing on his own feet and making his own way in the world.

Mrs. B. J., aged 34, complained of nausea, excessive fatigue, insomnia, irritability, and a lack of interest in her home, husband, child, and everyone else. These feelings, present for many years, varied in intensity, but never entirely left her. Repeated examinations revealed no pathology, and her symptoms were always labeled "neurotic." The label did not mitigate her unhappiness nor relieve her symptoms.

From childhood, Mrs. J. had been unhappy. Materially she was more fortunate than most children; but she had no freedom. Her companions were chosen, her clothes bought; even the musical instrument she was to study was decided by her father. Her life was well organized—too well. Her hours of practice, study, and recreation were fixed in accordance with what her parents "knew would be best for her." She was taken to concerts by the "best" musicians; the "best" writers were made available, and her friends were chosen from the "best families"—best socially and financially. Though sent to the "best schools" Mrs. J. was never a student, preferring daydreaming to studying, since only in phantasy could she be carefree and gay.

When Mrs. J. reached what her parents considered the marriageable age they brought home the young man who would "be just right." He was "well-connected," ambitious, and a financial success. He was handsome and attentive; her parents were enthusiastic about him and her friends envious. Though her feelings were not what she "expected being in love to be like" and though many of his ways and mannerisms irritated her, so accustomed was she to following the dictates or opinions of others that she accepted the consensus that he was "the man for her" and married him.

After marriage, having nothing to do, she soon became very bored. Her mother chose the house furnishings and employed the servants. Mrs. J. had no interests, no responsibilities. Her girlhood had been strictly regimented and ordered; now she was utterly aimless. Her husband worked ha d, often in the evenings; and when he did not, was too tired to go out. Her friends envied her because her husband "gave her everything she wished." Though Mrs. J. "had everything," her days were lonely, empty, meaningless; and her evenings with her husband soon changed from periods of boredom to active irritation. Her parents, friends, and husband thought she was "just spoiled" and should "have some responsibility" some interest to "take her out of herself." She should have a baby.

Her pregnancy was the happiest time of her life. She loved all the preparations and made countless plans. After the baby was born, however, Mrs. J. was overwhelmed by her sense of inadequacy. She "didn't know enough to bring up a baby"; was terrified whenever the baby cried; was afraid that the food formula was not right, that he did not sleep enough, that he was dressed too warmly or not warmly enough, etc. She would not make the simplest decision without consulting her mother. Far from solving her problem, the baby intensified Mrs. J.'s feeling of inadequacy and helplessness. She became acutely depressed—to the point of contemplating suicide, and developed tension symptoms of insomnia and gastrointestinal disturbances.

Essentially, she had always been so dependent upon her parents that she had developed a general pattern of inadequacy and helplessness. Her life had been lived for her, her decisions made, her responsibilities met; consequently, she was unable to make the adjustments every adult must manage: she did not know how to find, make, or keep friends; she had no conception of, much less technique for, the coöperative rôle a wife must play; she could not "run" her household; she was bewildered by the responsibilities of motherhood; though chronologically adult she was emotionally still a child, as un-self-reliant as an infant.

Before her nausea, headaches, and insomnia could be cured and the fog of her melancholy lifted, it was necessary to change her whole general reaction pattern of emotional dependence. Such a change can be achieved only by: (1) analyzing and undertsanding underlying causes; (2) accepting intellectually and emotionally the new attitude to be developed; and (3), most important of all, putting the new attitude into effect by specifically practicing it daily, hourly, in definite concrete situations. Hard as it is to learn self-reliance even with intelligent help from parents it is even more difficult to break down habits of emotional dependence and substitute ability to face and solve one's problems. But it can be done; and with much guidance and moral support, Mrs. J. eventually learned not to send out an S.O.S. to her mother at every real or imagined crisis; she learned to decide for herself, to profit from her mistakes, to manage her own life with at least a modicum of maturity.

Emotional dependence may be *upon a person other than one's parent.* An entirely normal manifestation of this attitude is found in the "crushes" or the "hero worship" so charasteristic of adolescence. The "normalcy" of such an attitude is determined in large part by its intensity and its perpetuity. Sometimes the attachment is wholly one-sided, and the stronger or more dominant personality simply exploits the other. Whether the "dependee" is fine or base, selfish or generous, the relationship is still a dwarfing and stunting one for the person who resigns his own wishes, looks to another for his decisions, lets someone else "live his life for him." One can learn from his own mistakes, and there is possibility of growth when one meets—even unsuccessfully—his own problems; but flabbiness of will and initiative inevitably result from dependence, no matter how superior the other person may be. Many factors may play a rôle, but generally it is true that one who devotes himself in complete self-abnegation to another is a person who previously had little self-reliance. In other words, a person who is in the habit of making his own decisions, meeting and solving his own problems, rarely suddenly turns over his life to another: a tree whether it be a giant of the forest or a sturdy little scrub oak does not become a clinging vine.

Impersonal emotional dependence.—The most obvious form of emotional dependence is that which involves a close personal relationship. Less patent and therefore harder to recognize or cure is the dependence in which one looks to some impersonal source, some organization or institution for the solution of his problems and to relieve him of the responsibilities of making his own decisions and assuming his own responsibilities. There is no simple explanation of this pattern of behavior, whether manifested by a single person or by groups. Part of it lies in desire for security; part of it, in training. It may be that the parent, church, state, or any other source of dictation and direction "knows best"; it may be that blind subservience, unquestioning obedience, would result in more *immediate* comfort for all involved; but it is tremendously important to remember two things. First, *the human quest is for happiness, a positive and a vital attitude, not for comfort, which is at best a negative state, meaning little other than the absence of immediate disturbance.* Secondly, *the very nature of our civilization* with its demand for delayed satisfactions and with its establishment of "long term" goals *carries with it the implication that not only the person but society itself profits most when efforts are directed toward the achievement of significant values* rather than toward the pursuance of immediate whims. Only by mature men—men whose intellectual maturity makes them capable of visioning such values and whose emotional maturity enables them to accept the responsibility of actualizing their visions—can true personal happiness be found; only by mature men can a "good world' be wrought.

Let us be more specific. The quality of affection and appreciation which a child who is encouraged and helped to become a person in his own right can give his parents is more significant, more heartwarming than the sickly dependence of a chronologically adult child, terrified of the dark—whatever the dark may be—whining his little disappointments, never knowing his own mind, for the best of all reasons that he has never been permitted to have a mind of his own. In the same way, any organization—church, state, or any other institution—gains incalculably more from intelligent, loyal sharing of ideals and willing coöperation than it can hope to have from the timorous acceptance or hysterical devotion which too often characterizes adherents who blindly "resign" their thinking and "bow their wills" to a force whose dictates they accept without question. Granted they have the same equipment, an army force that knows what it is fighting for, and is doing its own will is more effective than can be the most rigidly disciplined "forced" corps. Such a statement is not a glorification of selfish individualism, nor does it imply that a particular judgment is necessarily superior to the one superimposed: it is merely the assertion of a "fact" that countless times has been demonstrated; namely, that coöperative endeavor tends to result in much more efficient activity, much more permanent good, than can slave labor—whether the slavery be physical, mental, or emotional.

Everyone on occasion is so overwhelmed by what he must face or endure that he would gladly turn his problems over to someone else. Sometimes we need to do just that. If you are desperately ill you put yourself into the hands of competent physicians and nurses; they make your decisions; they take care of you; but when you are well again you resume your responsibilities. Likewise, if you are involved in bewildering business dealings you rely upon the judgment of a trained lawyer; but after you have had that temporary and necessary help you do not assume the attitude, "Someone else will have to run my business for me." Similarly, a person may have temporarily to depend on his community to take care of him; but he does not expect to escape indefinitely his moral obligation to be as intelligent and self-reliant as possible. The point we are endeavoring to establish is twofold: (1) the limitations of our own personalities and the organization of our society make absolute self-reliance impossible; and (2) protection is valuable only when necessary and only to the degree that it aids growth or the establishment of self-reliance. Don't let your parents choose your clothes, your friends, your amusements, your profession; don't let your church, your state, or any other organization choose your ideals, your goals. Don't, because you and your father love each other and because he sat up with you every night when you were seven and had diphtheria, expect him to continue "sitting up with you" every time you meet a major or a minor crisis. Don't let him, even if he wishes to. Don't, because you love your country, and because it at least promises security in time of trouble—as happened in Germany in the twenties and thirties—let the country tell you what to think, what to read, what to see, whom to hate. *Don't expect and don't accept a totalitarian family or state,* no matter how pleasant the present rewards, no matter how fair the future promises. The family, the state, and you will be healthier and happier to the degree that you exchange parasitic dependence for mature self-reliance.

Self-reliance is a general attitude toward life, toward one's responsibilities and one's obligation and ability to meet those responsibilities. It is both a feeling tone and a pattern of acting. The self-reliant person meets and to his best ability solves his own problems—because he can and because he should. Stated in reverse: the man who solves his own problems, reaches and carries out his own decisions thereby develops a feeling of self-reliance. Action and feeling tones are simply different aspects of the same behavior pattern, each being both cause and effect. Moreover, self-reliance is an habitual and cultivated attitude, the outgrowth of repeated experiences of assuming responsibilities, of building a sense of self-confidence, paying the price for poor judgment or ill-advised actions and reaping the rewards of good judgment and actions. Self-reliance is not primarily an intellectual concept; it is not sufficient that you *think* every person, including yourself, should assume responsibility, arrive at independent conclusions, have the courage of his convictions, and put those convictions into operation: to *feel* self-reliant you must be self-reliant.

Do you "go to pieces" in times of crisis? Do you expect someone else to do your disagreeable tasks? When you are in a "jam," do you look to someone else for deliverance? Do you wish another to make your decisions (crediting yourself if everything turns out well, and having an excuse if not)? Do you think the world owes you a living, or anything else? (For what service?) Do you "run home to Mama" every time life becomes complicated? Does Papa have to solve your financial problems, as he once helped you with your arithmetic? Do you assume your children will support you, when you are entirely capable of caring for yourself? Do you have the courage to express convictions that are not "in line with" those of your group? To what degree can you "keep your head" and remain objective in the midst of mob hysteria? How much do you *do* about sharing your social obligations? Do you dismiss problems of corrupt civic government as being of someone else's making and therefore no concern of yours? What do you do to alleviate poverty, bring about better health conditions, secure justice for others, soften hatreds and prejudices, alleviate suffering, etc.? By your answers to such questions you can estimate the degree of your self-reliance.

It is a rather sardonic commentary on human nature that usually the person most convinced that the world owes him a living is one who has done least by way of self-support—in every sense of the word. Such an attitude is an inculcated one, stemming from overprotection, inexperience in "making one's own way," and failure to learn that responsibilities are in direct proportion to one's capacities and opportunities.

Coddling does not necessarily take place only where there is wealth. It is amazing how effectively the job may be accomplished on meager resources! The shirked responsibilities may differ and the expectations vary; but whenever a person looks to another for support (material or emotional) and whenever he refuses to grow up and assume responsibility for his own life, he may properly be labeled "dependent," lacking in self-reliance.

R. M., aged 21, was an only child. Since the age of three Robert had been supported by his mother, who was resolved he should be dressed as well as anyone's child, have as much spending money, in no way be made to "feel inferior." Far from training him to share responsibility, she refused to let him work, determined that he should have a carefree childhood. Of course he grew to be thoroughly selfish. He allowed her to send him through high school and business school. He secured a good position; lived at home; and assumed that his mother would continue to pay all household bills and "wait on him hand and foot." When she mildly suggested that he meet some of his own expenses, he accused her of being selfish and of wishing to rob him of all the good times that he had waited so many years to have.

Self-reliance is not a single attribute but the end expression of many attitudes: objectivity, emotional stability, willingness and training to face facts and bear responsibility, self-discipline, faith in the validity of one's own judgment, practice in making decisions and abiding by the consequences, training in depending on one's own resources, abilities, and initiative. Implicit in all that has been said is the realization that *self-reliance is primarily a pattern of action*. We have deliberately reiterated that in the well-integrated person, the happy, healthy, efficient, and mature person, there is synchronization of thought, action, and feeling. We have shown how misplaced or disproportionate feeling can cripple and hinder action, how action undirected by intelligence can be self-defeating, and how intelligence which refuses the high call to action is useless. If self-reliance is to be an actualized rather than a merely verbalized ideal it must be motivated and directed by intelligence, accompanied by the appropriate feeling of self-confidence, and expressed in action. Action calls for at least two further factors: *courage and energy*. So important is the element of "energy" that the next chapter will be given over to its discussion; and here we should like to be a little more specific as to just what we mean by "courage."

COURAGE

Courage is ability to meet dangers and difficulties with firmness and with fortitude. The word "courage," comes from the Latin "cor," meaning heart; and it takes a stout heart indeed to live in this dangerous world without quailing, running away, or giving up the battle. Courage, as we conceive it, is not an "extra" quality, a gift of the gods to the favored few, a shining weapon to be used on rare occasions. Instead it is an everyday necessity, an acquired attitude, within reach of all, the best armor in which man may array himself for the conflict. That there will be conflict there is no doubt, what with all the natural dangers of our environing life plus all the dangers and difficulties of our own creation. There are different kinds and degrees of courage, but they all require Man to meet his dangers squarely and make every effort to overcome them, lest they overwhelm him.

We are inclined to label as courageous occasional deeds of conspicuous bravery, and to forget the unsung heroes, the unmarked battle-fields. The suicide bomber diving to certain death, the fireman risking his life to save that of a child trapped in a blazing house, the captain going down with his ship, the man flinging himself into the river to save a drowning stranger: these are the ones we instantly recognize as heroes and to them we give our medals. But what of the man who, having lost his job, trudges from one possibility to another, refusing to be *dis*couraged by repeated failure? What of a physically deformed man, shrinking alike from pity and aversion, who forces himself into the world when he would much rather retreat from it? What of the mousey little clerk working overtime at a deadly dull routine job to make extra money to insure his son's education? And what of the son, who despite the fact that he is socially and financially underprivileged, has resolved upon a certain career and bends all efforts toward that goal? What of the man who voices the deep convictions of his heart, when he knows that such utterance will bring down upon him avalanches of disapproval and hatred? Courage is an everyday matter and manner, an attitude which says in effect, "Yes, I realize the danger or the difficulties; I see all the possibilities and appreciate all the implications. But it is a situation which can be handled, and to the best of my ability I will manage it." Such quiet determination, such unyielding persistence, calls for even greater endurance than does sporadic and spectacular action, no matter how "heroic" that action may be or appear.

Courage does not mean absence of fear. The old saying, "fools rush in where angels fear to tread" applies. The more clearly you apprehend all the risks involved, the greater your courage. There is nothing "heroic" about a ten-year-old's scrambling about the ruins of a demolished building; he does not even know that danger is involved; he is merely being adventurous. The man who *knows* the dangers of crumbling masonry, is fearful of "live wires" but yet will investigate because the situation needs his attention is being courageous. The extrovert, self-assured high school youngster does not have to summon courage, before he can get up to talk before a group of students; but it takes real courage for the timid, self-conscious student to register for a course in public speaking in order to overcome his shyness. In other words, courage is not an absolute, abstract virtue; it is a relative and specific quality, an essential element in the technique of effective living.

To know the varieties of courage, any or all of which *you* may be called on to have, we need only review civilization and list the inherent dangers and difficulties: physical, psychological, and social.

Physical courage.—For a long, long while the primary dangers (and satisfactions) were almost wholly those of a physical nature: the destructive forces of nature—storms, freezing cold, scorching heat, earthquakes, lightning, bloodthirsty animals, and stronger men. Consequently, courage expressed itself largely in acts of physical daring which required physical strength, we have noted how the human body is organized and geared to respond physically to physical attack, how it automatically gets ready for defense or assault. We still automatically strike out against whatever hurts or threatens; we automatically clench whatever someone would wrest from us. Whether a particular act involves courage will be determined by two factors: the amount of actual danger involved and the "feeling" present in the "actor." For animals and in many human situations these two elements are identical. For example, it does not take courage for a lion to rip a rabbit to tatters—the rabbit is neither an actual nor a potential danger. For a lion to fight for his life against the quicker movements, the sharper claws, the more cunning ways of a Bengal tiger would seem to necessitate more courage. In like manner, there is nothing courageous about the "bully" who always "picks on" someone smaller and weaker than he is. On the other hand we unconsciously "take sides" with the smaller, the less fit fighter who, apparently oblivious to the fact that he is outmatched, keeps slugging away as best he can. There are two or three things to be remembered if we are not to be misled in our judgment. For one thing, what often appears courage may be mere foolhardiness or the inability accurately to size up a situation, or it may be an expression of the desperation of the moment, wherein the person strikes out blindly in an effort at self-preservation. Courage is neither desperation nor "taking wild chances"; it is deliberate facing of dangers with the will and the effort to overcome them. Secondly, we need to guard against over-evaluating physical prowess and bravery to the exclusion of other types. Actually, other kinds are equally if not more important at our present state of civilization.

The fact that a man is a physical weakling, incapable of performing acts which demand physical courage, does not stigmatize him as a coward; and vice versa. Finally, we must realize that the "feeling" about the particular "danger" is a determining factor to be considered in estimating the courage of any act. What may seem most hazardous to one may to another be child's play, a mere matter of course. Are you afraid of high places, and do you consequently marvel at the "courage" of a window-washer scrambling around on the window ledge of the forty-third story of a building? Does your claustrophobia lead you to amazed admiration of submarine crews? On the other hand, are you, as a master electrician or an expert mountain climber, amused and a trifle embarrassed to have persons ask or exclaim, "Aren't you scared to death to fool around with those dangerous wires?" or "How you have the courage to climb sheer precipices is beyond me!" The world still has many physical dangers and there is still urgent need for physical courage; but there are multitudes of other more subtle dangers, more intangible difficulties which call for a different, and perhaps a "higher" kind of courage.

Super physical courage.—Having gained at least a partial technique of control over the physical world and its attendant dangers, we have enlarged the scope of our desires, and consequently of our fears, to include many elements which offered no problem to primitive man. Our memories, anticipations, and forebodings enable us to live in the past and the future as well as the present; so that we react to past experiences and future possibilities as well as to immediate exigencies. We must have courage to see in perspective, to forget old mistakes, old wrongs, old injustices; to face squarely the multitudinous sources of danger and difficulty we daily encounter; not to be overwhelmed by our fears of what the future may hold, and at the same time to face actual possibilities.

Most of our satisfactions must be arrived at indirectly and most of our dangers must be warded off or escaped in the same fashion. Our bodies being organized as they are, it would be much easier on them and consequently on our total organism if we were able to *do* something in every situation which arouses fear; for thereby our mobilized energy would be released. We must still "do something"; but the action is for the most part nonphysical. Primitive man confronted by a wild beast began to wield his club and pit his physical strength against that of his assailant. Modern man confronted by loss of his job, must reason out the best possible solution, and then work toward achieving it. Primitive man's encounter was soon over, with one participant the undisputed victor; the second situation calls for sustained courage and unflagging effort. There are delays, disappointments, unexpected and complicating factors; and the battle is never finished. While you are working through one problem, others constantly appear so that your courage must be constantly available. We have talked enough about the infinitude of fears to which man is heir to make repetition unnecessary; moreover, if you will review your own life, you will see that even on the relatively uneventful days there are situations which demand your best wisdom, ingenuity, and courage. It took courage for the pioneer woman to stay alone in her rude shack of a home, to care for her children, to be constantly on the watch for Indians, to keep up her spirits when her husband did not return at the expected hour. It takes courage—different in kind but not in degree—for her great-great-granddaughter uncomplainingly to stretch an inadequate income, to offer encouragement to her husband when he is "down," to provide a sense of social security for her children, etc. It takes courage to operate—to pit one's skill and training against all the dire possibilities; it takes courage—maybe even more courage—to be neither patient nor surgeon but the anxious one who awaits the outcome of the operation. But it is not only in dramatic moments that courage is essential. For most of us there are relatively few events of cataclysmic import; our days are an endless round of little duties, unimportant tasks, small problems, minor irritations, each calling for courage: the ability to meet each situation objectively and without undue emotional stress and *to do whatever one's best judgment dictates should be done.*

Having the "courage of our convictions."—Granting all the limitations to which human beings are subject, and being fully aware of how partial is our knowledge, we still assert that most of our problems—both personal and social—could and would be solved if we had the courage of our convictions. We rarely do our best; we seldom meet the demands of our best knowledge. We assume that the problem is too big and our own powers too feeble.

We worship the great gods, expediency and opportunism; we "pass the buck," and "let things slide." As physical daring without appreciation of what is involved and without direction tends to be sheer bravado, so conviction of what is right and knowledge of what is true without the courage to put that knowledge into operation is a worthless mental gymnastic. Courage is active, not passive; courage demands not your intellectual assent but your active co-operation.

Moreover, courage is an habitual response; it is not an attitude to be saved for rare occasions. Don't fool yourself: you won't any more suddenly acquire moral courage than you will intellectual honesty. If by silence you give assent to gossip you know to be untrue, don't salve your conscience by trying to believe that if it were anything important, you'd certainly speak out. The chances are you wouldn't. Understand why others are craven-hearted, why they "play safe"—because they fear social disapproval, because it is easier to run with the herd than to stand alone. Understand, and don't judge too harshly; but don't condone your own cowardice.

Are you convinced "the labourer is worthy of his hire"? Then don't dream of some far-off Utopia wherein there will be no "wicked capitalists" to exploit the masses; have the courage of your convictions: pay decent wages to those who work for you. Are you convinced that our democratic way of life, imperfect though it be, offers more opportunity and happiness to larger numbers of persons than does any other scheme? Are you convinced enough to pay your taxes without too much grumbling? Enough to vote as intelligently as you can? Enough to take part in community enterprises? Have you sufficient courage to admit that many of your problems are of your own making, and the even greater courage required to make the necessary changes? You know your over-protection is robbing your children of their independence and self-reliance. Have you the courage to "let go" and permit them to grow up? Have you the courage to face your limitations—neither magnifying nor minimizing them—and to do whatever you can to eradicate or compensate for them? Sometimes one's courage is put to the test when he must accept an unpleasant situation which he is powerless to escape or modify; but don't ever confuse courageous acceptance with supine resignation.

No single action, divorced from its attendant circumstances, can properly be labeled "cowardly" or "courageous"; and no one can state specifically what situations will call for your courage. Sometimes situations call for the courage to change; other times you will need courage to "stand pat." There is the courage of silence and there is the courage of speech. It takes courage to blaze new trails and it takes courage to conserve old values. Your problems are highly individualized ones and your courage must be adapted to meet them. In general, however, one may say that the essential ingredients of courage are (1) willingness and ability to face facts and (2) willingness to carry through whatever plan your reason dictates.

The technique of courage.—Courage is not a theory; it is not an abstract ideal. It is a practical technique for everyday living, an attitude which is established and becomes habitual through usage. Once more let us reiterate that courage is not a feeling you "should" have to help you meet major emergencies but rather the consistently undaunted attitude which enables you to cope adequately with whatever exigencies arise. If you wish to know what aspects of your life call for more courage than you are in the habit of manifesting make a list of situations which arouse an inhibiting sense of fear. Note the qualifying word "inhibiting." Only a fool could be entirely fear-free in a world like this: a world in which one is forever encountering—if not in his own immediate experience, then in the lives of others—physical pain, mental torture, illness, accidents, poverty, injustice, stupidity, ignorance, selfishness, cruelty, defeat, frustrations, war, hunger, pestilence, and death. A healthy sense of fear; that is, an acute realization of just what elements in our own personalities and just what factors in the world outside offer actual or potential danger, is essential if we are to make ourselves and the world healthier and happier. But we said a fear which robs us of ability to act and which overwhelms our judgment, a fear which only adds one more danger. Courage requires that—fully aware of, and sensitive to, the implications of the situation, you *do* all in your power to evade, circumvent, mitigate, overcome, annihilate, or accept the danger. Which technique you must employ will be dictated by circumstances; but in every instance, the courageous act will be a reasoned-through and followed-through plan.

Many of our attitudes of courage we learn through imitation; and fortunate is the child of courageous parents, who with a maximum of reasoned efficiency and a minimum of emotional stress meet situations as they arise, and take it as a matter of course that they and their children will do whatever is necessary to be done. The child who learns to share his toys is learning through practice a kind of courage he will need throughout his life: a courage which realizes that the ways of selfishness lead to unhappiness. The child who learns not to whimper every time he hurts himself is establishing the habit of a courage one needs for living in a world where bumps are inevitable. The child who learns automatically to climb out of his warm bed and go to school when he'd much rather not is learning courage for the life most of us lead—a life in which the day's work must be done, irrespective of our personal wishes. The child who learns to forego today's ice cream cone for next month's circus is learning the kind of courage essential in a world of delayed satisfactions and long-time goals. The child who learns to plug away at his arithmetic, though he "hates the stuff" is laying the foundation for automatically doing instead of evading unpleasant tasks. The child who learns to "stand up for" the little new foreigner despite the fact that he looks different, talks different, and is the target of persecution and bullying by other children is learning the courage of tolerance, and of resisting mob prejudice. The child who learns to curb his "show off" tendencies for the good of the team is learning the courage necessary for coöperative endeavor, so essential to our social welfare. The child who learns to get up and turn on the light when he is sure that he "saw something moving in the corner," instead of shuddering under the covers or yelping for help is learning the courage to face his fears— which fortunately as often as not turn out to be "nothing."

You will perhaps have noticed our repetition of the word "learned." There is no royal road to courage; it is not an endowment nor a gift. It is a technique, a general orientation toward life; and, like every other skill, it is acquired and perfected through practice. You cannot by harsh discipline or by platitudinous preaching *make* your child courageous; but you can, by example and by teaching him self-reliance, greatly aid him in becoming so. Children as surely reflect the general attitudes expressed in their home as a parrot does the language. If you are habitually courageous, probably you are not particularly conscious of so being; and probably, also, your child will quite unconsciously imitate your pattern so that courage becomes part of his "second nature." Let us be a little more specific about that last sentence.

If you are an expert driver, you perform all necessary motions smoothly, automatically, and without conscious thought. You became expert through practice. The same statements can be made about any skill you have acquired—whether it be typing, swimming, selling life insurance, running a switchboard, or living courageously. If you are in the habit of meeting difficulties squarely, sizing them up for what they are worth, reasoning out the best possible solution, and then *doing* what your judgment tells you: you probably will meet today's problems and tomorrow's in much the same fashion, and you will do so without any conscious evoking of courage. If you have reasoned through and carried through, if you have learned to take troubles in your stride—not discounting or refusing to acknowledge them but at the same time not permitting them to "get you down," if you have developed your sense of self-reliance to the degree that you have confidence in the validity of your own judgments and a keen sense of your moral obligation to assume your personal and social responsibilities, then whether or not you are aware of it you have been living courage-ously and you have the technique for meeting today's dangers and difficulties. Has your child seen you go to pieces over some major irritation or an accumulation of minor ones? Has he seen you rush for the neighbors or the telephone every time something has gone wrong, or is he used to seeing you handle situations as they arise? What have you done about his mistakes—scolded or berated him? Dissolved into tears and lamentations over the "disgrace" he has brought upon you? Tried to hush it up? Or have you listened as calmly and objectively as possible to the whole story and tried to get at all the facts? Have you helped him see why and how he was wrong and then have you *en-couraged*—not forced—him to admit his mistake and do everything within his power to correct it? What about your mistakes with him? You have made plenty; even the most nearly ideal parent does. Have you had the courage to admit your fault, change your tactics, reverse your too hastily spoken decree? If some financial crisis has arisen, what kind of talk has he heard, what attitudes has he seen expressed? Emotional blaming of your associates, the government, or yourself; a frantic search for "ways out"; an atmosphere of hopeless defeatism? Or has he heard you in "family council" work out the problem, and then has he seen you resolutely pushing the new plan "for all it is worth," refusing to be stopped by attendant hardships or to "lose heart" because of partial failures? Do you admonish him not to be a "cry baby" when he hurts himself or suffers some childish disap-pointment; and then does he hear you vocalize for hours about how tired you are after a hard day at the office or a strenuous seige of house cleaning? What do you do about your own disappoint-ments? Has he witnessed you refrain from telling the truth and heard your weak excuse, "Why stir up an argument. After all it's not important." Or heard you rail about some injustice only to conclude with, "Of course in my position I cannot *afford* to say what I really think."

The questions just asked—a host of similar ones might well be added—have two purposes: to indicate what we mean by the every-day courage which is an essential for living life at its best; and to point out that it is your acts of courage, not your words, which impress your child.

A little while ago we used the analogy of the expert driver who has had so much experience that his excellent driving is almost a reflex matter. But there will come ice storms, washed-out bridges, slippery roads, tortuous mountain trails, traffic jams; and it will be necessary for him to focus his attention, call on all his resources, make an extra effort. The same holds true for the management of your life; crises demanding extra courage will arise; and there will be situations in which so much is involved that the temptation to evade doing what you are convinced is right will be extraor-dinarily great. If, however, your general orientation toward the everyday dangers and difficulties is one of courage you will have two major advantages when you must meet the big issues. You will have already well established the general plan of *how* to cope with the situation; and you will bring to the problem your best strength, undissipated by ineffectual and tension-producing living.

Remember, too, that courage is a relative and not an absolute term; it is an ideal to be approximated. Allow a margin for human frailty; don't expect the impossible of yourself or anyone else. With the best of intentions and with the best judgment of which you are capable, you will make mistakes. You will have the courage of your convictions—you will say or do what you think is "right"—and you will fail to bring about the desired result. Even though in the particular instance you fail, it is better for you as a person and for the society of which you are a member that you did carry through what your deepest conviction led you to believe you ought to do. You and society suffer far less from honest and courageous mistakes than we all do from the defeatism and inertia which keep men from making the effort. At best our progress toward personal and social goals is a stumbling, halting succession of steps;

but the steps must be taken. Action demands effort, and courage is the driving power behind the effort; courage is the will, the determination to reduce the number of dangers and difficulties and to increase the number of satisfactions for yourself and for mankind.

Don't think that even your most ardent and consistent practice of courageous living will reward you eventually with immunity from fear. When your child screams with the pain of a mastoid infection, terror will seize your heart; but your courage will keep you from collapsing and will enable you to carry out your physician's orders. You will have black moments when your plans fail; but your courage will drive you on to another plan—maybe a better plan, maybe only the "next best" plan; and your courage will keep you hoping "Till Hope creates from its own wreck the thing it contemplates." When you see or hear about chain gangs, "third degree" methods, concentration camps, you will be afraid of the cruel savagery which makes such conditions possible; but your courage will not let you turn aside; it will force you to do and say all that you can whenever and wherever you can to take truth from the scaffold and wrong from the throne. You will league yourself—your resources, limited or great, material and spiritual—with the agencies, the groups, the other courageous because fearful persons and do all you can to overcome the danger that lies behind the "might makes right" philosophy so rampant in the world today. You will be afraid when war sweeps the world: afraid of the waste, the pain, the suffering, afraid perhaps that the effort is futile; but your courage will drive you to decide what stand you must take and to follow through with whatever action your conviction dictates.

CHAPTER XVII

ENERGY EXPRESSION

Our "civilization," our "culture," call it what you will, is the resultant of many factors, most of which we share with other forms of life, but one of which seems to be pecularily our own. This distinctive characteristic is our capacity for directed and sustained energy expression. Our cortex enables us to delay responses in order to choose the most advantageous ones; but this directing capacity is of little or no value unless we have also the energy to carry out that choice. Since there are various sources and levels of energy and since some kinds offer man his staunchest ally while others work to his destruction, it becomes important for us to know: (1) how to mobilize what energy we need; (2) how to prevent creation of excess amounts; and (3) how to channel all that we have.

Many persons with an unusual degree of intelligence accomplish little; many do little with their wisdom, save verbalize it. Energy undirected by wisdom is at best wasteful and at worst destructive; but wisdom unsupplemented by the driving, constructive force of energy is impotent, lifeless. No matter how fine its engine a car will not run without gas; no matter how logical and "true" your intellectual solution of your problems, there will be no change or improvement until you implement your ideas with action. Our personal and social problems arise not so much from lack of "knowing" as from our unwillingness or inability to *do* that which we know. Our major problem, then, becomes a matter of developing the right kind of energy, reducing the generation of the wrong kind, and directing into socially constructive and personally satisfying outlets that which we have, or that which we mobilize.

KINDS OF ENERGY EXPRESSION

There are at least four levels of energy expression, all of which are present in every person but in widely varying degree and proportion.

Daydreaming.—Just outside the door of unconsciousness lies the least active form of energy expression: daydreaming. The mind during this state is sufficiently active to permit the appearance of a more or less steady succession of more or less amorphous and nebulous ideas, conjectures, and phantasies. Our wishes and fears shape and give color to this ghostly parade—what we'd do if we had his money or her beauty; how nice it would be to have a home of one's own with a garden and a fireplace; the day of triumph when one has accomplished "wonders" and one's friends have "to take back" their accusations of laziness; the dignified but crushing retort to one's boss; if only I had married that other man, or woman, how different things would be today: I'd . . . if I had my life to live over, I'd certainly . . . when I get the kind of job I really want, then I'll . . . and so on endlessly. We all daydream: regretting the past because it is past or because it was not different; skirting around our present wishes or fears but never coming to grips with them; dreading the dire possibilities or anticipating the joys of tomorrow, without planning either escape or actualization. Daydreaming may be and is valuable to the extent that it furnishes goals; but, unfortunately, it usually is little more than a substitute for intellectually and actively solving our problems—a wholly inadequate substitute.

Physical effort.—A higher level of energy expression than daydreaming is that manifested in physical effort. The accusation that man was "born lazy" has a large element of truth; insomuch as the basic physical law of inertia (all things tending to come to rest in the presence of friction), holds for animate as well as inanimate objects. The force of this principle has, in the case of man, however, been counterbalanced and outweighed by the urgency of his fundamental drives for hunger and sex satisfaction. He needed physical strength and energy to get food, to get his mate, to protect himself from physical dangers, and he survived by virtue of the fact that his organism was so constituted as to enable him to mobilize the requisite energy. Though his needs were relatively simple and uncomplicated, as compared with our pyramided wishes and fears, they were none the less demanding. The obstacles he had to overcome were almost wholly physical; consequently it was necessary for him to develop superior strength and to expend great physical energy in his effort to maintain a satisfying life. Obviously, in such a set-up, the greatest man would be the physically strongest man.

But the scene has shifted, the values enlarged and the fears multiplied, the technique of achievement and avoidance has radically changed; and what was once the highest form of energy expression—physical effort—is now low in the scale and relatively unimportant. For even the most sedentary person a minimum essential of physical energy is necessary—for the effort involved in eating, dressing, and getting to work, if for nothing more. Much of the world's work still calls for physical strength and endurance; and just as physical effort without direction is largely wasted energy, so plans for the city beautiful will never be actualized without physical effort on the part of countless men. But *physical effort is not enough*. The farmer, the steel worker, the man doing the heaviest work on the construction gang has problems which his superior physical strength alone will not enable him to solve; he has wishes which need more than physical energy to attain; he has fears which he cannot crush with the strength of his hands; and he is part of a society whose needs call for more than merely the expenditure of physical energy.

Problem-solving.—A much more complex and demanding level of energy expression than that required in physical effort is that used in mental work, and particularly in problem-solving. Obviously, some types of physical work require more sheer strength than do others—a hod carrier uses more strength than does a telegram delivery boy—and some call for a more complex muscular coördination than do others—a typist uses a more complex skill than does a man pushing a wheelbarrow. There are comparable gradations in the realm of mental work, some calling for far greater energy than do others. If a task is merely a routine application of knowledge, it can hardly be called mental work, except by grace of the absence of physical effort. More particularly we have in mind the kind of energy called for when one must solve a problem.

The more complex the problem, the more mental energy must be expended in its solution. In addition to the inherent difficulty of the problem there must always be taken into account the training of the thinker. It is not so much a matter of native intelligence, as of experience in the technique of thinking through to a conclusion. Just as physical strength is increased through exercise, and just as one's habitual physical energy output is proportionate to the demands of his work and his mode of life, so one's mental energy develops with practice; and the identical problem which seems a hopeless maze to one person will offer no especial trouble to another who is in the habit of putting forth as much problem-solving energy as the varying conditions of his life have demanded.

There are at least three steps in the problem-solving technique: defining the problem, considering all pertinent and available facts, and formulating the best solution.

Defining the problem to be solved.—The more definitely you can define your problem the more certain you are of working out a solution. Your problem is a financial one. What specific problem? Do you really have a problem, or are you just worrying on general principle about "what may happen—what with unfair competition, labor troubles, shortage of materials, the country going to the dogs, and this war and all"? Are you producing too much? Is your overhead too big? Are you overstaffed? Do you need to expand or to retrench? If your business affairs really are in an ailing condition, the first thing to do is to find out just what the trouble or troubles are. We are all prone to confuse every issue by bringing in associated problems, fears, and wishes so that we become bewildered by the resultant, apparently hopeless welter.

This failure to define problems clearly is even more characteristic of our social failures than of our personal mismanagement; for often, far from clearly defining the situation which needs change or amelioration, we even fail to recognize the existence of the problem. We know "things are not right"—that there is neither logical nor ethical reason back of the inequitable distribution of the world's goods; that too many persons are underprivileged both materially and spiritually; that justice too often miscarries; that hatreds, bigotry, and prejudices are vitiating; that too many persons have to work too hard and too many persons who wish to work have no opportunity to do so; that wars are wasteful and at best only temporarily decisive; etc. In other words, we "sense" that the problems exist; but we never clearly formulate them, and, more important still, never define specifically just what part of the problem is ours to tackle. This first step in the problem-solving technique—defining the problem—is not easy, so accustomed are our minds to dodging issues and zigzagging off on detours of wishes and fears; but it is one that is richly rewarding. It does at least three things. First, it automatically solves many problems, insomuch as many difficulties have no substance other than the shadowy stuff of our vague fears. Secondly, it conserves the energy which otherwise would be dissipated in worry and prevents creation of the tension which results from unreleased mobilized energy. Finally, it serves as a measuring rod, when we proceed in the second step; namely, the assembling and evaluating of pertinent facts.

Finding and evaluating available and pertinent facts.—The only point in defining your problem is that you be able to proceed to solution. A general planning a strategy for his army does not consume time and energy in vaguely wishing to "win the war"; he defines his problem: a certain city must be taken. He must plan *how* to take the city, and if his plan is to have any likelihood of working he must take into consideration all the related facts he can learn. He must know, for example, the topography of the land, the strength and weakness of his own troops, the amount of equipment available, the morale of his men, etc. These facts he can determine with a relatively high degree of certainty; but there are others which he must evaluate as closely as possible: the probable strength of the enemy; vulnerable points of the city; the attitudes of the resisting forces; etc. This kind of problem-solving is much more demanding than that which an engineer faces when he must with exactitude calculate stresses and figure out proportions. The engineer deals with objective facts and applies intricate but established knowledge; the general must also estimate and weigh intangibles, variables, and imponderables. The same kind of effort is demanded when you have such problems as choosing a career or deciding which school your child should attend. The more pertinent facts you consider the greater are your chances of coming to the "best" solution. The pitfalls in this stage are those we have pointed out earlier: facts themselves are relative, and we tend to interpret facts in terms of our wishes and fears. The more adequately one is able, however, to evaluate fairly all pertinent facts, the better position he will be in for the final stage: arriving at a conclusion.

Arriving at conclusions.—The final stage of the problem-solving technique, that is, arriving at a conclusion as to what is right, what one should do, what is the best way to meet the situation, is even more difficult than the first two. There may be *a* best way to skin a cat or solve a problem; but usually we need to formulate several ways, try them out in imagination, and then choose the one which seems most likely to work. We have great need for *realistic imagination,* the ability to foresee probable consequences. Such imagination is not to be confused with idle daydreaming, wish-thinking, or fearful foreboding. Understanding ourselves and human nature; remembering past experiences—failures and successes—in similar situations; taking into account the differing elements in a particular set-up, and evaluating their potentialities should give us realistic ground in which to root our imagined solutions. Mentally try out your "best" solution; and you will often find that the one that looked best on paper has ignored some important and success-prohibiting element. It may be an intrinsically unimportant element—like your employer's pet enthusiasm—but one which disregarded will defeat your plan. The "best" solution is always the "best possible solution"; for only when the mentally arrived at conclusion is carried over into action does it have any real value.

Initiative.—The most complex and least used form of energy is that involved in initiative, in carrying through to completion that which the mind has decided. Mentally working out the best solution of a problem certainly involves far more effort and energy than does idle daydreaming; but it is wasted effort, a profitless expenditure of priceless energy unless one has the further energy, or initiative, to put the solution into operation. Let us say again that most of our personal and social difficulties stem not from our inability to figure out solutions, but from lack of courage and initiative to try them out.

You are unhappy in your work. Though it is not difficult and wages are adequate, it is monotonous; it has no future and your boss, given to petty faultfinding, delights in holding the threat of dismissal over your head. You have always maintained that the one "sure fire" way to make money is to sell good food: "Why, if a man sold only three things—the best hamburgers, the best apple pie, and the best coffee in town—he'd have more business than he could handle." You've saved a little money; you could borrow on your life insurance; your wife is willing to help; there's a little store for rent on High Street. . . . Well, what are you going to *do*—stay chained to your distasteful job, go on being irritated by your boss until you are as jittery as he is? Will your solution become one more vague daydream or will you take the risk, muster the initiative to actualize your solution? Of course there's risk involved; there always is.

You are convinced—at least we hope you are after reading this book—that many of your physical symptoms and much of your unhappiness result from your habitual overreacting, your tendency to worry, your lack of objectivity and emotional stability; and you *know* that the answer lies in retraining your specific and your general responses. But it is not enough that you know cause and cure; you must take the initiative, you must follow out in action all the implications of what you know.

Youth generally has more initiative than does age. To carry out plans, to follow thought with action, to *do* something about getting out of distasteful situations or into desired ones: these are customary attitudes of youthful vitality. That many mistakes result is inevitable, since Youth, handicapped by lack of experience, is often incapable of the sound judgment which should precede action. On the other hand, the greater wisdom of Age, the more carefully thought out and hence better solutions are often not even tried out, because sufficient energy of initiative is not mustered to overcome personal inertia and social indifference or antagonism. Not until men of good will have enough *intellectual energy* to work out the best possible solution of their personal and social problems, and, not until such men have sufficient *energy of initiative* to put those solutions into actual operation shall we ever approximate the good life for ourselves and all the other children of earth.

If all our accomplishments from self-preservation to actualization of our loftiest social visions are dependent, in the last analysis, upon energy, it becomes apparent that the problem is a twofold one of: (1) mobilization of energy and (2) utilization of energy.

MOBILIZATION OF ENERGY

Energy cannot be created; but energy which is latent, whether in wind, waterfall, coal, or man, can be mobilized and used for constructive or destructive ends. Man's energy-problem is twofold: (1) to mobilize sufficient energy to accomplish established goals, and (2) to avoid the mobilization of excess energy which tends to express itself in detrimental fashion. The three major sources of energy are: inherent constitutional energy, routine, habitual energy, and energy resulting from frustrations.

Constitutional energy.—Fundamentally, all energy is dependent upon the inherent nature of the man, and whether a specific person does much or little depends in large part upon the constitution. That statement is not so clarifying or so simplifying as it may appear on first reading; for as yet science knows little about what makes constitutional differences and cannot explain why in a given family one child should be "naturally" lazy or mentally sluggish and another "naturally" energetic both physically and mentally. That such differences exist needs no demonstration; all the whys of their existence are as yet unknown. Moreover, what often appears as constitutional energy or lack of it is in reality a manifestation of the second source: work habits.

Energy from work habits.—Whether we accomplish much or little and whether that accomplishment is with a maximum or a minimum of exhaustion seems dependent not so much on our "constitutional energy" as upon our "work habits." There are three major categories of persons, with countless variations within each group and with no person consistently manifesting all the characteristics of his particular classification. There are the habitually lazy ones who expend and therefore have little energy. They do as little as possible, bestirring themselves only under the lash of necessity. Such laziness may be physical, mental, or both. In this category belong persons whose inertia is habitual: those whose mobilization and expenditure of physical and mental energy is adequate for their needs but who accomplish little because they are not habituated to carrying through to completion either the physical or the mental tasks which they start. The completely lazy person, of course, does not even "start." In the second classification are those persons whose efforts are sporadic, who work "by fits and starts." Stimulated by some new desire or some temporary awareness of "danger" they mobilize sufficient energy to initiate the work necessary for accomplishment; but it is only a spurt of energy—interest lags; some new interest supervenes; the task appears too big; and the person abandons the project to lapse into the laziness of exhaustion or to repeat the performance of starting but not consummating another task. That worthwhile results are sometimes obtained from such "false starts" cannot be denied; but it is important that you remember two things. One is that if the work thus flashily initiated has potentialities of significant accomplishment and if those potentialities are ever actualized it will be because someone else does all the routine and sustained work necessary to complete that which was started. The second thing to remember is that usually such sporadic efforts accomplish little and that, however great or little, the accomplishment is minimal in comparison with what it might have been.

In the third classification are those persons who have been trained or who have trained themselves for sustained, persistent effort, who steadily mobilize their energy for the steady pursuance of their task, whatever the task may be. These are the ones who really achieve, whether their success be modest or spectacular. The latent energy is there: it can remain dormant (the habitually lazy); it can be sporadically and temporarily evoked (those whose efforts are scattered, partial); or it can be mobilized into a steady stream of power and force. This steady, uninterrupted flow of energy is the result of work habit, the amount and the quality being dependent on what we habitually require and use.

Even on the lower level of energy expression—physical effort—it is the steady worker who is retained when other men are "laid off." How much physical energy do you have? The answer is in most instances identical with your reply to: "How much physical energy are you in the habit of using?" Miss B., in charge of the safety vaults in a small bank—a position requiring much stretching and bending, said, "At the end of my first week, I discovered I had a million muscles; and every one of them ached like an abscessed tooth. Now I'm not even conscious of my gymnastics." The latent energy was there; her job demanded that she mobilize and continually utilize it; and the result was that the supply became automatic—an effortless effort. Miss B.'s further comment, "Of course, I always get a few twinges the first day after I come back from vacation," is illuminating. The more steadily energy is mobilized and utilized the more automatic and unconscious is the process. The most efficient worker—whether the work be floor scrubbing, paper hanging, bricklaying, or furnace stoking—is the one who has been "on the job" long enough so that his body, having learned how much energy the task requires, automatically mobilizes the optimum amount.

The same principles hold for the higher levels of energy expression: those involved in mental problem-solving and those used to put plans into operation. *The more problems you have reasoned through and the more solutions you have implemented with action the more mental energy and the more energy of initiative you have.* The inherent difficulties in the problem-solving technique and the inertia-inducing elements in his own nature and the social structure will offer many hurdles for the "trained" thinker and for the person who habitually tries to put his convictions and his ideals into operation; but the more accustomed he is to thinking before he acts and acting after he has thought the more closely will he approximate the realization of his best plans. We cannot too strongly emphasize the importance of so constantly and persistently tackling our problems with reason, and so pertinaciously attempting to work out our solutions that we automatically mobilize the energy necessary for successful completion of tasks which require mental energy and the energy of initiative.

Inculcating good work habits.—As we have elsewhere noted and as you know from your own experience, learning a new skill or establishing a good habit is much easier if one does not first have to "un-learn" the wrong way or break down a bad habit. The rule applies to the establishment of effective work habits, of routinizing our energy mobilization so that we automatically meet and fulfill our tasks. If you are habitually lazy or if you are in the habit of alternating between spurts of activity and quiescence, if you are accustomed to "jumping to conclusions" on the basis of your wishes or fears (usually missing the mark) instead of reasoning out your best plan of procedure, if you are given to daydreaming instead of to acting, then you have a hard task ahead of you, its difficulty being proportionate to how consistent and how deeply ingrained your bad habits are. It takes days, weeks, or even months to accustom the body to mobilize sufficient physical energy so that certain physical work can be done automatically, with a maximum of efficiency and a minimum of strain. It takes a lifetime to approximate perfection in the problem-solving technique or in the techniques for actualizing our well-thought-out plans. Hard as the task will be, there is one even harder—and certainly less rewarding: to go on existing as you are, doing everything the hardest way (hardest because not routinized), overwhelmed by the problems which you inevitably encounter, accomplishing little for your personal gratification and contributing little to the society of which you are a part. So you'd better start mobilizing energy right now—you'll need it in your effort to establish effective work habits!

The procedure followed in teaching your child, or rather in helping him learn, the work habits which will guarantee that he will automatically mobilize the energy needed for the effective performance of his tasks is much the same you will have to employ in teaching yourself. Perhaps the following suggestions will be helpful.

Don't try to make life "easy" for your child.—Life is not easy for anyone. Maybe it ought to be; maybe some day it will be; but it never has been and it is not now. The sooner one learns he has work to do and problems to solve the sooner will he start mobilizing energy for doing his share. Paradoxically enough, you make life ultimately much easier by expecting and, if need be, insisting that he do his work, than if you do it for him. The steadier the stream of mobilized energy, the less exhausting the work; and the steady supply is furnished only by actual doing.

Teach your child the nature of work.—Work is effort directed toward accomplishment. It is accomplishment that gives significance to effort. If the "end" is something very much desired, the effort expended seems more fun than work; but there are many tasks which must be performed irrespective of whether they are immediately pleasurable. If you and he can "make a game of" his task—fine; but the important thing is that he learn to do whatever work has been assigned him or that he has undertaken. Scale what you expect to his capacity—neither to his lowest level of ability, nor to the utmost effort he can make. The ideal toward which you are moving is to be able smoothly, automatically, and almost effortlessly to mobilize the "right" amount of energy—hence the necessity for avoiding extremes of under- or over- mobilization. Teach him to be reasonable in his self-expectations. Much of our inertia and lack of initiative comes from discouragement over previous failures when we expected the impossible of ourselves. Be generous with praise: desire for approval is one of the strongest motivating forces in human life. If he has done a slipshod, careless piece of work, don't let him "get by with it"; but don't on the other hand, stand by in Olympian disapproval, proclaiming ultimatums. Show what is wrong; and if he needs help, help him. Be firm but not rigid in your assumption or insistence that your child do his routine tasks in routine fashion. One of Tommy's "tasks" is after supper to empty the garbage pail and feed the dog before he starts out to play. He's been doing it for six months now, rarely forgets, and rarely protests. Feeding the pup is fun, and emptying the garbage is not fun; but he does both tasks routinely and as a matter of course. As you are finishing dessert, the fire engines scream by and you see clouds of smoke pouring from a roof in the next block. Does the establishment of your child's good work habits demand that you sit back and say, "You may go just as soon as you have done your chores, washed your hands, and hung the towel up neatly." Not if you are still human; the chances are ten to one that you, he, and the dog will all be on your way to the fire to see what you can see; and the same chances hold that when the excitement is all over and you have come home, you'll say, "You'd better feed the dog, while I take care of the garbage for you."

Teach your child that a task undertaken must be carried to completion.—It is tremendously important if we are to accomplish much that we learn the discipline of finishing what we start. How many careers have you seen start brilliantly, but the brilliance was pyrotechnic, of short duration? How many things have you started to learn or do, and then stopped because you "lost interest," it was "too hard," or something else attracted you attention? Not the brilliant start but the finish of the race determines the winner; and it is safe to make the generalization that every profession entails much work which is neither thrilling nor exciting and that every significant accomplishment necessitates sustained effort in the face of discouragement. Don't clutter your child's life with so many toys that he literally doesn't know which one to play with; don't let him enter so many activities that he can't possibly do any one well; if he badgers you into letting him take a paper route, don't let him fall down on the job; if he starts building a rabbit hutch see to it that he finishes it before he begins on the dog kennel. By insisting that he carry through whatever he starts you will not be taking the joy out of life for him; on the contrary, you will be helping him develop one of the most sustaining sources of pleasure: joy in accomplishment.

Teach your child to take joy in work well done.—Avoid as much as possible bribing or bullying your child into doing his work. The world is not so organized as to give us a pat on the head or a slap on the hands according as we do well or poorly. Indeed, the reverse situation seems often to obtain. If we are to mobilize the energy necessary to work out and carry out solutions of our personal and social problems we need to have faith in the value of the accomplishment toward which we are expending our efforts, and we need to take satisfaction in realizing that our efforts are the best of which we are capable. The greater and more significant your contribution to Society, the less likelihood is there that you will receive plaudits and honors within your lifetime. The scientist, the inventor, the creative artist does not ask, nor is his continued effort contingent upon popular acclaim; his joy is in his work; and the demands made by his own desire for perfection are far more stringent than could be any superimposed from outside. Most of us do not belong in the category of the "great"; but no one of us is barred from experiencing the same quality of pride and joy in accomplishment.

Your child must learn, and you must learn, that for everyone some tasks are "naturally" hard and some "naturally" easy; but that one must expend the amount of energy necessary—whether much or little—for successful accomplishment. The fact that it takes him twice as long to get his arithmetic as it does "the other kids" is no excuse for failure to get it and no occasion for whining self-pity; it is simply a demand that he expend more energy. Help him if he needs your help; but take it for granted that he will do his work, and by your pride in his work communicate to him a sense of achievement, of work well done.

The whole point of this exhortation about the value of inculcating good work habits is simply this: there is much work which in the natural course of events you will *have* to do. There is much more which you as a citizen of the world *should* do; and since accomplishment is one of our major sources of pleasure there is much work which you will *wish* to do. To work one must have energy. Your reservoirs of energy await your use; they can be mobilized upon demand. Practically all goals—major and minor, personal and social—demand steady, persistent pursuance; and for such unremitting expenditure you will need an unbroken supply of energy. Work habits that make consistent demands on the reservoirs of your energy will guarantee an automatic mobilization. You may occasionally be so desirous of some satisfaction or so mortally afraid of some danger that you call forth a great burst of hitherto unused or even unsuspected energy to help you get or get away from; but you will be left exhausted, winded, spent—unless you have your automatically mobilized and normally adequate supply of energy to fall back on. The race still goes to the tortoise and not the hare.

Energy from frustrations.—Another powerful, though seemingly contradictory, source from which energy is mobilized is frustrations. It seems odd that energy should come from that which upsets, balks, or thwarts us; but such is the case. This mechanism will not be hard to understand if you recall what you know about the creation of tension. Tension is simply another term for mobilized but unreleased energy.

Our marvelously organized bodies function automatically to help us obtain satisfactions and escape or overcome dangers. But it is for direct, immediate, overt, and physical activity that our bodies get ready, that our bodies mobilize energy. For example, we are hungry and want food: the total organism wants it. When our body-mind is thus oriented, appropriate glands begin preparations for the intended activity: the mouth begins to water, the stomach to increase its number of contractions, the digestive process to become active. The body starts mobilizing the energy which will be required to digest food. Or we sense the presence or approach of danger; and our body begins preparations for defense or flight: the heart beats faster, more adrenalin is pumped into the system, the blood sugar rises, more oxygen is brought to the muscles, etc. The body is mobilizing energy needed to overcome danger. Should food not be available, the energy mobilized for digestion and present in the body will serve as an irritant to drive the body to greater effort in food-finding and thus mobilize still more energy. Unless the energy thus mobilized is released by getting the food, or in some other manner, it will remain pent up within the system and create tension. Similarly, unless the energy mobilized to aid the organism to meet and overcome danger is somehow released and dissipated it will remain seething in the body.

All of our wishes and all of our fears mobilize energy, the amount being in proportion to the intensity of the feelings. Whether this "calling out of the reserves" is good or bad will be determined by how fully you avail yourself of the assistance proffered. If you utilize it either for the purpose for which it was originally intended or along some other equally "releasing" channel it will be valuable. If you do not expend it, your body is in much the same position a small town would be if it called out the militia, prohibited the militia from performing any useful function, and then the militia refused to leave. The town would eventually be eaten out of house and home—particularly so and more rapidly so if it continued foolishly to call in more and more "assistance" to be mismanaged in similar fashion. The person who by his host of wishes and his hordes of fears is continuously mobilizing more energy than he needs or can use is not securing help but simply inviting trouble.

Much of our excess mobilized energy is the wrong kind, "wrong" in that it is not adequate for the situation. You wish fame and power; and in proportion to the intensity of your wish your body tries to help you get what you want. Your muscles become tense, your glands overactive, etc.—all worse than wasted effort; for eventually the tension thus created acts as a boomerang and causes new difficulties. Or you are constantly irritated by your employer; and your body as constantly mobilizes energy to help you "smite your enemy." In primitive society, such reinforcement would have been invaluable because it would have been released in physical blows, with you perhaps the victor. In any event, the fight itself would have consumed the "extra" energy. Instead, the unreleased energy mobilized by constant irritation acts as a further irritant to call forth still more energy and consequent tension. Primitive man, fearful when he sees a track which he recognizes as that of a tiger, is helped by the rise of his blood sugar and by the extra secretion of adrenalin—helped to run. Twentieth century man, fearful over the falling stock market, is as definitely *not* helped by the overactivity of his endocrine system; in fact, it only creates one more problem: how to get rid of the useless mobilized energy which, unreleased, will result in tension symptoms of one kind or another.

Whenever we wish or fear, we mobilize energy; whenever the wish is frustrated or the danger causing the fear is not met, we are left with mobilized but unreleased energy. Granting that much can and should be done to minimize the amount produced, and recognizing that situations are primarily frustrating in terms of how we "feel" about them, we must still admit that in every life there are bound to be some frustrating experiences and consequently some excess energy mobilization. This more or less constant stream of energy mobilized from frustrations is inevitable; it is well that we can direct and channelize the supply so that it can be of constructive benefit instead of being at best wasted and at worst destructive. But first let us look at those factors which interfere with the adequate mobilization of energy.

OBSTACLES TO ENERGY MOBILIZATION

Disease and age.—Both disease and malnutrition make the mobilization of energy difficult. There are some particularly debilitating disease processes—tuberculosis, tularemia, Malta fever, chronic diarrhea, and hookworm—which tend to reduce energy output to its lowest level. Vitamin deficiency (particularly the B complex) can also bring about a startling lowering of resistance, strength, and activity. Conquerors have exploited this knowledge in their treatment of the vanquished; for victims of malnutrition are not only less energetic physically but are also more docile, more inclined to follow what seems at the moment to be the path of least resistance.

If there is marked or sudden diminution of your "pep," energy, and vitality, and even if you are one of the host who seem to have been "born tired," by all manner of means have a complete physical check up. Don't berate yourself because you "seem unable to concentrate" or because you "no longer enjoy going out"; find the cause of your "limpness," sluggishness, and disinclination for effort. How serious are the inroads on your "normal" health and energy will be determined by: the nature of the disease or the degree of malnutrition; the duration or chronicity of the difficulty; your basic amount of constitutional energy; and, to an amazing degree, on the amount of energy you are in the habit of mobilizing. Automatically supplied energy, the reward of our consistent mobilization and use of our latent energy, supports us, even when some disease process is temporarily sapping our strength.

Mrs. A., aged 54, had for fifteen years after her husband's death been supported by her children. She cruised from doctor to doctor, finding them all "stupid," since they agreed that she had no organic pathology and would feel better if she would do something. She fed and dressed herself; but otherwise was as completely lazy as it would be possible for a human being to be and still exist. She lived in a hotel—at her children's expense—because she "didn't have the strength to take care of an apartment." Sewing "strained her eyes"; and she even refused to read the newspapers because she found them "too upsetting." Last year she had a mild case of flu. She remained in bed literally weeks after her doctor had told her that she could, she should, and finally that she must get out. She was too weak to feed herself, too weak to change the position of a pillow, etc. Not all her behavior was deliberate malingering. She had habitually lived at such a low level of energy mobilization and expenditure that even a mild infection was too much for her to cope with.

Of Mr. W., aged 63, all his friends say, "If he had been anyone else, he would have been dead long ago." He was born with a "frail" constitution. Determined to get an education, he, at the age of 15, left the farm where for two years he had been doing a man's work and found employment in a mine. He worked and saved toward his goal of going to college. It took him seven years to complete his education: eighteen months he was in a tuberculosis sanitarium, and at other times he dropped out to work. Throughout his life he has carried unusually heavy responsibilities—financial and otherwise—many of which he could have avoided but all of which he assumed as a matter of course. He has never had enough strength to do the work he has done; but he has so constantly mobilized his latent strength to accomplish his goals, he has wasted so little energy in vain wishes and futile fears that despite his six forced returns to the tuberculosis sanitarium and despite many illnesses he has worked steadily, effectively, and happily, making a success in his profession, and what is more important, in his personal life. Last year when for weeks he suffered from a particularly distressing siege of shingles and all his friends urged him to take it easy, his reply was, "I've been fighting this old body of mine for more than fifty years; I'm certainly not going to 'give in' to it now. Anyhow, I think less about how I feel when I come on to my office as usual."

These are extreme, though actual, cases. Granted all the other personality differences which undoubtedly exist, one must still recognize the important rôle played by their radically different *habits* of energy mobilization and expression. The implication is not that *every* "do-less" person is a selfish, self-indulgent shirker, nor that *every* person of limited inherent energy and subject to many debilitating diseases can, or even should, make a superhuman effort to disregard them; it merely indicates that our latent energy, if habitually mobilized and systematically utilized, will steadily increase in volume and dependability.

Another factor which operates to prevent the mobilization of energy is *old age*. Many chronologically old persons are physically active, mentally alert, and both interested and instrumental in bringing about changes; but as a rule, persons in the declining period of life have diminished energy. It is difficult to determine whether it is an ebbing life force or an accumulation of caution-teaching experiences which accounts for the typical "conservatism" of old age; but the fact remains that most significant changes are initiated and carried through by men at the time of relative youth. It is important for society and for persons to distinguish between fearful timidity and true wisdom, and equally important that we learn to let the wisdom of accumulated experience guide the reins of youthful enthusiasm.

Attitudes of apathy and defeatism.—Our necessities and desires, our dangers and difficulties stimulate us to activity. In the absence of such stimuli we do little. Even with such a basic drive as physical hunger "abnormal" things may happen. A person who during a long illness has eaten little loses interest in food and doesn't care whether he eats. To a literally starved person, eating is definitely painful. "Apathy" stems from two Greek words meaning "without suffering"; and the apathetic person is one who no longer responds sufficiently to stimuli to do anything about his pleasure or his pain drives.

In the case of population apathy, living is beset by so many difficulties that persons have, beyond getting enough food to maintain existence, given up the struggle. Group apathy is found in such situations as the tenant farms of the American South, the steppes of Czarist Russia, or in caste-bound India. That a person or group should "give up" after countless futile efforts and when the odds seem inescapably and overwhelmingly against him is understandable; but such an attitude is bound to lead to ultimate defeat. The suffering of the moment may be less acute; but in the long run it is better to take or even invite sharper pain if it holds any promise for ultimate release. (It is, we recognize, infinitely easier to make this *ex cathedra* statement than to live it.)

So far as particular persons are concerned, this attitude of apathy is often associated with other marked manifestations of personality difficulty. An extreme manifestation is found in the simple schizophrenic who has so completely withdrawn from life's stress and problems that he literally lives in another world, the world of his own phantasy. The most common expression of this lethargic attitude is the all-too-prevalent philosophy of defeatism: "What's the use?" "I've always been this way." "You can't change human nature." "Better men than I have tried and failed. Why should I even try?" "There have always been poverty and wars, hatreds and injustice; and there always will be." "We are hopelessly caught in the net of our lust, avarice, and stupidity; why attempt escape?" Dozens of times each day you hear or perhaps utter variations of the same theme song of defeat. Maybe the prophets of gloom are right; maybe there is

> . . . neither joy, nor love, nor light
> Nor certitude, nor peace, nor help for pain.

One certain way of making their assertions come true is by accepting their philosophy, damming the resources of our energy, and taking defeat lying down.

We tend to be even more defeatist about social than about personal problems: perhaps because the problems seem bigger and their solutions less obvious and capable of immediate realization, perhaps because the suffering they entail does not so immediately and poignantly impinge on our individual awareness and we have insufficient creative and realistic imagination to appreciate that their solution is up to us. The more general and pervasive the apathetic attitude and the defeatist philosophy, the more certainly are we doomed. Our only hope is in formulating personally satisfying and socially beneficial goals and then persistently mobilizing and directing our energy toward their accomplishment. Perhaps Clough was right in believing that if "past hopes were dupes, present fears are liars."

> It may be, in yon smoke concealed,
> Your comrades chase e'en now the fliers,
> And, but for you, possess the field.

Since it is our only chance, it is surely a chance worth taking.

ENERGY MANAGEMENT

Recognizing then that whatever may be your inherent constitutional energy you have vast resources of latent energy which *can* by your demands be mobilized for effort and which *will be* mobilized by the inescapable frustrating experiences of life, and appreciating too the fact that these reservoirs of energy can be inhibited by the health condition of your body or your defeatist, apathetic attitudes, you are then faced with a threefold problem: (1) to mobilize as nearly as possible the right amount of energy; (2) to prevent as much as possible the production of excess energy; and (3) to release as constructively as possible whatever excess energy you may produce.

Adequate energy.—Your goals will determine how much and what kind of energy you should mobilize. If your major objective is to be a champion prize fighter, then certainly you must mobilize more physical energy and condition your body much more rigorously than will another who plays tennis for recreation but whose major ambition is to become a great lawyer. A lawyer needs skill in the problem-solving technique, and his constant demand will be on his resources of mental energy. If your guiding dream is to effect social change and reform, your energy of initiative must be constantly mobilized and utilized. The kinds of energy and effort are not, of course, mutually exclusive; everyone requires physical fitness; everyone has problems to solve; everyone needs to be able to carry out his plans. The difference is one of emphasis or degree.

How much energy should you expend in pursuit of a particular goal? First answer the question, "How much is its attainment worth to me?" Obviously it would be absurd to mobilize and expend energy out of all proportion to the value of the accomplishment; and equally obviously is it "mismanagement" when you stop short of realization when you can call forth the little extra required effort. The ideal is to mobilize as much as accomplishment requires with a maximum of effectiveness and a minimum of wear and tear on you. Some of your goals will be reached with a minimal output of energy, others will demand all you have—the difference lying in the intrinsic nature of the goal, in your fitness—both "natural" and cultivated, and in your attitudes.

If everything takes too much energy, if nothing seems worth the effort, or if you feel inadequate for what you must do, let alone having energy enough for doing either what you think you should or what you would like to do—then your first problem is to find out *why* you are mobilizing too little energy. Some disease process may be robbing you of your natural vitality; have a complete physical examination and institute whatever measures are necessary to bring you back to par. Your habits of energy mobilization may be poor. You have alternated between excessive demands, leaving you exhausted and little or no demand, leaving you flabby; if so you must *by practice*—by mobilizing and utilizing the optimum amount of energy—convert your hitherto sporadic energy outbursts into a steady and automatically functioning supply. You may have, by the dead weight of your defeatist attitude, changed a manageable load into a crushing and unbearable burden; if so you must "will" to change. This "willing" is a practical, not an abstract, matter. Choose a goal your judgment tells you is within the limits of your capacity for attainment; mobilize the energy necessary for working toward it; stick to your purpose despite temporary discouragements and your success—even though only partial—will demonstrate that effort is not futile, that it is possible to move toward what we desire.

Preventing the mobilization of excess energy.—So great are our resources of latent energy and so responsive is it to demand that in this day of multitudinous stimuli, the problem confronting most of us is not how to muster more energy but what to do with the "too much" we already have and are steadily augmenting. Learning to reduce the amount produced is synonymous with cultivating *relaxed attitudes.*

Being relaxed does not mean being indifferent, unconcerned, phlegmatic; it is a positive, not a negative state. The fictional South Sea islander, lolling in the sunshine and waiting for the ripened fruit to fall is not "relaxed"; he is "collapsed." The person who is unaware of his own or anyone else's pain is not "relaxed";

he is "unconscious." The person who, far from assuming, refuses even to recognize his responsibilities is not "relaxed"; he is merely a "shirker." Nor does "relaxation" necessarily have anything to do with the tautness of your muscles, the concentration of your mind, or the resolution of your purpose. The muscles of the expert tennis player are not flabby; the lawyer while pleading a case does not permit his mind "to wander"; the crusader does not call a truce. It is important that one be properly "toned" or "keyed" for his undertakings; but just as the strings of a violin may be so taut that they will snap or so slack that all the tones are blurred so if we mobilize too little energy our accomplishments will be poorly executed and if we mobilize too much, there is likelihood not only that our achievements will be less effectively accomplished but that we will "break" in the process. It takes much time and practice to learn to tune a violin properly; and it takes even more ingenuity, skill, and perseverance so to attune our attitudes to our tasks and problems that we can "play" both easy and difficult passages with ease, smoothness, and harmony.

By relaxed attitudes is meant ability so to orient oneself toward the innumerable irritations in life that one will not become needlessly aroused, while simultaneously maintaining sufficient arousability so that he can be motivated when action is required. Relaxed attitudes are the means toward the greatest happiness as well as the greatest efficiency in life. Here, as elsewhere throughout the book, we are pleading for the "golden mean," the avoidance of extremes. Had we no emotional unrest, no "divine discontent," we would become stagnant and smug, and progress would cease; but the opposite extreme of excessive emotionalism and unrest leads to the defeat of our personal happiness and our social effectiveness.

THE TECHNIQUE OF DEVELOPING RELAXED ATTITUDES

If you realize that you expend more energy than is necessary, that you become excited and jittery out of all proportion to the gravity of your problems, that you often are so "wrought up" about situations that you feel powerless to do anything about them, and if you further appreciate that your happiness and effectiveness result from "acting" you can evolve your own technique for working instead of straining toward accomplishment. There are, however, a few practical aids we should like to suggest.

Reduce the number of your desires and fears and thereby reduce the amount of mobilized energy.—You can't do, be, and have everything you would like. Time, ability, and opportunity limit what is possible. You can't be a great surgeon, a great engineer, a great research scientist, and a great statesman in one lifetime; and if you consume energy and produce excess energy by wishing, longing, and striving to be, and still more energy in vain repining and regret because you cannot be, the chances are you won't be a great anything except a failure and a misery to yourself. Most of our "impossible" and contradictory wishes are not so patently absurd. But do you know persons who wish and try to do too many things, and do none of them well enough to bring any kind of satisfying enjoyment?

Mr. J., a university professor, does research work in his specialized field, writes short stories, and is an amateur photographer. He is "nervous," tense, irritable, and mediocre in achievement—not because his "wishes" are not legitimate and even laudatory and not because he is lacking in ability; but because there are only 24 hours in a day. He resents the demands his children make upon his time; is impatient to finish teaching to "get at" his writing; leaves his desk to develop "just one film"; comes back and is irritated because he can't write but must grade papers; while grading papers he is unhappily aware that he should go over his notes for tomorrow's classes. He suddenly and aggrievedly recalls that he promised his son to mend his skate; and that he hasn't even started preparing the lecture he must give next week.

The trouble with Mr. J. is not the inherent nature or number of his wishes or ambitions, but rather his inability to organize his time; departmentalize his interests; and utilize his mobilized energy to pursue his goals instead of forever, by his attitudes, creating tension which prevents accomplishment.

A second practical aid in cultivating relaxed attitudes is *learning to take one thing at a time*. Of course you will "get in a dither" and become frantic, tense, and irritable if while you're washing dishes you worry about the rest of the housework. You stop the dishes to make the beds, and while doing that remember that the groceries must be ordered. You "can't possibly" finish your housework because you promised to go at eleven o'clock to see your ten-year-old Jimmie "be George Washington" in the school play. After the hurried lunch and confusion of getting the children back to school, you are confronted by the still unfinished beds, groceries to put away, more dishes to wash—and you "haven't had a minute to call your own." By feeling sorry for yourself, you mobilize still more excess and harmful energy, energy which, far from helping you finish your work, actually interferes and hinders. The same kind of thing happens if, as you prepare a brief, you also worry about when you'll get time to make out your income tax, and try to decide whether or not to let your son drop out of college. You stop to make an important telephone call and while making it remember another you must make. You need a reference book and go across the hall to borrow it. By the time you have finished a long-winded conversation with your neighbor lawyer you must rush to get to court. You mobilize more energy to meet your court appearance; and even though you expend it adequately, you still have the excess from the morning's uncompleted tasks and from your worry. You produce still more—and it entirely without function—by feeling abused because you must return to the office and complete your morning's unfinished work.

There is a vital difference between singleness of purpose and rigidity or perfectionism. We are not urging you to have a single track mind or recommending that every task major or minor should claim your zealous and undivided attention; but we are insisting that budgeting your time and energy will help you carry on more efficiently and will help prevent mobilization of energy which you don't, and, in the very nature of the situation, can't use at the moment. Don't order ten cabs, when you are going only one place!

Sometimes one must not only appear to be hard-hearted but must in reality steel himself against responding to appeals which under other circumstances would and should mobilize his energy as well as his sympathy. An illustration will suffice to make this point clear.

Mr. A. has been unemployed for three months and his small savings are about gone. His neighbor, who is active in war-relief work, has asked Mr. A. to contribute money and help solicit funds. Mr. A.'s wife faces an operation which they cannot afford. Mr. A.'s ability to meet the second and third problem is tied up with the first. He will be able to do more about all three, if temporarily he devotes his attention to finding a job, and as much as possible disregards his other worries. Permitting himself to be distressed about his wife's condition or disturbed by his inability to help a worthy cause will mobilize energy which since he cannot expend will serve only to make him less able to cope with his most pressing problem. There are countless occasions when what appears to be both heartless and heedless behavior is in reality not only the wisest course but ultimately the most altruistic.

In addition to limiting our wishes and fears which serve as generators of tension (mobilized but unreleased energy) and to learning to pursue our objectives with efficient singleness of purpose, *we need to define our goals quite concretely and specifically.* Frequently persons who perpetually strive and struggle but accomplish little are ones whose goals are undefined. They have the illusion of working hard and of making tremendous efforts, and in a way they are; but it is the same kind of exhausting and profitless expenditure of energy exhibited by the frantic rushing around of a rat in a maze. The very defining of a goal tends to bring it within the possibility of achievement; for if we formulate our wishes in terms of what we are willing to work to achieve, we are not nearly so prone to set some impossible task for ourselves. Time and time again persons have "done the impossible"; but they were able to do so because they so clearly saw the desired end result that they were able to mobilize—despite difficulties that to a less resolute person would seem insurmountable—the necessary energy and to direct it all toward accomplishment. "Wishing for the moon" rarely eventuates in anything other than your vague unhappiness and discontent; "hitching your wagon to a star" can be a tremendously important step toward achieving personally satisfying and socially valuable goals. Your movement toward the "star" will be more certain if you can proceed in relaxed fashion—not too impatient of delays, not straining to do in a day what you know will take weeks, not demanding perfection of yourself, being willing to detour if necessary.

Limiting our wishes, defining them concretely, and tackling them in the most "economical" fashion possible are aids toward developing and maintaining relaxed attitudes; but the real heart of the problem lies primarily in *controlling the intensity of our desires.* Paradoxically enough, we have much more certainty of "winning the race" if we move along with trained and toned but not tense or strained muscles; we are much more likely to realize our highest hopes and actualize our finest dreams if we are not too frantic and furious in their pursuit. For example, the desire for recognition is basic and natural; but it is, or should be, one among many desires, and certainly each person is only one of many. If a person's desire for recognition is so intense that it blinds him to all other values and makes him unaware of the rights and sensitivities of others, before he can hope to attain that which he most wishes he will have to decrease the intensity of his wish, cultivate a relaxed attitude.

Mr. S. R., aged 53, suffered from peptic ulcers. Often when there had been no change in his prescribed routine he would experience definite accentuation of his symptoms.

Mr. R. had "always been discontent, dissatisfied, and unhappy." No matter what he had, he wished something else or something more. No matter what he accomplished he was envious of others' achievements. In college, he ranked first in his class; but was wretched because his roommate was voted the "most popular man."

His promotions in work were steady and though all readily agreed there was no question as to his ability, no one liked him. An executive position was opened—the one position for which he had been working all his life. Mr. R. interviewed the president, vice-president, and secretary of the corporation, pointing out that he was the best qualified, the only man for the job. He was as voluble in depreciating every other candidate as he was enthusiastic in his own praise.

Another man secured the much coveted position. Mr. R. drank himself into a stupor; but the exacerbation of his ulcer symptoms discouraged him from that escape mechanism. He fell into a deep depression, became morose, slept poorly, suffered from palpitation in addition to intensified ulcer symptoms, was continuously explosive at work and irritable at home.

This man was efficient, intelligent and energetic. He had most of the qualities for success; but his tense aggressiveness had alienated his associates as well as manifested itself in physical symptoms of tension (such as the ulcer). All his attitudes were so tense as to be self-defeating. He had to reëvaluate his goals, by determining what he really wished most out of life. He had to understand his own personality; to understand that unless he changed his attitudes no matter what position he ever reached he would still be discontented because he would always find something else that he desired even more intensely. He had to learn that his present unhappiness did not result from his failure to achieve a particular goal and that his physical symptoms were not organic in nature; but that both alike stemmed from the identical source—a hypertense and striving orientation. He had to learn that his basic attitude was wrong, his outlook on life warped, and his feelings keyed to a pitch incompatible with either efficiency or happiness.

He had to learn what we all need to learn: we have one life to live. There are satisfactions, pleasures, and joys that have nothing to do with "advancement" or recognition. He had to learn that without internal harmony no man can be happy, and that peace and quietness of spirit accomplish far more than does straining at the leash. He had to learn to work earnestly but not intensely, to work toward but not strain after; he needed to learn to laugh, and play—to live each day at its highest level of satisfying accomplishment.

Obtaining relaxed attitudes towards specific problems is perhaps the ultimate goal; yet in practice, the surest way of achieving a "general state of happiness" is by cultivating a general orientation of such freedom from tension, such objectivity and emotional stability that one can face life with equanimity, with courage to face unflinchingly whatever needs to be faced, with ability to bear up under the responsibility that rests with all free men in a free society, and with simultaneous tolerance of one's own and of others' inadequacies and resolution to effect improvement. Each man should learn how to obtain his greatest satisfaction and pleasure, not only purely momentary happiness, but also long-term satisfactions. We need not routinization or regimentation but understanding and control of emotions.

Being "relaxed" in one's attitudes is just another way of saying "having an adequate philosophy of life"—a philosophy rooted in understanding of the world as it is but reaching and working toward the world as one dreams it could be, a philosophy which makes allowances but not excuses for human limitations, a philosophy which sees big things as big and little things as little. Such a philosophy is not a theory about life; it is a way of life, a technique of feeling, thinking and acting, a general orientation toward life as a whole which manifests itself concretely and specifically in our handling of the particular situations which make up our lives.

Providing outlets for excess energy.—The "perfect person," so far as energy mobilization and expenditure are concerned, is one able to call into use exactly the right amount and kind required for realization of his greatest personal satisfactions and accomplishment of his highest social value. This perfection like all other ideals is a relative, not an absolute, state; it is a goal toward which we may move (the closer we get, the happier and more significant will our lives be), but which we shall never fully attain. The more or less constantly present and continuously mobilized but unreleased energy which the frustrating nature of many of our experiences makes inevitable can be greatly reduced by cultivating relaxed attitudes; but it can never be entirely eliminated. Accordingly, the third aspect of energy management is what to do with excess energy. Our failure to provide adequate outlets is certain guarantee that we will be its victims. Like every other powerful force it will be destructive or creative, depending on how we use it. Your tension symptoms may be distressing and incapacitating, or they may be little more than the nervous mannerisms of smoking continually, clenching your hands, shaking your foot, fiddling with your clothes, biting your nails, or moving restlessly about the room; but whatever they are, you can use that wasted or harmful energy and make an asset of a potential liability. There are four major categories of energy outlets: (1) intelligent vocalization; (2) recreation, including hobbies and avocations; (3) socialization; and (4) work.

Intelligent vocalization.—One of the best ways "to get it out of your system" is to "speak your mind." Something arouses your anger: your body as well as your mind is angry; automatically you start mobilizing energy to meet the situation, energy which if unreleased will result in physical tension symptoms, symbolic psychologic symptoms, or general irritability. Speech may seem a mild substitute for the physical blows of our primitive ancestors but in many instances it is an entirely adequate safety valve. Talking about what has made you angry, telling and retelling it to everyone who will listen and with each repetition lashing yourself back to your initial state of anger certainly does no good; it merely increases your tension. Likewise gossip and nagging have no constructive value as energy outlets, the former being sure and sadistic evidence of the gossiper's own frustrations and the latter being little other than articulate grudge-bearing. Talk with the person who has aroused your anger—*with*, not *to*. Hurling an avalanche of invective on the person who has angered you will not relieve the situation; nine times out of ten it will merely intesify your anger. Be thoroughly selfish: speak to make yourself feel better, not to demolish your irritant. Doubtless you can make some cutting retort, some ego-wounding speech that will disturb him; but what will it profit you? Vocalization serves two purposes. In the first place, the very act of putting our feelings into words diminishes the intensity of our emotion. You are worried, and you often discover in the telling—when you come down to actual facts and get rid of the shadowy host of vague, undefined fears that so frequently surround our concerns—that the situation is not in reality so bad. The same principle works so far as other emotions are concerned. Just what made you so angry? So hurt? So humiliated? So misunderstood? Secondly, vocalization frequently "clears the atmosphere," not only resolving the immediate anger-producing situation into nothingness or complete unimportance but paving the way for future understanding. It is amazing how often when persons finally "get together," each expressing his side of an "irreconcilable" difference they discover that their terminology rather than their fundamental principles are at variance, or one discovers that he has misunderstood and been misunderstood. Vocalization, then, can not only "let off steam" but sometimes also establish better relations. Don't jump to the conclusion that everytime you express yourself honestly you are going to make a convert to your point of view or are going to turn an enemy into a bosom friend. But it is true that persons whose civilization is a matter of, to some degree, having substituted reasoning for fisticuffs ought to be and often are capable of agreeing to disagree agreeably.

Talk calmly, reasonably, objectively. If your attitude is one of belligerency the chances are you will whip up more anger within yourself (thereby increasing rather than decreasing your tension) and arouse more antagonism. Don't, however, pretend to a "sweetness" you do not feel. The important element is not your manner or politeness, but how you feel. Your true calmness and objectivity will be rooted in your practiced and habitual attitude of respect for the personality of another, in willingness to admit that you may be wrong and the other right, in intelligent awareness of just what you are doing and of why you are doing it. There are, of course, situations in which this way of energy-release will be inadvisable; and your common sense will have to guide you. You are not, for example, solving your problem of excess and tension-producing energy if you permit yourself the luxury of telling your pompous and self-important boss just how little you think of him if by so doing you merely increase his antagonism when he is in the position where he can and is so constituted that he will delight to make your situation even more irritating. Don't deliver ultimatums unless you can carry them out; and don't feel you must give voice to your every random and minor irritation. It's amazing how many potentially irritating situations you can train yourself to shrug off as unimportant, how many will not even "register" when you have learned the technique of relaxed attitudes; but when energy has been mobilized and tension is present, if the situation is such that expressing yourself will literally "get it off your chest" then vocalize. You may thereby actually change the situation; even if you don't you will have "let off steam."

Recreation.—Aside from the fact that often it is inexpedient to make our feelings articulate, the amenities of life restrain us from "saying all we feel." Though useful, vocalization is a rather indirect fashion of releasing energy which is physical in origin and which so frequently takes its toll by making our bodies suffer. A more satisfying and more easily accessible form of expending surplus energy is recreation. Play is as essential to a well-balanced and happy life as is work; and though the person who makes a fetish of work and a slave of himself may accomplish more than one who fritters away his life, dissipating all his energy in having a good time, nevertheless he is bound to be "lopsided," and sardonically enough achieves less than he otherwise would or could. Play like sleep offers release from care, but it not only loosens taut nerves and smooths ruffled dispositions; it literally rebuilds, gives new life and vitality, recreates.

Have fun. No one can tell you how; for what seems fun to your neighbor may be your idea of hard work, and activities you find refreshing and pleasurable may seem quite the reverse to another. Whether a particular activity is or is not "fun" will be determined wholly by how the participant feels about it. Do you enjoy swimming, hiking, dancing, ice skating, tennis, making scrapbooks, movies, hearing concerts, knitting, building bird houses, reading, looking at the "comics," gardening, playing some musical instrument, golfing, playing bridge, pitching horseshoes, collecting first editions, stamps, donkeys, or anything else, "tinkering with" machinery, dabbling with paints or clay? If you enjoy any or all of these activities, that's fine; but it's equally fine if you don't. There are no obligations about what you should enjoy; what constitutes "fun" is a highly individualized matter. There are, however, two or three considerations which we should like to note. First, whatever you do for fun should be done in just that spirit—you're playing, not working; you're releasing, not mobilizing, energy. Don't make a chore of your play. If you have temper tantrums on the golf course, whether you manifest your irritation by hurling the clubs at the caddy, by making excuses or by stewing and fretting internally, then obviously you are not "playing" golf. Have you seen persons "settle in" for an evening of bridge—the light of battle in their eyes and a grim-jawed determination to win. If one is unhappy about his mistakes, irritated by his partner's, and discontented if he does not make high score, then obviously he is not "playing" bridge. Fun and play are their own reward—things that you do for the pure love of doing them and not to win the prize. Keep your recreations "amateur"; the minute you start working toward "professional" status you have ceased playing.

Have variety in your recreations, as (and for the same reason) you have variety in your diet. Do you know persons who feel there is nothing to do if they can't find a fourth for bridge, and others who are "lost" on rainy Sundays when they can't golf? If you limit yourself to a single line of recreation you can so easily "run it into the ground," wear out its interest. Moreover, "the world is so full of a number of things," there are so many possible pleasures, why confine yourself to one? Be experimental, as you are about new foods. Your hunch may be right: perhaps working crossword puzzles will be boring; if so, do something else. But you may have maintained a hearty and superior contempt for mystery stories because you have never read a good one. (We—or rather one half of we—are still looking for that one!)

Finally, in some of your recreational outlets be an active participant. So many persons get all their fun vicariously. They watch athletic contests, listen to music, look at movies—always as "audience." You may never become a Burbank, Kreisler, or Wren; but to the pleasure derived from going to flower shows, concerts, and art galleries, add the joy of planning and cultivating your own garden, playing your own violin, or "trying your hand" at designing houses. The more things you enjoy doing the better off you will be; and the more nearly you do them just because to you they are fun, the more tension-releasing they will be. If you "work" at having a good time and play because you think you should, you will miss both the fun and the side effects of tension-dissipation as well. "Make yourself have a good time" is as much a contradiction in terms as is the phrase, "You must relax."

Socialization.—For most persons the greatest release of tensions comes from social activity. Man is naturally gregarious and does best when not thrown back wholly on his own resources. Some persons are *too* dependent on outside stimulation, and have no ability to "enjoy their own company." Certainly everyone needs "a room of one's own"; but it is equally true that we need companionship and shared activities. We have no significance save in terms of social worth; our burdens are less when shared and our joys more intense. Half the fun of reading a good book or seeing a good show is in talking about it with someone else; and ordinarily speaking, any work or play is more meaningful when it is a shared rather than a solitary undertaking.

The tendency of many persons who are distressed or disturbed—particularly those who are naturally shy—is to "crawl into their shells," brood over their troubles (thereby increasing them), and shun the effort of seeing others. Such a person often declares he feels even worse when with others and would far rather be alone. It is tremendously important that he make himself go out, no matter how he dislikes doing so and no matter how much effort it requires. There is something contagious about the enthusiasms and interests of other persons; and most of us need to think less about ourselves and more about others or about impersonal subjects. The human spectacle is a diverting performance; and though you may find slim comfort for your ill luck in discovering "the other lad had no luck at all," the point is that when you stop riveting your attention on your loneliness, misfortunes, and worries, your luck starts improving. Get out with other persons; do things with them; go places with them; make their interests, joys, and troubles yours; contribute your much or little; travel many roads; make many acquaintances. You are fundamentally a social being, no matter how isolated a "lone lorn critter" you may at the moment fancy yourself, and you will be a much more valuable and a much happier person if you live closely associated with the work and play of other persons, who no matter how different they may appear are, in the last analysis, just like you.

Work.—Of all the methods of tension-release in this civilized world the best, the most effective, and most creative is work. The world is not finished; it is in the process of being made, and we are the makers. If it ever becomes a good world for little children to be born into, a place in which every man will have opportunity to live at the level of his highest and best potentialities, if the time ever comes when active and happy participation is rewarded by mellowed wisdom and the satisfaction of having lived life at its fullest and best, then it will be because we have worked to create such a world.

Too often "work" is considered synonymous with "drudgery"; and unfortunately it cannot be denied that much activity is little more than physical or mental servitude. There are many physically exhausting jobs and many that are deadly routine and monotonous: jobs which offer little if any opportunity for creative self-expression. The ideal would be for every person to fit himself for and pursue whatever occupation would interest him most. We shall have, however, to turn many corners before we reach that ideal state; and part of each man's work—whatever his present job may be—is to do all in his power to bring that day about. In the meantime, any work is better than none. Everyone should work; no one is exempt from assuming his share of responsibility, though what that share is varies widely with circumstances, opportunities, necessities, and abilities. Work has the somewhat negative value of diverting our attention from our own petty or major concerns or troubles; but it has also many definitely positive values. It gives a center around which to organize our lives; and the directed life is always more useful and more satisfying than the aimless, drifting one. It, more adequately than anything else, serves to mobilize a steady and sustaining supply of energy. It gives meaning to your life and adds meaning and purpose to the life of the world. Though your job is humble and personally not particularly satisfying, if you can adjust your attitude to it so that you conceive of it as being part of the human endeavor—an essential though infinitesimally small cog in a great machine—its monotony will irk you less, its limitations will irritate you less.

This glorification of the worth of work does not mean simply that the job by which you earn your livelihood is important. It is; but for the vast majority of persons such jobs consume less than a third of their time and even less of their ability. There is all the other work too: to heal the suffering of humanity, to eliminate poverty, hatreds, ignorance, injustice, and cruelty—Herculean work that for its accomplishment demands the best efforts of everyone of us.

Society will gain immeasurably if it assumes its responsibility of providing adequate outlets whereby the mobilized energy of man can be turned to constructive work, and of offering social goals of such compelling worth that they will challenge man to mobilize still more of his latent energy that he may utilize it to move closer to the realization of the good life for all men.

CHAPTER XVIII

CHANGING SOCIAL NATURE

Our thesis, throughout this book, has been that man can, by changing his own nature, live on a much higher level of personal health and happiness. But man's life is not a thing apart; he lives in a world of other men; his individual happiness is conditioned on the happiness of the world; he is, perforce, his "brother's keeper." Oddly enough, solving the world's problems makes infinitely easier the solution of one's personal difficulties; for achieving individual objectivity and emotional stability would be facilitated greatly by a world wherein stresses were reduced to a minimum and where social goals were established on the basis of seeking to know the truth and achieved in a spirit unclouded by vain wishes, undaunted by fears, yet resolute to actualize the fairest dreams of our realistic-creative imaginations.

Standing in the way of the development of objective, emotional stability for Society as for the Self are two obstacles: external threats and internal attitudes. The external threats are the hardships that threaten man's very existence: lack of food and the other minimum essentials and war, that not only intensifies existent physical problems, but adds the danger of sudden and physical destruction.

Contributing directly to and always intensifying these physical dangers is the second set of obstacles: the attitudes of men and of those congregates of men called nations. Probably no other social attitudes are more far-reaching in their detrimental effect than are: *lust for power,* manifested not only by men in their personal relationships, but by the activities of special interests and by autocratic and "totalitarian" governments; *lack of formulated and planned idealism; vacillation* in action; *sadistic* (fear-induced) treatment of minority groups and other nations; and passive acceptance or savage *condoning of evils* existing within the social organism.

Group psychologies are both cause and effect: they not only reflect the attitudes of their component members but by the process of group interaction spread and intensify them. A vicious cycle results: the more members of society are immature, the more will the total social personality be characterized by instability; and the consequent customs, taboos, and laws make it more difficult for each person to achieve that intellectual honesty and that emotional integrity and stability so essential to health and happiness. It is, therefore, important that each citizen make constructive efforts to help correct the attitudes of his group in order to benefit himself, if for no other reason. This goal of social correction must be part of the philosophy of each person who wishes to rise to a higher level of personal integration. The task of changing social nature does not belong solely to the social psychiatrist but is the work, the responsibility, and the privilege of every citizen.

Adults can do much to remold their unstable selves; but much of this instability could be avoided if there were proper molding early in life. Thus, one of the first steps is the proper education of children who must continue the task of "building this world nearer the heart's desire."

The education of our children needs radical modification. Children are today taught "facts"; they need to be taught principles and techniques of thinking and of feeling. Children must learn the "three R's" but it is even more important that they be taught how to solve the problems of life. What they must learn is the *technique* of thinking, and the *technique* of emotional control. And since the habits which are laid down in childhood carry on throughout life, it is important to initiate such education early in life. Such education needs be carried out in the school and in the home.

Mental hygiene is not a separate course to be taught as such. Rather, in *every* class the process of thinking and reasoning should follow the patterns of intellectual objectivity. In the understanding of any subject, rules are trivial and unimportant except as expressions of relationships. The child should learn the how and the why of each subject; and not simply memorize "that which is so."

In addition, there should be discussions of daily topics, with intellectually objective methods of analysis applied to current events. Children should evaluate, within the capacities of their age and intelligence, what is current in the world about them, and learn to insist upon knowing all the facts. Moreover, they should participate in both school activities and community enterprises. Emphasis must be, not so much on *what* they are doing, as on the *way* they are doing it. The way of doing must be based on intellectual honesty.

In similar fashion, the child's pattern of emotional reacting must be guided and established. The emotional attitudes expressed both by the teacher and at home are extremely potent influences in retarding or aiding the child's efforts toward maturity.

It is most important that those who guide the emotional development of the child be themselves emotionally capable of such guidance. Many teachers, despite their excellent professional training, are by virtue of their own emotional problems actually emotionally disturbing to the child. On the other hand, phlegmatically stolid teachers are often unaware of the child's sensitivity and his need for assistance. Teachers should have not only integrated personalities and proper training but also ample time for counselling and guiding the child, instead of being driven by huge classes in an efficient "machine-like" organization that glorifies records and reports above all else.

Much that is accomplished by the teacher may be undone by the home. If there are emotional problems, with bickering, quarreling and abusive parents, or if the economic situation at home deprives the child of physical security and psychologic stability, these problems should be investigated and dealt with. Toward this end, school children who are obviously emotionally unstable should be studied carefully; social workers should aid in determining the family pathology; and corrective influences should be brought to bear by well-planned and morale-building economic relief, or in the form of psychiatric counsel for the parents as well as the child. Such emotional training will not only improve the family stability but remove the emotional pressure upon the child. Parent-teacher's associations may be of great value in such a program.

COMMUNITY MENTAL HYGIENE

The development of community mental hygiene is essential if social ills are to be mitigated or removed. This mental hygiene cannot be achieved by flag waving or the utterance of hortatory, condemnatory, or promisory phrases. True mental hygiene in a community, like happiness in a person is not a *thing* in itself. True mental hygiene is a *way* of thinking, feeling, and living. It is a way of being efficient yet considerate of human frailty; it is determined yet not ruthless; it is happy without sensuousness; it is courageous without bravado; it is the capacity to face facts without defeatism and without false optimism; it is the ability to make decisions and bear responsibilities without egoistic proclamations and "iron-willed" invincibility; it is the ability to be progressive technologically, sociologically, and psychologically, yet to balance between the unchecked idealism of the "ultraradical" and the immovable inertia of the "arch-conservative."

True mental hygiene is not a garment to be donned or doffed at will. True mental hygiene, which should permeate every fiber of the social organism, can be achieved only through experience and effort. All our concrete, specific actions are expedited or hindered, are mechanical actions or human processes, depending upon the mental hygiene background.

Every citizen can do much toward developing sound community attitudes. It is still true that he who would gain his life must lose it; and the more Man advances the interests of society rather than himself, the more he advances his own interests, the more he advances the efficiency and happiness of others, the better will be their service to him. In addition to this very selfish gain which man experiences in advancing social causes, there is the immeasurable emotional satisfaction derived from feeling that one is a meaningful part of the whole.

Man cannot lie comfortably basking in the sunshine of our technological advances and avoid his responsibility to and for the social organism. We must personally see to it that our government is made for man and not man for the government. In our natural inertia lies the seed of self-destruction; for when the control of our lives, social, economic, or otherwise is given into the hands of a few, we become the subjugated, the subservient, the helpless, the dependent, and eventually the destroyed. All living things carry the germs of self-destruction; and plants, animals, and men survive not so much by destruction of the "germs" as by maintaining a constant high level of resistance. Once this resistance drops, the living thing falls prey to many foes. Similarly, in the body politic there are innumerable "germs of destruction"; and only high resistance and dynamic healthiness will enable it to survive.

Understanding that your personal happiness is in large measure dependent upon the kind of society in which you live is not enough: you must *assume your responsibility* as physician for a sick society and creator of a new world. Among our favorite excuses for inaction are: persons in authority should make the necessary changes; individual efforts avail little; there are too many pressing personal problems, etc. Don't try to comfort yourself with these easy speeches. Remember that experience has repeatedly shown that if we would avoid the holocausts precipitated by permanent rulers, we must constantly be on the job, never delegating authority, more than temporarily, to any leader or group. Remember, too, that you are free to carry on your personal duties and interests only so long as your government permits; so it is "up to you" to see to it that it is the kind of government under which you and other men can live most happily, most productively.

You must carry to your task of changing society the same attitudes which are so essential if you would modify your own reaction patterns: objectivity and emotional stability; and you must be prepared to mobilize and expend your best problem-solving energy and initiative. Don't start worrying about the bigness of the task, at least until you have done all that you immediately can. In a democracy our greatest weapon of defense and our most valuable tool for constructive building is the right to vote—a right, the privileges and responsibilities of which we all too often treat lightly or abuse. A better world will be wrought not by agonizing over present miseries or dreaming about far, faint Utopias, but by passing social and economic legislation and by giving our leadership into the hands of men of integrity, world-vision, and daring initiative. Most of us will not personally accomplish great deeds; but we can all play a significant rôle in their achievement. Toward that end, there are several specific suggestions worth considering. (1) *Be acquainted with current issues,* local, national, and international. Learn all the facts; get as close as you can to the truth of every situation. Expand your tolerance to the extent that you are not only willing but eager to *hear both sides of every question.* You must know what the other man is thinking, saying, and believing; you must learn to recognize truth, even when spoken by your opponents; you must realize that the highest level of intellectual objectivity is obtained by *seeing similarities in differences.* (2) Having obtained all available and pertinent facts, make them yours by *thinking about them.* Digest their contents and subject them to your best judgment, which stems not from your wishes or fears but from your past experience and your total knowledge of human and social nature. The more times you go through this process of conclusion-seeking (problem-solving) the more perfected will your skill become. When you have done your best to arrive at a "true" conclusion, (3) *subject your ideas to the opinions of others.* In your block, your office, your club, wherever you talk with men who face the same problem, discuss your ideas and check the validity of your conclusions by their knowledge, judgment, and experience. Be more eager to listen than to expound. It is amazing how many paths there are to the same goal; and it will be a happy day for society when we learn to pool our knowledge, arrive at composite conclusions, make free use of truth and wisdom from no matter what source they come, and formulate our decisions in terms of the common good instead of personal gain or petty loyalties. (4) *Having arrived at your decision, implement it by action:* vote, write to legislators, form or participate in action groups, etc. *Do everything you can to actualize whatever you have decided is "best."*

LEADERSHIP

Probably no other one factor is more potent in determining the kind of world we shall have than is the quality of our leadership. We can have our choice: we can lazily turn over our lives to men dominated by the lust for personal gain or controlled by special and selfish interests or we can place our trust in men of personal integrity, social vision, and daring initiative. That we can make this choice is at once the glory and the terrifying responsibility of living in a democracy. If we bungle our opportunity, shirk our responsibility, let our inertia or our short-visioned selfishness prevent the mobilization and direction of our energy toward the selection and support of real leaders, we have only ourselves to reproach, that in a world of plenty there is want, that the law of the jungle still prevails, that the Four dread Horsemen still ride across a terror-stricken multitude.

Too often we have daintily "washed our hands," preferring the pursuit of our personal interests or the quiet seclusion of our "ivory towers" to the grime and stench of politics. We have blindly thought—if at all—that we were doing our part if we kept ourselves "unspotted from the world." Today, as perhaps never before, men of good will realize that good will alone will not suffice for themselves or for the world. We need all the serpentine wisdom we can muster and all the constructive energy we can mobilize to outwit the powers of darkness. The Devil—whether you call him familiarly by the name of Hunger, Political Corruption, or War—cannot be wished out of existence nor can our fearful flight guarantee us safety; but he can be "out-smarted," and out-fought. It is *your* intelligence, *your* courage, and *your* effort that can win the day.

Perhaps the most immediate way that we as individual persons can throw our weight on the side of right is by doing all in our power to see to it that our representative leaders are truly *representative* of our best wisdom, our best plans, our best goals. As it stands, many of our potentially best leaders are lost to us. They too hesitate to "get mixed up in the dirty mess of politics"; they have seen too many others fail in their effort because of half-hearted support. That we are skeptically surprised when we hear of a politician with a "clean record" is a sad and sardonic commentary not so much on the all too frequent quality of leadership as on our wholesale indifference and irresponsibility that make such a condition possible. Then, too, we often lose good leaders because we permit our insistence on nonessentials to obscure our objective judgment. Great leaders do not necessarily have good manners, come from good families, have the "right kind of names," or the "right kind of religion"—they need not, indeed, "belong to the right party."

Examine records before you vote, paying little attention to fine phrases and glowing promises, but using all the objective, truth-seeking judgment of which you are capable. Even more important, concentrate on finding and supporting men who have the essential qualities of great leadership: (1) true social interest; (2) intelligence (not just professional degrees); (3) energy to carry out the ideal goals of those whom they represent; and (4) courage to subordinate self or local interests to the good of the many. Having found such a leader is the beginning, not the end of your responsibility. Your leader's obligation, as your chosen representative, to implement your will and carry out your wishes presupposes your reciprocal obligation to support his efforts. Again it should be reaffirmed that leaders should never have authority permanently delegated to them; their responsibility should continuously stem from the public; and their authority should exist only so long as they truly represent "You—the People."

A WORLD STRUGGLING FOR PEACE

It seems that mankind has to learn everything the hard way. We go on having avoidable accidents, letting mild infections spread and become virulent, permitting our uncontrolled emotions to play havoc with our health, until we have to invoke the "miracles" of surgery, medicine or psychiatry to help us get well again. Sometimes we wait too long. Even when we don't, we must pay exorbitant bills of needless suffering, wasted energy, and lost happiness. Sometimes we profit only temporarily from restored health and then fall back into the old harmful way of living.

We have taken the same reckless chances with the health and happiness of the entire world; and today a war-ravaged world struggling for peace is paying the price of that folly. That our present tragic state could have been averted seems as certain as that you could have avoided developing many of your distressing physical symptoms and self-defeating attitudes. Over and over again we have insisted that your present troubles are not occasion for self-reproach or vain regrets but a challenge to mobilize all your energy to remedy the situation while it is still possible to do so. What is possible for you as one suffering person is possible for the whole sick world, provided—and only provided—our knowledge is put into practice.

Now as never before do we need to *face facts* and *stabilize our emotions*. We must understand just what dangers confront us, realize the magnitude of the task before us, and honestly measure just what we are doing for the peace effort as against what we could do. We must maintain our sense of proportion, avoid blind prejudices and hatreds, and control our natural tendency toward hopeless depression over minor failures or fatuous hopefulness that "everything will come out all right." We must conserve our emotional forces and *mobilize our latent energies* for the purpose of directing them into constructive channels.

Military victory was won at a staggering price—a senseless waste, a cruel mockery unless we win the even more arduous, baffling, and demanding struggle for peace. Now, as never before, must we maintain at as high a level as possible our *intellectually honest* and *emotionally steady habits of reactions;* now, as never before, must we develop to their highest potentiality our *problem-solving* ability and our dream-created, reason-directed *initiative*.

For the quest has not changed. We know at last that our own "pleasure" is to be found only in a world wherein all men are guaranteed, to the limit of our corporate endeavor, their right to the pursuit of happiness. We know that we can most surely avoid "pain" in a world wherein every man senses his brother's danger and helps him overcome it. We have within our grasp the technique for changing our own little worlds and the whole great world of society. We can more certainly than ever before move steadily toward the enduring human goal—Happiness.

INDEX

Abstract theories and terms, 201, 212
Acceptance
　of inescapable facts, 282
　of responsibility, 298
Accidental determination of symptom
　site, 61, 62
Accusation, 139
Achieving Maturity, Ch. XV
Action
　habitual nature of, 270
　importance of carrying through, 274,
　　326
　necessity for, 242, 272, 300
　relation to thought and feeling, 27,
　　122, 201, 300
　vs. belief, 133
　vs. contemplation, 242
Adequate energy, 335-336
Adolescence, sex interest during, 183
Age, effect on energy, 320, 330
　lack of imagination in, 153
Amnesia, 174-175
Amoeba, 7-10
Anal pruritus, 116
Anaesthesias, 169-170
Anger
　effect on stomach activity, 83
　in primitive man, 24
Anticipations, 122, 304
Anxiety, 56
Apathy, 333-334
　vs. stability, 230
Aphonia, 173-174
Appearance, see Manners
Approval, desire for, 255
Assets and liabilities, 241-243
Asthma, 103-106
Attitudes
　affected by illness, 45-47
　affected by personal relationships, 43

Attitudes—*Cont.*
　affected by traumatic experiences, 45-
　　47
　changing, 4, 14, 43, 48, 66, 72, 160-
　　161, 176, 192-193, 206, 212, 235,
　　263, 282
　contradictory, 51-52, 138, 241, 338
　detrimental to Society, 352
　General, 39-50, 191-192
　habitual nature of, 269-270
　imitation by children, 39-40
　immature, 49, 233, 236-239
　mature, 49, 202, 286 ff.
　relation of General and Specific, 210-
　　211, 215, 234
　relation to one's philosophy, 210
　relation to physical diseases, 119-121
　relation to symptoms, 54, 122, 201
　Specific, 50, 52, 210, 234
Automatic Bodies in a Changing World,
　　Ch. III
Automaticity
　failure of, 17, 23, 24-25, 54-55, 122,
　　243-244
　nature and purpose of, 38 ff.
Autonomic nervous system, see Nervous
　　systems
Awareness, as cortical function, 23

Basal ganglia, 21
Basic drives, see Drives
Bed wetting, 110
Belief, nature of, 145-146
Bladder, 110
Blatant optimism, 205
Blood pressure
　mechanism of, 74
　see High Blood pressure
Blurred vision, 97
Blushing, 112